Hydraulic Dredging

The General Tremblay, One of the World's Most Powerful Dredges. (Marine Industries, Ltd., Canada)

Hydraulic Dredging

THEORETICAL AND APPLIED

By

JOHN HUSTON, P.E.

CONSULTING ENGINEER

CORNELL MARITIME PRESS, INC.

Cambridge   1970   Maryland

Standard Book Number ISBN 0—87033—142—6

Library of Congress Catalog Card Number: 71-100659

Printed in the United States of America

Copyright © 1970 by Cornell Maritime Press, Inc.

To

R. R. Manatt and G. W. Warner

who gave me my start in dredging, and

To

Kathleen

who has put up with it

Foreword

On the premise that a profession is known by its literature, dredging might well be eliminated. Its available literature is almost nil. In general those who are familiar with dredging are not inclined or motivated to write about it. Those who do are few. Most of what has been written, particularly in the United States, is composed principally of job or equipment descriptions. These contribute practically nothing to the advancement of the profession and offer little learning opportunity to those not directly connected with the industry.

Since those words were originally written, a World Dredging Association (WODA) has been organized, and in 1967 a World Dredging Conference (WODCON) was held in New York. Thirty papers related to dredging were presented (1). Although many of them were hardly more than accounts of equipment, jobs, or processes, a considerable amount of useful information was presented. Before this book went to press, another WODCON was held in Rotterdam, Holland, from which some additional useful papers emerged (2).

There have also been other meetings in the United States over the past few years which have produced some worthwhile information on dredging. One was the 1966 Dredging Symposium of the Society of Naval Architects and Marine Engineers in Tampa, Florida (3, 4, 5). However, most such meetings have been widely dispersed and unfortunately relatively unheralded.

In Europe there have been several books published (6 through 12), but they, as the papers of the symposiums, have not been relatively available, translations have been generally unobtainable, and the greater part of the body of the dredging profession is either unaware of them, or cannot benefit because of the language barrier. In general it can be said that most of the useful dredging information that has been provided has been sown broadcast, and either has not taken root or has not been harvested.

England, Germany, the Netherlands, and a few of the other European countries have produced far more informational literature than the United States. To my best knowledge the only useful, available, organized literature that has originated in the United States, other than that from manufacturers, the United States government, isolated papers of the Societies' Journals, and sources such as those just mentioned, can be credited to only a few rare individuals, such as the authors of references 16 and 83. Without their efforts the literature of United States' dredging would be practically zero.

From the beginning it has been thus. The dredging pioneers recorded very little of their experiences. They saw the development of the dredge happen through random trial-and-error rather than by plan. Interested in the practical aspects of making money, rather than academics, they put into writing little of what they did and started the circumstances which constitute the situation today—there is a dearth of usable, available, organized dredging literature.

One would think that because of the dredge's wide usage, great output, ease of spoil disposal, efficiency, and economy, a profuse amount of descriptive literature would be in evidence. Not so. Less has been written intelligently about the dredge than any other piece of excavation equipment in existence. The reasons for this are many.

Perhaps one of the reasons is the comprehensiveness of the dredging process. Describing and explaining the operation of a unit of another type of excavating equipment, such as a tractor or scraper, cannot be compared with explaining the dredging process.

Results obtainable with most excavating equipment are fairly easy to predict, as the equipment generally has a regular cycle that produces the same result time after time. This is not the case with the dredge. Factors controlling its operation and production are numerous, and any one of them by varying only slightly will affect a remarkable change in the dredge's output. For example, consider the material it digs. Soft materials cause pumping capacity to limit production, while hard materials cause cutting ability to be limiting. Also, pipeline length affects pumping velocity, and any change in length will change the output correspondingly. These two factors alone, among the many others, compound the difficulty of predicting production.

On the other hand, hesitancy of dredgemen to write about their work contributes considerably to the lack of information. Theirs is not an academic endeavor, to say the least. There are no pressures on them to write a book or present a paper. They just dig mud and tend to keep their innovations and improvements to themselves.

Then, there is another stumbling block—dredging's technological progress. Compared with industries of comparable size, the dredging profession is near the bottom of the list in time, effort, and money devoted to training and study. Men introduced into dredging are placed on the dredges and left in an informational vacuum. Application of the fundamentals acquired in school is left to time and chance. Where other professions and the trades rely for their propagation on an apprentice system based on study along with practice, the dredging industry completely ignores the former (13).

But whatever are the reasons for the lack of information, the unfortunate fact remains—only those who work and live with the dredge have an opportunity to obtain more than a passing knowledge of its operation and capabilities. Dredging is a complicated and empirical business, and men spend their lives in it learning almost wholly by experience. Others, who would normally be able to acquire a fair knowledge by studying the literature, have little opportunity to learn.

My experience in being introduced to dredging was, as I recall, being told to report to a certain dredge at a certain location on a certain day. Upon doing so I was introduced around and then turned over to the acting civil engineer. From that time henceforth my memory fails me if I was ever given or advised of any available information on dredging.

I might say, however, that I was fortunate in having an authoritative verbal source of information. This was in the person of George W. Warner of the Atlantic, Gulf & Pacific Company. If such a category exists in dredging, I would place him in that of the foremost authority on hydraulic pipeline dredging in the world today. Whatever dredging knowledge I have accumulated over the years has been in a great part due to my continued consultation with this dredgeman.

Others have not been so fortunate, and in this state of affairs I have always felt that a usable and practical book about dredging would be valuable. I have compiled it principally for the layman, the student, the beginning dredgeman, the younger engineer, and the engineer or executive in other industries. However, it is hoped that it may be of use to whomever is interested in this special field.

As no one can fully understand dredging without some familiarity with its past, the first chapter gives a brief history of dredging, and discusses modern-day dredges in general, their operation, and how they are used. Following chapters are devoted to the ramifications of the operation of the hydraulic, pipeline, cutterhead dredge. Practical and empirical information has been stressed, but scientific and theoretical principles have not been disregarded.

The British system of weights and measures is used throughout the book. In some instances where a comparison between the British and the metric system is necessary, metric units are shown in parentheses following the British unit. Conversion tables are provided to convert from one system to the other.

Some of the book's text has been previously published. In 1967 I prepared a paper, *Dredging Fundamentals* (13), which was published in the Journal of the Waterways and Harbors Division of the American Society of Civil Engineers. The paper was an abstract of some of the material from the first draft of this book, much of it being verbatim. Also, several articles were written for *World Dredging and Marine Construction* (14). These articles were also taken from the text material. Two of them were *Shafts and Couplings* and *Ropes and Sheaves*.

In assembling the book I drew from multitudinous sources. As in any technical work, it is difficult, and often impracticable, to credit all the sources of information. Much of the material presented has been taken from my notes which were collected over the years. Unfortunately I often failed to indicate the source of many of the data. Consequently throughout the book there most certainly will be passages, excerpts, or details which may appear elsewhere, but which are not acknowledged. I would appreciate hearing from anyone who may identify them, so that credit can be given in the first revision of the book. Wherever possible I have attempted to continually refer the reader to the sources of information. Most sources are indicated by parenthetical numbers, e.g., (5), referring the reader to similarly-numbered references of the Bibliography, a selected list which should also be of value to anyone interested in further perusal of the subject.

It is hoped the reader will understand and appreciate that the great bulk of the information presented is original only with the generations of dredgemen—living and dead—who knowingly or not have made it possible for this book to be written.

Corpus Christi, Texas   JOHN HUSTON, P.E.

Contents

Chapter 1.   The Antecedency of Dredging

Chapter 2.   The Pipeline Cutterhead Dredge—Components and Plant

Chapter 3.   Permits—Mobilization—Commencement of Dredging

VOLUME CALCULATIONS

Chapter 5.   Plans—Specifications—Contracts—Investigations—
Estimating—Bidding

ADVERTISEMENTS AND BIDS

INVESTIGATIONS

Chapter 6.   Costs—Management—Personnel

COSTS

Chapter 11. Characteristic Curves

Chapter 12. Prime Movers

Appendix

PER-UNIT CONTRACTS

SPECIFICATIONS

RENTAL CONTRACTS

Hydraulic Dredging

Chapter 1

The Antecedency of Dredging

1. Introduction. Today's dredge is an unparalleled excavating plant. When sufficient water is available it has no economic competitor. Without the dredge, commercial navigation of waterways and rivers would be ended, waterborne industry would collapse, and ocean shipping as it is known today would be nonexistent.

Dredges ply the waters of the world. They dig canals, ports, and harbors, do maintenance dredging in rivers, canals, and waterways, excavate for construction of piers, wharves, docks, dams, and underwater foundations. They provide spoil for the reclamation of swamps and marshes; they construct dikes and levees, and dredge sand,

Fig. 1. Six-inch Dredge Digging in Shallow Water. (Ellicott Machine Corp.)

gravel, and shell, as well as coal, gold, tin, diamonds, and many other minerals for commercial purposes. Pipeline dredges excavate underwater solids and transport them without rehandling to almost any location. With the aid of booster pumps, solids are pumped almost unlimited distances.

The dredge's scope of operation is broad. Small dredges operate in water only a few feet deep. Figure 1 shows a small, six-inch dredge working in Argentina. Designed by the Ellicott Machine Corporation of Baltimore, Maryland, it can operate in only three feet of water. Larger dredges require more draft, but can dig to greater depths. Figure 2 shows a 30-inch dredge designed and built by PACECO— division of Fruehauf Corp., Alameda, California. It can move more than 40,000 cubic yards per day over distances greater than four

Fig. 2. Thirty-inch Dredge Digging in Deep Water. (PACECO)

miles. Table 1 gives typical specifications for five other dredge sizes. Figure 3 shows average characteristics.

Although the dredge's output is understandably greater in soft materials than in hard, it can excavate almost anything. It digs mud, silt, loam, clay, sand, hardpan, gravel, coral, and even rock. Boulders weighing 1,000 pounds and more have been excavated and transported by dredges. Today's dredge however, is a considerable contrast to the early dredge.

2. World's First Dredge. Probably the world's first dredge was the *Spoon and Bag Dredger* (10).* Used by the early artisans many

Table 1. Typical Specifications for Five Sizes of Dredges

Item	Size of Dredge, in inches				
	12	16	20	24	28
Length, in feet	100	120	140	160	175
Beam, in feet	35	40	45	50	50
Depth, in feet	8	9	10	12	15
Displacement, in tons	560	840	1200	1850	3000
Pump Power, in brake horsepower	570	1000	1500	2700	5000
Pump Speed, in revolutions per minute	500	400	350	325	300
Cutter Power, in brake horsepower	150	200	400	750	1000
Cutter Speed, in revolutions per minute	5–30	5–30	5–30	5–30	5–30
Spud Length, in feet	55	60	70	90	100
Ladder Length, in feet	50	55	60	70	80
Maximum Pipe Line, in feet	2,500	4,000	5,000	7,000	9,000
Maximum Width of Cut, in feet	160	200	220	270	325
Minimum Width of Cut, in feet	50	60	70	90	90
Maximum Digging Depth, in feet	35	40	45	50	60
Minimum Digging Depth, in feet	4	5	6	8	12

thousands of years ago, it has seen little change. Even today if one will voyage up the Thames in England, he may have the opportunity of viewing one of these early dredgers (Figs. 4 and 5).

It consists merely of a barge or raft upon which is mounted one or more poles on pivots. On the outer end of each pole is a bucket, bag, or some other receptacle. The bag is lowered into the water, dipped into the material to be excavated, and then raised by the pole and swung aboard. The contents are dumped into the hold and the operation repeated until the barge is full. The Dredger is then pulled or poled to shore, and the spoil is scooped out and deposited on the bank.

Holland and Italy both claim to have originated the Spoon and Bag Dredger. It is probable that Holland deserves the credit—hers is a history of mud and water from antiquity. But it is more likely that the Dredger was first introduced in western Europe and England by the Phoenicians, or possibly the Romans, who during their journeys and conquests in the eastern countries, saw the Dredger and brought the idea westward.

Probably not until 1400 were any significant improvements made in dredging. The Spoon and Bag Dredger remained supreme. One of

---

* *See* the Bibliography for parenthetical reference numbers.

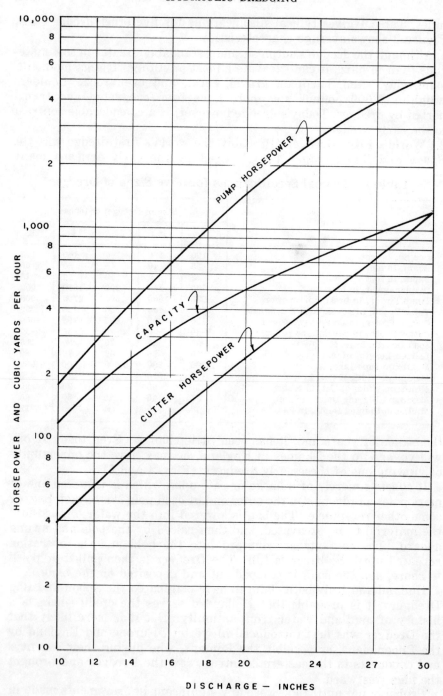

Fig. 3.   Average Characteristics of Pipeline Dredges.

the first recorded improvements was in 1435, when a Kraggelaar, or *water harrow*, was used in the town of Middleburg, Holland (10). It was a ship-like affair with a harrow or plow attached beneath its stern (Fig. 6). Moved by the wind on aboveboard sails, and by the tide on underwater wings, it plowed and loosened the bottom when the tide was ebbing. As late as 1800 the Water Harrow was in use in some parts of Holland.

3. Other Early Dredges.   A later improvement, and undoubtedly the best, until the invention of the steam engine, was the *Amsterdam Mud Mill* (10). Invented before 1600 and often called *Noah's Ark* in its later years, the Mud Mill was probably the ancient ancestor of all dredges.

Fig. 4.   Spoon and Bag Dredger in the Thames. (Brown, Son & Ferguson, Scotland)

The Mud Mill was made entirely of wood, and was operated by a treadmill turning an endless chain of buckets. The material scooped up by the buckets was dumped into a scow astern. At first men operated the treadmill (Fig. 7), but in 1620 a horse-driven mill was used (Fig. 8).

Between 1778 and 1793 there were mud mills in use in Amsterdam, Holland, that had five horses aboard, two pulling and three resting. These mills were reported to have been capable of dredging 400 tons of mud a day to a depth of 10 to 15 feet.

Fig. 5. Spoon and Bag Dredger from an Early Woodcut. (Technical Press, Ltd., London)

Fig. 6. Model of the Water Harrow. (Martinus Nuhoff, The Netherlands)

Fig. 7. Model of the First Mud Mill. (Martinus Nuhoff, The Netherlands)

Fig. 8. Model of the Amsterdam Mud Mill. (Martinus Nuhoff, The Netherlands)

The Mud Mill was very popular throughout Europe, and for 250 years it stood off all competitors. Throughout its history few changes were made. Even as late as 1835 it was holding its own, according to

Fig. 9. Early Scraper Dredge. (Technical Press, Ltd., London)

Fig. 10. Early Manpowered Dredge. (Technical Press, Ltd., London)

Van Ronzelen, the hydraulic expert who built the port at Bremerhaven, Germany. However, with the advent of the steam engine and its adaptation to the dredge, the Mud Mill was finally made obsolete. Figures 9 through 12 show pictures of other early dredges.

Fig. 11. Early Grab Dredge. (Technical Press, Ltd., London)

Fig. 12. Early Manpowered Bucket Dredge. (Technical Press, Ltd., London)

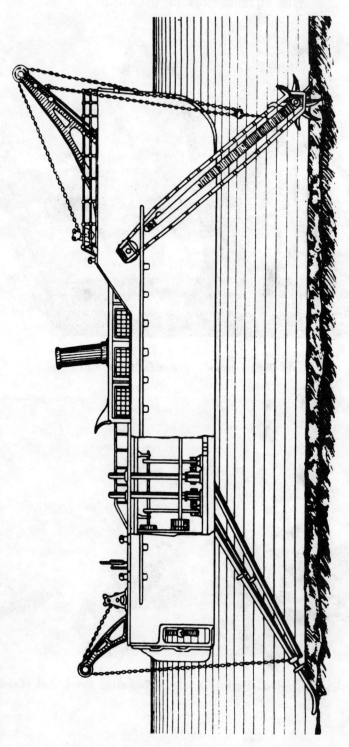

Fig. 13.   Model of Bazin Dredger. Note plows at bow and drag at stern.
(Technical Press, Ltd., London)

4. The First Hydraulic Dredge. It is possible that the first use of water and a centrifugal pump to transport spoil may have been by the French hydraulician, M. Bazin, circa 1864 (7).

Bazin built a pump which is believed to have had a 12-inch discharge. The four-vane runner had a diameter of about 24 inches and a speed near 350 rpm. When two vanes broke off, the pump worked better, so a two-vane runner was used from then on. Best results were alleged to have been obtained in sand and gravel, the proportion being about five to one.

In 1875 a review of a model of a Bazin dredger was given in *Revue Industrielle,* and a translation appeared in the *Tijdschrift van het Koninklijk Instituut van Ingenieurs* for the year 1876-1877 (7). This review had the following to say: "The dredge can suck 3,000 cubic meters of sand per day at depths of eight to 12 meters. The pipe of 25-centimeters diameter passes through the hull two meters below water level. Thus a difference in levels is obtained which produces moving power so that a swift current carries along a considerable amount of sand and mud. The ground is first raked loose by scrapers and the vessel moved forward by a propeller." (*See* Fig. 13.) "It is interesting to note that the two-meter static suction head was given the credit for the movement of the material with no mention of the pump being made."

5. The First United States Hydraulic Dredge. In the United States in 1855, Nathanial H. Lebby conceived what is generally recognized as the first successful United States dredge—if not the first in the world—based upon hydraulic principles (15). Named the General Moultrie, it was used by James and Thomas Eason to dredge the bar at Charleston, South Carolina. Although the Moultrie was no pace setter—it averaged 325 cubic yards per day—it motivated suction dredging in the United States.

6. The First Pipeline. The discovery of the practicability of transporting spoil through a pipeline can probably be attributed to Alexis von Schmidt (16). Born in Russia in 1821, but reared and educated in the United States, he is generally acclaimed as the originator of pipeline dredging. With his brother Julius, he designed in 1874 what is believed to have been the first practical pipeline suction dredge.

In 1876 von Schmidt obtained a patent for *A Dredging Machine* (Fig. 14). This dredge had a round bow and a square stern. It had three spuds, one at the center of the hull, and one at each of the stern corners. The discharge pipe was suspended by wires guyed from a mast. The cutter had four blades, similar to a ship's propeller, that were mounted around a vertical axis. The ladder, on which was mounted the suction pipe and cutter, moved from side to side on wheels rolling on a circular track on the bow of the dredge. Later modifications fixed the ladder to the dredge and the dredge was swung from side to side. With the dredge swinging, the suspended

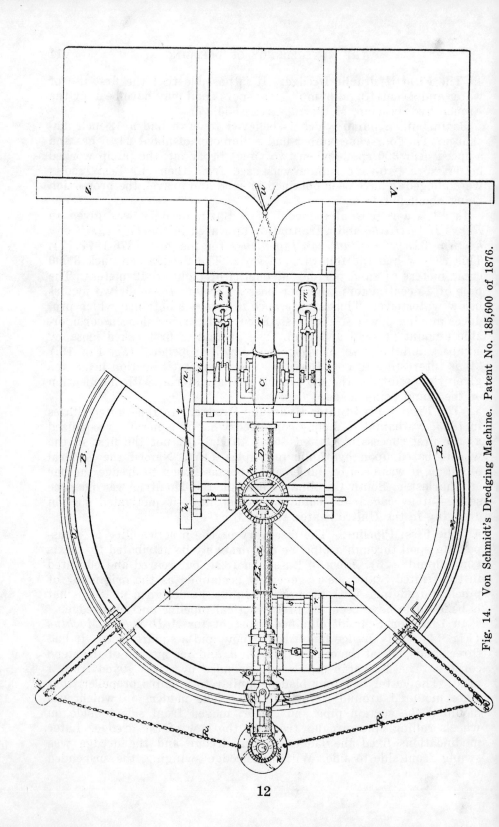

Fig. 14. Von Schmidt's Dredging Machine. Patent No. 185,600 of 1876.

discharge pipe swung also. This was cumbersome, so it was not long until a floating line came into use (16).

7. The First Two-Spud Dredge. Most likely the first man to question the need for three spuds on a dredge was Horace B. Angell (16). In 1884 he obtained a patent for a dredge with only two spuds (Fig. 15). This dredge contained nearly all the elements of the modern cutterhead dredge. It had a ladder swinging in a vertical plane, a swivel elbow in the suction, and a cutter engine on the ladder.

8. Modern-day Dredges. The development of the dredge occurred because of a need to excavate submerged or water-logged materials. Because of the different classes of materials and varied excavation requirements throughout the world, many different types of dredges evolved. It was a geological and geographical, as well as climatical, type of evolution.

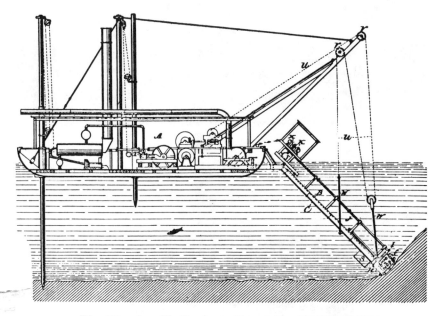

Fig. 15. Angell's Dredger. Patent No. 341,539 of 1884.

As an example of the different demands on dredging today, consider most of Europe where the population density is high and reclamation of land is not in great demand. Excavated material is generally disposed of at sea. This requires the use of large, hopper-type, dredges or barges that can store the material aboard and then transport it to sea to be dumped.

In the United States however, the land is not yet so populated and there still exists a great amount of unreclaimed land. Dumping at sea is not therefore often required, and the pipeline dredge has thus become more popular.

Kicking spud

Fig. 16. Five-cubic-yard Grab Dredge. (A, Top) Bow View; (B, Bottom)
Stern View. (Ellicott Machine Corp.)

Although the main purpose here is to discuss the hydraulic, cutter-head, pipeline dredge, a review of today's other types of dredges is desirable to lay a foundation for the operation and need for this most popular United States dredge. Following are the principal types of dredges in use throughout the world.

9. Types of Dredges. The two basic types of dredges are the *bucket* and the *hydraulic*. Bucket dredges are sometimes referred to as *mechanical dredges*, and are classified as *grab*, *dipper*, and *ladder*. Hydraulic dredges are *plain-suction*, *draghead*, and *cutterhead*.

A. BUCKET DREDGES. All bucket dredges have one limitation—the discharge must be alongside the place of excavation, or when the spoil cannot be placed alongside, scows or barges must be used to carry it away. For large-quantity, widely-dispersed excavating, this type of dredge is not practical.

Fig. 17. Dipper Dredge.

1. Grab Dredges. The grab dredge is essentially a grab bucket operated from a derrick mounted on a flat-topped barge (Figs. 16 A and B). It is used extensively around docks, piers, and particularly in the corners of cuts where it has the ability to get in close without damaging structures. This dredge works well in silts and stiff muds and is particularly effective where there are obstructions and trash. In hard materials its production is poor, and in stiff and hard clays it is unsuitable. Its dredging depth is practically unlimited, being restricted only by the length of the hoisting wire. However, the deeper the dredging, the less the production, because of the increased hoisting time. Depths of 100 feet are not uncommon.

Fig. 18. Ladder Dredge. (Technical Press, Ltd., London)

16

As its digging action depends upon the weight of the bucket, it does not have sufficient penetrating power in hard materials to obtain a good bite or a full load. It also leaves an irregular bottom, making digging to a specified depth difficult, and much time is lost because of the twisting of the opening and closing cables.

Two general types of grab buckets are used—the *clamshell*, for mud or stiff mud, and the *orange peel*, for loose rock or other hard or bulky materials.

A large grab dredge with a one-cubic-yard bucket may raise 45 to 55 cubic yards of mud per hour when working in 15 to 20 feet of water. In clay about half this production can be obtained.

2. Dipper Dredges. The dipper dredge is merely a power shovel operating from a barge. It is almost exclusively American (Fig. 17). It is most effective in hard materials such as till, soft and broken-up rock, and shales. It works well where there are obstructions such as boulders, snags, or timbers. It requires a small crew—five or six being about the maximum. It can dig its own flotation and remove high banks without worry of their collapse. In rock that has to be blasted, the bucket sometimes has a rock-piercing shaft that tears the rock apart as it excavates.

On the hull there are two forward spuds and one stern or *kicking spud,* similar to those on grab dredges. The two forward spuds are used to lift the barge above its normal flotation and thereby obtain additional weight for absorbing the reactions of the digging oper- ation. The *kicking spud* is used to move the dredge ahead (Fig. 16B). Digging depth is limited by the length of the boom, 65 feet being about the maximum.

Bucket capacities vary from one to five cubic yards. In soft mate- rial a dredging cycle of about one minute can be expected. Hard materials may double the cycle time. With a one-cubic-yard bucket in muds, 50 to 250 cubic yards can be dredged per hour. In clay about half this is possible.

3. Ladder Dredges. The ladder dredge is probably the oldest of the dredges in general use today (Fig. 18). It originated soon after the invention of the steam engine, replacing the once popular Mud Mill. These dredges do their excavating with a continuous chain of buckets which are supported on an inclinable ladder and move up and down around two pivots called tumblers. As the buckets go around the lower tumbler they scoop up the material. They then carry it up the ladder and dump it into a shoot or trough as they pass over the upper tumbler.

Single-ladder dredges have the ladder collinear with the centerline of the hull—double-ladder dredges have the ladders set on either side of the centerline. The double-ladder dredges are practically obsolete however, inasmuch as they have a multiplicity of moving parts, have poor hull trim resulting in unsteadiness in the water, and have a broad beam making it difficult for them to pass through narrow locks or channels.

18 Cubic Foot Dredge Operating Near Marysville, California

Fig. 19.   Eighteen-cubic-foot Yuba Gold Dredge.

The single-ladder dredge is by far the most popular European dredge. Its only general application in the United States is in the production of gold (Fig. 19), and in some instances, sand and gravel.

One of the disadvantages of this dredge is that it has to be moored with five or more lines and anchors. These moorings are a constant hindrance to traffic and moving and resetting them is time consuming. Not only does this dredge have poor mobility as a result of the moorings, but it is not at all stable when being towed, principally because of the high center of gravity caused by the ladder, A-frame, and ponderous buckets.

Where traffic is limited and where there are rocks, piling, and other such obstructions, this dredge is highly practical. It works well in soft clays and rocks. In areas where pump-ashore methods cannot be used, or where flotation is a problem, it is quite economical.

The ladder dredge is swung across the cut by hauling in one bow wire and paying out the other. When the dredge reaches one side of the cut it is hauled ahead by the forward mooring wire and then the swing operation is repeated.

It is not a rough-weather dredge. In disturbed water the buckets lift out of the material—waves of three feet or more make it practically nonproductive.

The size of the buckets and the speed of the bucket cycle is dependent upon the materials being dredged. Small buckets are preferred for rock and other hard materials; large buckets are generally used for soft digging. Bucket sizes vary between five and 55 cubic feet (Fig. 20). In silts and muds the bucket-cycle will average 22 to 30 buckets per minute. In medium soils the rate may be 18 to 24 buckets per minute, but in hard or stiff clays the rate can drop to as low as nine to 12 buckets per minute. An 85 per cent bucket-fill is considered average. Maximum digging depth for most of these

(Yuba Industries, Inc.)

Fig. 20.   Five-cubic-foot Buckets on Lower Tumblers. (Yuba Industries, Inc.)

dredges is around 40 feet, but 75 feet is not uncommon.

Generally speaking, in comparison with other types of dredges, the ladder dredge has low efficiency. One of the main reasons for this is the extra power required to turn the bucket chain. Costs for dredging with this dredge are about twice that of grab dredging.

ENGINE ROOM

DRAG SUCTION

SIDE DRAG

OVERFLOWS

HOPPER SECTION

PUMP ROOM

Fig. 21. Suction and Draghead on Hopper Dredge.

20

B. HYDRAULIC DREDGES. All hydraulic dredges have one thing in common—they have a centrifugal pump discharging either into the hold of the dredge itself, into barges alongside, or ashore. They also all have a suction line through which the pump is supplied with material. The means of loosening and picking up the material is where they differ.

1. *Plain-suction Dredges.* Plain-suction dredges are similar in hull construction to a regular ship, but they often differ from other dredges in the location of the suction pipe. The plain-suction dredge often has its suction pipe in a well at the bow, whereas other types, such as the hopper-drags, have their suction pipes alongside.

The suction pipe, regardless of its location, extends through the hull to the pump. The pump discharges either into hoppers within the dredge itself or into barges alongside. Occasionally there is a

Fig. 22.   Converted T-2 Tanker. Two 24-inch discharges extend 290 feet outward.
(National Bulk Carriers, Inc.)

pump-ashore arrangement. The modern plain-suction dredge often has water jets installed at the lower end of the suction. High-pressure water is forced through the jets to break up the material. The end of the suction is also often flattened out in a rectangular shape much like the mouthpiece of a vacuum cleaner, and the jets are attached around the perimeter.

These dredges operate best when they are able to remain stationary and can dredge a hole into which the surrounding sand can run. In hard materials they are not very effective.

2. *Draghead Dredges.* The plain-suction dredge often uses a special suction head called a *dustpan* or *draghead* attached to the end of the suction (Fig. 21). Dredges using these attachments are generally hopper dredges, but occasionally they pump into barges tied alongside, or have side-casting booms (Fig. 22).

The draghead dredge requires the drag to be in contact with the bottom and the dredge in motion while dredging. It usually has a moulded hull and is self-propelled (Fig. 23). Built-in hopper capacities vary between 500 and 8,000 cubic yards. When the hoppers are full the dredge stops dredging and transports the material to a disposal area. This is the main disadvantage of the hopper dredge—it has to stop dredging to transport the material.

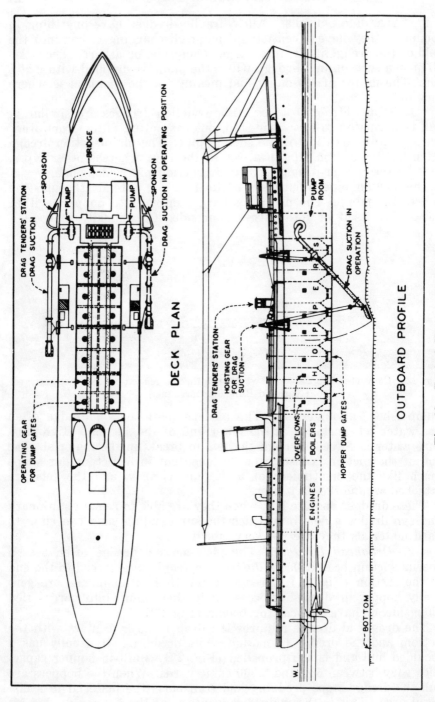

DECK PLAN

OPERATING GEAR
FOR DUMP GATES

DRAG TENDERS' STATION

DRAG SUCTION

PUMP

SPONSON

BRIDGE

PUMP

SPONSON

DRAG SUCTION IN OPERATING POSITION

OUTBOARD PROFILE

DRAG TENDERS' STATION

HOISTING GEAR
FOR DRAG SUCTION

PUMP
ROOM

DRAG SUCTION IN
OPERATION

HOPPERS

OVERFLOWS

BOILERS

ENGINES

HOPPER DUMP GATES

W L

BOTTOM

Fig. 23. Typical Hopper Dredge.

22

Some European hopper dredges operate at a mooring and by hauling ahead push the drag into the bank. These dredges are not common however. The vast majority dredge while in motion and are generally called trailing-suction dredges.

Some of the latest hopper dredges cost more than $15,000,000. One of the United States' newest is the *McFarland*, built for the Corps of Engineers. It has controllable-pitch propellers, swell compensators, bow-thrusters, elevators, air conditioning, closed-circuit television, radioactive density and magnetic flow meters, and even a helicopter landing pad (Fig. 24).

Fig. 24. Modern Hopper Dredge. Boom is 160 feet long. (Corps of Engineers)

This dredge is one of the first hopper dredges to carry a side-casting boom which enables it to discharge spoil more than 160 feet from the side of the cut. Its diesel engines develop 6,000 shaft horsepower. It has a speed of from three to seven knots while dredging, and up to 13 knots when running. Hopper capacity is 3,140 cubic yards.

C. DRAGHEADS. There are several types of dragheads in use in the United States, the most well known being the *Ambrose, California Coral, Newport Bay,* and the *Fruehling* (15). These are principally on government dredges, as the private dredging industry has not yet seen fit to invest in such type dredges.

The *Ambrose* draghead is a general purpose drag which is best used in mud, silt, soft clay, light gravel, loose sand, or stones. It is not effective in firm sand since the head will not dig into the material and thereby allows an excessive amount of water to enter. It is not adjustable for different depths (Fig. 25).

The *California* draghead (Fig. 26) was developed to provide a more efficient drag for sand dredging. It is self-adjusting for changes in dredging depth.

The *Coral* draghead (Fig. 27) was developed for dredging in the atolls of the south Pacific. It was a row of teeth along its bottom

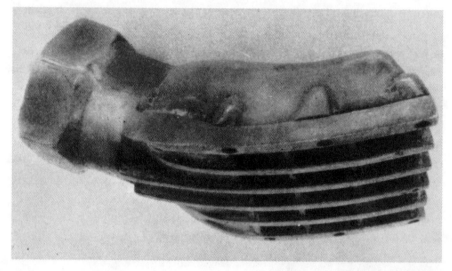

Fig. 25.   Ambrose Draghead. (Corps of Engineers)

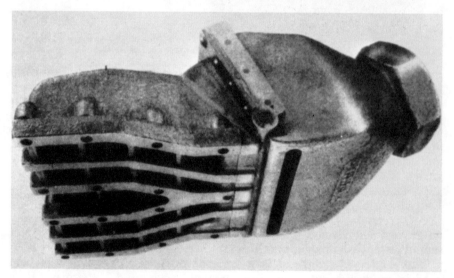

Fig. 26.   California Draghead. (Corps of Engineers)

which break up any coral not previously broken by blasting. It can be adjusted for different depths, but it is not self-adjusting.

The *Newport Bay* draghead was built to dredge on sloping banks of hard-packed sand. Where other types of drags slide down the banks, this drag has serrated bars which cut into the bank and prevent the drag from sliding.

The *Fruehling* draghead, named after its inventor Otto Fruehling, has a curved lip which gives it a scooping action (Fig. 28). It is sometimes outfitted with water jets to loosen the material. It operates effectively in soft mud, but poorly on sand bottoms. Because of its scooping action, it requires a lot of pulling power.

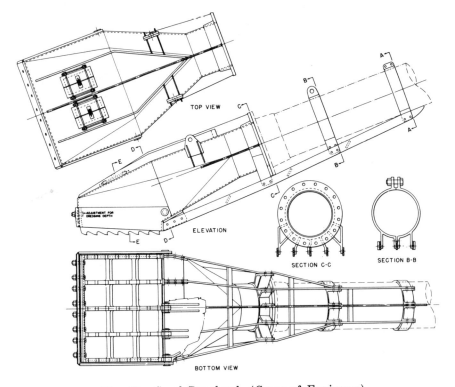

Fig. 27.   Coral Draghead. (Corps of Engineers)

Most dragheads have grates across their bottoms to keep out obstructions. When the grate openings are too large, over-size objects can pass through the suction and become lodged in the pump. When the openings are too small, suitable material is rejected and the openings often become clogged with rubbish (Fig. 29).

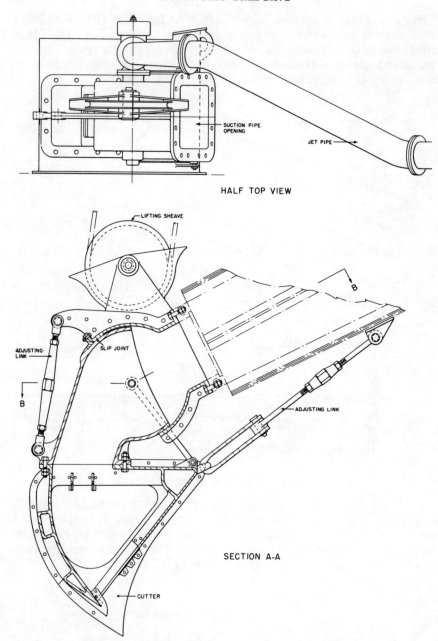

SUCTION PIPE
OPENING

JET PIPE

HALF TOP VIEW

LIFTING SHEAVE

ADJUSTING
LINK

SLIP JOINT

B

ADJUSTING LINK

SECTION A-A

CUTTER

Fig. 28.   Fruehling Draghead.   (Corps of Engineers)

Fig. 29. Draghead Bottom Showing Grates. (Posey Iron Works)

Chapter 2

The Pipeline Cutterhead Dredge—
Components and Plant

10. Introduction. In Chapter 1 principal types of dredges were discussed. However, one type was not dealt with—the pipeline, cutterhead dredge. In conjunction with its supporting equipment it is the most versatile and popular dredge in the world today. Essentially a combination of all other dredges, its prime function is to excavate and move material hydraulically to some other location without rehandling. It is generally referred to by the size of its floating discharge line—for example, a 24-inch dredge.

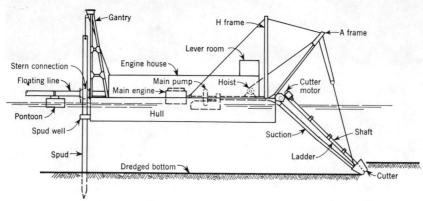

Fig. 30. Dredge Components.

11. Dredge Plant. The dredge, per se, is comprised generally of a ladder, cutter, suction pipe, A- and H-frames, cutter motor, hull, house, lever room, hoist-machinery, main pump and engine, spud frame, and spuds. Figure 30 shows these components and their location on the dredge.

During operation, a floating discharge line and shoreline are attached to the dredge. Supporting equipment is comprised generally of a derrick, one or more tugs called *tenders,* fuel and pipe barges, surveying craft, and other special equipment that may be required for a specific job. The dredge with its pipe and all supporting equipment is referred to as the *plant.* Figure 31 shows a plant owned by the J. S. Gissel Company of Houston, Texas.

28

12. Cutter. The cutter is attached to the forward end of the ladder. Connected by a shaft to the cutter motor, its rotation agitates soft or loose material or cuts hard material which is then picked up by the suction. Figure 32A shows a large dredge cutter. Figure 32B shows a view of the cutterhead. Both were made by the Florida Machine & Foundry Company of Jacksonville, Florida. Some cutters weigh as much as 40 tons and are as large as 12 feet in diameter.

Fig. 31.   Dredge Plant. (J. S. Gissel Co.)

A. TYPES OF CUTTERS.   Cutters are usually classified as *basket* or *straight-arm*. Figure 33 shows five types of United States cutters. The *basket* cutter has a front hub, a back wearing ring, and several spiral-shaped blades integral with the hub and ring. A closed-nose basket with spiral blades is best suited for digging in soft materials or loose sand. An open-nose basket is suitable for clay or hard materials, because when dredging in stiff clay, a cutter with blades close together may become clogged. A closed-nose basket with chisel-pointed teeth closely spaced on the blades is used in hard materials.

The *straight-arm* cutter with its blades extended beyond the hub and attached with bolts to a *spider* is used in hard clays. In exceptionally hard materials, serrated blades or blades with shovel-type teeth are used. Pick-shaped teeth work well in coral and other brittle materials.

In the early days objects which might clog the pump were excluded by steel straps or cables welded around the periphery of the cutter. Properly-designed cutters have now eliminated the need for this. When rocks, roots, or stumps are numerous, one or more steel bars

Fig. 32.   (A, Top) Cutter with Pick-Type Teeth; (B, Bottom) Basket Cutter.
(Florida Machine & Foundry Co.)

still are often welded across the suction mouthpiece, and occasionally a vertical bar is welded across the eye of the pump.

B. CUTTER RATINGS. Horsepower applied to the cutter varies with the job and size of the dredge. Small dredges (8 to 12 inches) may have as much as 400 horsepower. Larger dredges may have more than

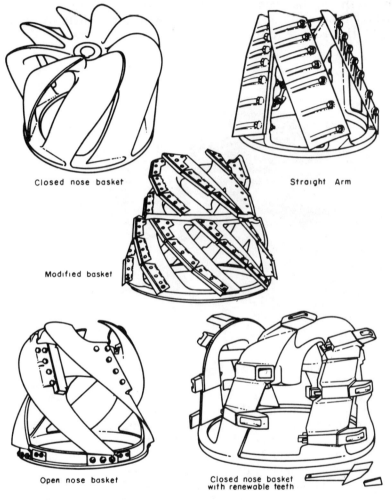

Fig. 33. Five Types of Cutters.

4,000 horsepower. Speeds at which cutters are turned usually are between ten and 30 rpm, depending upon the materials being dredged and the size of the cutter.

The cutter is supported at the end of the ladder by a shaft and a special underwater bearing. This bearing has to hold up against the most severe conditions. Combined with the impact loading of dredging, the abrasive materials encountered are rough on a bearing.

Packing has been unsuccessful in keeping abrasive material out of the bearing, as the rough service makes it difficult to maintain a satisfactory seal.

Cutless bearings have been very successful for cutterheads, however. For dredges, these bearings are usually made with shells of bronze. Inside the bronze shell is an oil-resisting, tough, and wear-resistant rubber lining which is vulcanized to the shell. As shown in Fig. 34, this rubber lining has a number of water faces and grooves.

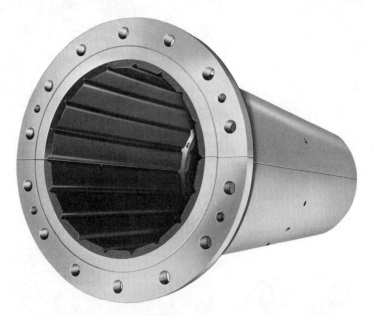

Fig. 34.   Cutless Bearing.   (Lucian Moffitt, Inc.)

The shaft is supported in the bearing by a film of water which is pumped into the bearing through the grooves. The amount of water usually applied is around 50 pounds per square inch, but 90 pounds per square inch will give a better lift to the shaft. For most dredge bearings there should be at least two gallons of lubricating water per minute for each inch of bearing diameter.

The cutter is usually attached to its shaft by a high-pitch, ACME thread (double or triple), and it is usually backed up against a lead washer to prevent sticking. When it is necessary to remove it, the cutter is blocked and the cutter motor reversed. Cutter changes should usually be made in less than 30 minutes.

C. CUTTER DESIGN. Cutters are made of wear-resistant steel. The leading edge of the cutter blade should have a hardness of at least a 500 Brinell or 51 Rockwell C, and a yield strength of around 200,000 pounds per square inch (17).

Three important physical factors determine a cutter's configuration. They are its *cone* and *face angle,* its *sweep,* and its *rake angle* (17).

The *cone angle* is the angle formed by the profile of the cutter— this angle is approximately twice the angle between the bottom of the cut and the centerline of the inclined ladder. The *face angle* is one-half the cone angle. The *sweep* is the angular displacement of the cutter blades—the included angle along the periphery of the cutter

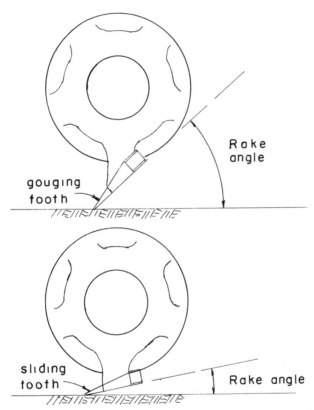

Fig. 35. Cutter Rake Angles. Top view, angle too large. Bottom View, angle too small.

of one complete blade. A three-blade cutter would have a sweep angle of 120°. The smaller the cutter's sweep angle, i.e., the more blades, the less vibration will be encountered—just as an eight-cylinder engine is smoother than a four-cylinder one. However, as the angle is reduced, the size of materials that can be dredged will decrease.

The *rake angle* is probably the most important characteristic of the cutter and important to its operation. This angle is that which is made by the tangent to the cutter's peripheral motion at the point of contact with the material being cut, and the slope of the line of the blade or tooth face (Fig. 35). The angle best suited for obtaining

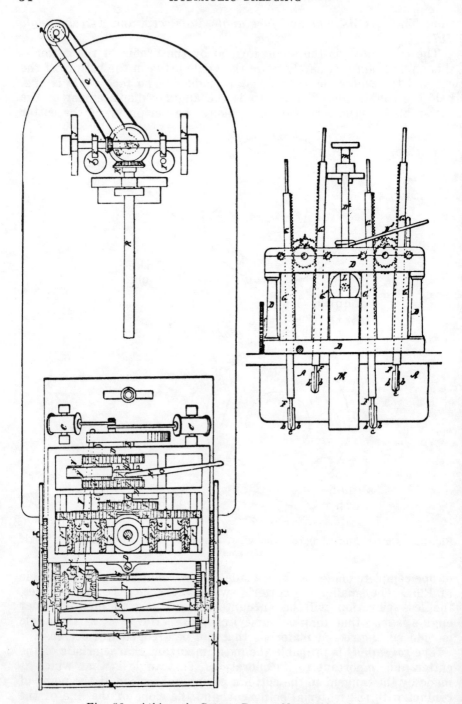

Fig. 36.   Atkinson's Cutter. Patent No. 39,194 of 1863.

maximum force is the angle which allows penetration of the material at the lowest torque.

With too small a rake angle—the blade or tooth slope being small— the cutter will tend to slide on the material. With too large an angle, the cutter will tend to gouge or stab into the material. Experienced levermen can tell the relative effectiveness of the cutter by observing the cutter-motor current, and are responsible for determining whether rake angles are proper.

Removable-teeth cutters allow quick teeth changes. This eliminates changing the entire cutter. Some dredgmen believe a pyramid-tooth is best for cutting soft or medium clay, a chisel-tooth best for cutting material that fails in shear, such as loose sand and clay, and a flared-tooth best for sand and stiff or hard clay.

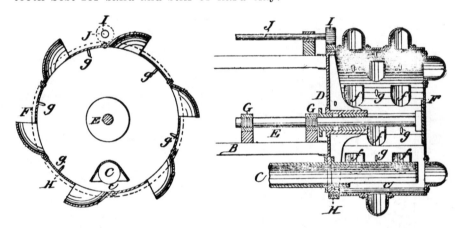

Fig. 37. Angell's Cutter. Patent No. 341,539 of 1886.

Most cutters are now assembled in sections. Whole-cast cutters are still made, but to maintain the requirements and quality of the different parts, they are difficult to build. Consequently, by casting each part separately and then welding them together, a better overall cutter can be obtained.

D. EARLY CUTTERS. The first cutters were not very successful. In the early days the understanding of the basic principles for obtaining a pumpable mixture was vague and attempts to develop a satisfactory cutter were disappointing. With the exception of sand and silt, dredging materials were hard and sticky—as they still are. Usually these materials have to be broken loose before they can be picked up by the suction. The early cutters were unable to do it (16).

The cutter's development included innumerable trials of jets, plows, knives, teeth, blades, and multitudinous other contraptions. Only after much time and experimentation was a suitable cutter produced. It had spiral blades with an inward delivery. Little change has been made over the years in this basic design. Even today the inward delivery cutter with spiral blades of different sizes, shapes, and number (some with teeth and some without, depending upon the material to be cut), is generally accepted (16).

Perhaps the first cutter was designed by William Atkinson of Brooklyn, New York in 1863 (Fig. 36). It had a number of knives similar to those on a lawnmower, revolving around a horizontal axis (16). A bank of vertical chisels, much like rock drills, was also included. It was too involved. A year later Bazin designed a cutter with a horizontal shaft set transverse to the axis of the dredge. The shaft was studded with a group of knives and long spikes, and the cutter rotated around its own axis (16).

Sometime later, Horace B. Angell obtained a patent for a cutter consisting of a rotating drum with numerous cup-shaped scoops attached to its periphery. These scoops were supposed to scoop the

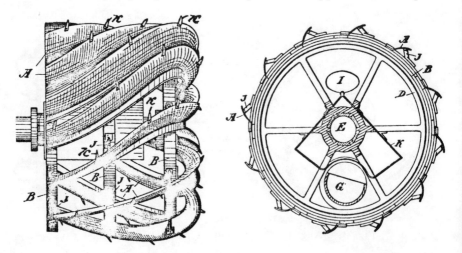

Fig. 38.　Lynch's Cutter.　Patent No. 365,140 of 1887.

material into the drum so the suction could pick it up. It was not too effective and was, in fact, totally useless in sticky materials (Fig. 37).

The *basket cutter* was probably first designed and patented by Henry H. Lynch. It was a major improvement. Basically it was a cylindrical cage (Fig. 38) around which a number of spiral knives were fixed. It was almost identical to the one now known as the Ellicott Cutter, named for the Ellicott Machine Corporation of Baltimore, Maryland.

In 1892, R. A. Perry designed the first sticky-clay cutter. It had straight, slightly-raked blades and a large-diameter spider with no back ring. Perry also designed the square, taper-end cutter shaft, and as well, the taper-socket hub for cutter connection. He failed to patent these, however (16).

Marshall C. Harris of the American Dredging Company invented and patented the renewable-tooth cutter. He also invented the slip-sleeve, knuckle joint for transmitting power from an engine on the hull of the dredge to a cutter shaft mounted on the ladder. In Tampa, Florida, in 1915, the dredge *Turbine*, using the Harris cutter, dredged

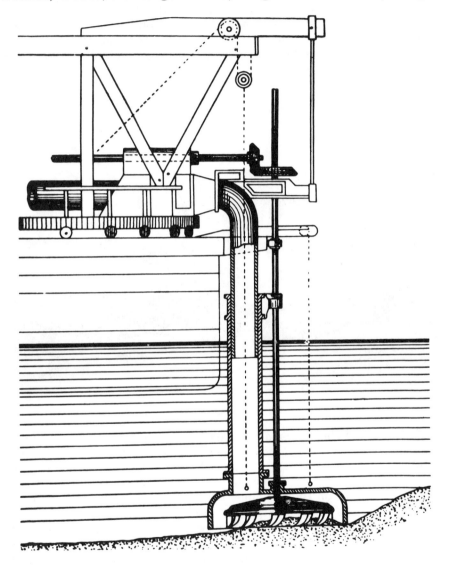

Fig. 39. Sectional View of Schmidt's Rotating Plow Cutter. (Technical Press, Ltd., London)

the first coral limestone ever dredged in the United States by the hydraulic method. Several years prior to the Angell and Lynch cutters, Alexis von Schmidt patented a *rotating plow* cutter (Fig. 39).

13. Ladder. In addition to the cutter, the ladder carries the suction pipe, lubricating lines, and most usually the cutter motor and its reduction gear. The aft or upper end of the ladder is supported by heavy trunions set in a well in the bow of the dredge hull. On small dredges the ladder is often mounted directly on the hull and no well is used. The ladder's front end is suspended from an A-frame by a multiline block-and-tackle connected to hoisting machinery within the dredge (Figs. 40 and 41).

Fig. 40.   Twenty-inch Dredge.   (Ellicott Machine Corp.)

The length of the ladder determines the dredging depth. Maximum dredging depth is generally considered as about 0.7 of the ladder's length—when the ladder is inclined at a 45° angle to the horizontal. This angular limitation is usually observed because a greater angle causes the forces on the trunions, which increase with the *Sin* of the vertical angle, to become extremely great.

The ladder is necessarily built to be tough and strong and generally is built with deep-web beams, girders, stiffeners, bulkheads, and large trunion housings. Stresses are highest in bending about its horizontal axis, and they increase in proportion to the square of the length. Ladders vary in length from 25 feet or less to 150 feet or more, and some weigh as much as 400 tons (U.S.).

14. Suction. The suction pipe transports material from the cutter to the pump. It is supported beneath the ladder (Figs. 42 and 46), and is flexibly connected to the hull by a ball joint, trunion elbow, or rubber sleeve. Its diameter depends upon the size of the pump.

Technically, the diameter of the suction is dependent upon the pump's output, the minimum velocity allowable in the pipe, and other criteria. The suction pipe diameter could be the same diameter as the discharge and have the same quantity of flow at the same velocity.

Fig. 41.   Sixteen-inch Dredge.   (Ellicott Machine Corp.)

However, the maximum suction available at the pump is about 28 feet—25 inches of mercury. (*See* Art. 141.) If most of this is used in overcoming friction losses there will be little left to raise the material; therefore, losses in the suction are kept as low as practicable, so that as much energy as possible is left for lifting material.

The parameters affecting loss in the suction are the discharge rate, the area of the suction pipe, and the velocity of the mixture. As the discharge rate is fixed by the pump discharge, and therefore by the

Fig. 42. Ladder and Suction Pipe. (Ellicott Machine Corp.)

velocity, reduction of loss in the suction must come through a decrease in velocity. The diameter of the suction is therefore usually increased sufficiently to reduce the velocity to as low a value as possible, but high enough that it will still carry the material in suspension.

Usually this is accomplished by making the diameter of the suction 1.25 to 1.50 times the pump discharge diameter. Practically however, the suction is usually sized one standard pipe size above the discharge. For example, with a pump discharge of 16 inches, the suction pipe might be 18 inches in diameter.

The suction pipe is suspended below the ladder in saddles attached to the transverse members (Figs. 42 and 46). It is assembled in flange-connected sections 10- to 15-feet long. Thickness of the pipe varies, but in general it is usually not less than 1/2-inch and more often 3/4-inch to 1-inch thick. Friction wears the bottom more than the sides or top, so rather than replacing the entire pipe each time the bottom gets thin, the pipe should be periodically turned 120° so that wear will be uniform.

Fig. 43.   Suction Pipe Fabrication. (Posey Iron Works)

The suction entrance is more important from a hydraulic standpoint than some dredgemen realize. It is generally accepted that a round entry with a bellmouth will give the lowest entrance losses. However, a shaft-supported cutter precludes a round opening, as the suction mouth must fit into the cutter below its center (Figs. 32 and 41). The suction mouth opening is consequently depressed on the top and widened on the sides, creating an elliptical shape (Fig. 43). The elliptical shape of the suction mouth should be of different area for different materials. However, the average area is usually about 125 per cent of the area of the suction pipe. A round opening could be obtained if a cutter of sufficient diameter was used, but such a size would be impractical because of the loss of torque from the increased lever-arm effect.

A. SUCTION CUTTER-DRIVE. A method of overcoming the difficulty of obtaining a round suction mouth opening was discovered quite early. Around 1890, L. D. Bates patented an idea of connecting a cutter directly to the suction and letting the suction pipe turn the cutter. Only recently, however, has this method been given any amount of acceptance (Fig. 44) and a lot of dredgemen do not accept it yet.

Fig. 44. Suction Cutter Drive and Jet Pump Attachment.
(PACECO)

Suction-mouth losses with the suction cutter-drive where round openings can be used, range from 25 to 50 per cent less than do those with regular depressed suction mouths. Also, it is generally considered that installation and maintenance costs are as much as 10 per cent lower.

Some of the other advantages of this arrangement are, (1) elimination of heavy cutter shafts and their unavoidable failures, (2) smaller cutters which provide higher torque and less cost—in extremely hard material such as rock, or hard-packed sand, effective tooth pressure can often be more than doubled by reducing the cutter size—and (3) elimination of ladder drag—the end of the ladder can be set farther back and consequently will not drag in the material. Also, as the cutter is located centrally, the suction can be extended into the cutter allowing closer contact with the material and conse-quently better pickup.

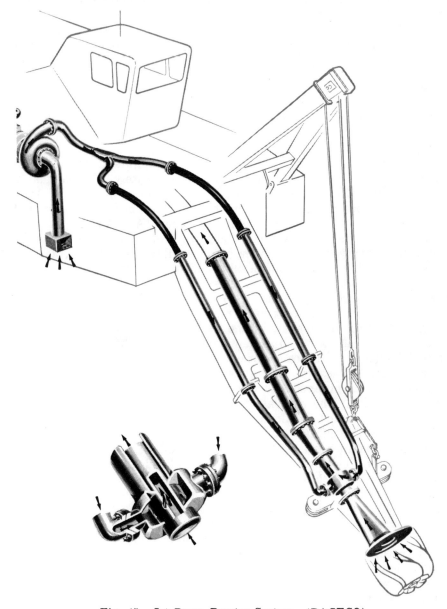

Fig. 45.   Jet Pump Booster System.   (PACECO)

As an example of how the suction-pipe drive eliminates heavy cutter shafts, consider a dredge with 30-inch suction. With a 1-inch wall thickness, the suction pipe would have the strength of an 18-inch diameter solid shaft—but its weight would be only about 35 per cent of that of the solid shaft. (*See* Art. 22 for means of determining these relationships.)

While considering the losses in the suction, and the need for as much energy as possible to lift the material, a method for obtaining extra energy should be discussed. This is the water-jet booster system.

B. WATER-JET BOOSTER. The water-jet booster system increases production by providing more lifting energy at the pump's suction. Not only is it advantageous when dredging at unusual depths, but production is sometimes improved at shallower depths, under certain conditions.

The amount of suction available to a pump is limited by the atmospheric pressure, which at sea level is approximately 14.7 pounds per square inch (34 feet of fresh water, or 30 inches of mercury). About 24 to 25 inches of mercury is all that will be practically available under normal operating conditions, however (Art. 141).

Some of this suction is always used up in overcoming friction and creating velocity, the remainder being available to lift the material. Where dredging is at a considerable depth, the friction, velocity, and entrance heads do not change appreciably from what they would be at some shallower depth, but the head to lift the material does. As the depth of dredging increases, more energy is required to lift the material. With no change in the hydraulic system, the amount of material that can be lifted as depth increases is continually decreased until at some point there is not enough energy to lift any material.

For instance, assume that at 50 feet dredging depth, 10 per cent solids are being pumped at a velocity of 15 feet per second through a 20-inch suction. The equivalent length of the suction line (from the cutter to the pump) is calculated as, say 100 feet. Suppose the material has a weight of 100 pounds per cubic foot.

In this instance the water vacuum would be the sum of the entrance head, velocity head, and friction head. The entrance head would be $H_e = 0.25 \ V^2/2g = 0.87$ feet, the velocity head would be $H_v = V^2/2g = 3.49$ feet, and the friction head (from Table 9) would be 3.06 feet. Specific gravity is not considered for this example. So the total water vacuum would be the sum of these heads, or $0.87 + 3.49 + 3.06 = 7.42$ feet, or 6.55 inches of mercury.

If the dredging depth were now increased to 100 feet—the equivalent length of the suction line then being 150 feet—the water vacuum would be increased only slightly, to about 8.88 feet, or 7.84 inches of mercury.

When material was introduced into the flow, the change in entrance, velocity, and friction head would be zero. Actually there would be a slight change in the friction head, as explained in Art. 142, but it would be small, and so for this explanation it is disregarded. There would be, however, an additional head required to lift the material.

At 50 feet, 100 per cent material would weigh $H_1 = (50)(100) = 5,000$ pounds, or have a pressure of $5,000/144 = 34.72$ pounds per square inch. At 100 feet, it would weigh $H_1 = (100)(100) = 10,000$ pounds, or have a pressure of $10,000/144 = 69.44$ pounds per square inch. For a 10 per cent material concentration, the pressure would be 3.47 pounds per square inch, or 7.07 inches of mercury, at 50 feet, and 6.94 pounds per square inch, or 14.15 inches of mercury, at 100 feet. So, at 50 feet the total head required would be $H_t = 6.55 + 7.07 = 13.62$ inches of mercury. But at 100 feet the total head required would be $H_t = 7.84 + 14.15 = 21.99$ inches of mercury—an increase of 8.37 inches for the same concentration.

It should be obvious therefore, that additional increases in depth, under the existing conditions, would use up all the suction available and result in lower concentrations, or possibly none at all. Consequently, some additional energy would have to be imparted to the suction if the dredging was to continue productively.

This is the purpose of the water-jet booster system. It injects a high-powered stream of water into or near the suction mouth at high velocity through a group of nozzles (Fig. 45). The velocity head is changed into pressure head by the jets and thereby energy is added to the suction system. Some jet systems have been claimed to increase the production as much as 40 to 60 per cent.

In adding to the energy of the system, the jet also allows the pump to operate further from the cavitation limit and correspondingly allows the use of smaller and higher-speed pumps. The water pressures and rates now being used in jet pumps are around 100 pounds per square inch at about 150 feet per second. Costs for commercial systems are high. For small to medium-sized dredges an adequate system would cost around $10,000 (1967).

It is quite important to realize that the jet system does not impart any energy to the pump. It is only beneficial when the pump is not being supplied the material it could be handling within its horsepower range. That is, if the pump and basic hydraulic system is producing a certain output which requires a certain amount of shaft horsepower, then the interjection of the jet into the system is not going to give a bit more output unless the horsepower is increased. If the pump is operating at full capacity, the jet system would be a detrimental addition, not an improvement. Consequently, when operating at normal depths the only advantage of the jet system would be in a condition where all the capacity of the pump is not being realized. In such a situation, installation of the jet would be like an aspirin to a headache—it relieves the situation but does not cure it.

15. Suction-to-Hull Connection. The suction pipe is connected to the hull of the dredge by a flexible coupling which is usually a rubber hose or sleeve (Fig. 46). Maximum angle of deflection of standard

Fig. 46. Flexible Connection. (Ellicott Machine Corp.)

Fig. 47. A- and H-frames. (White Motor Co.)

dredge sleeves is determined by the equation $B = (106)(L)/D$, where B = degree of bend, in decimal degrees, L = free length of hose, in feet (the part clamped to the pipe ends is not measured), and D = inside diameter of the hose, in inches.

The distance from the hull flange to a transverse line between the ladder trunions determines one-half the effective length of hose. In calculating the total length of hose required, a sufficient amount should be added for clamping to the flange of the hull and to the suction pipe. A longer hose however, would be of no advantage. It is important, therefore, that the distance between the hull and the trunion transverse line be sufficient to allow for at least a 45° bend of the hose to obtain the maximum digging depth.

Some installations have the connection of the suction pipe to the hull flange so adjusted that when the ladder is down 22.5° the hose connection is straight. In this manner only one-half the bending stress is placed on the hose at maximum depth, and a shorter length can be used.

Fig. 48.   Frame for Ladder in Deep Dredging.   (PACECO)

Suction hoses are standard from four-inch to 20-inch diameters. They can be obtained commercially from five to six ply. The safe working pressure varies, but about 200 pounds per square inch is the average maximum.

A swivel joint is sometimes used instead of a hose. One of the swivel's few advantages is that the degree of rotation is unlimited. On the other hand, it is difficult to keep the connection tight, and consequently suction troubles are more frequent than with hose connections.

16. A- and H-frames.   The A-frame is the main support for the block-and-tackle that supports the ladder (Fig. 47). It is usually pinned to the forward end of the dredge hull rather than being fixed rigidly. This arrangement allows for movement while the dredge is operating. It is tied back to an H-frame by flexible wires or sometimes steel rods.

Fig. 49. Cutter Shaft and Power Assembly.

Fig. 50. Hydraulic Motor Cutter Drive. (The Cincinnati Gear Co.)

The H-frame (Fig. 47), which is often called a *gallows,* supports the A-frame and transfers the load to the hull of the dredge. Usually it is tied back to a central location on the dredge by flexible wire-rope stays or *hog wires.* On large dredges a built-up structure utilizing the combined advantages of A- and H-frames is used for better structural strength (Fig. 2). A special frame used on deep dredging work is shown in Fig. 48.

17. Cutter Motor. The cutter motor is usually located on the rear or upper end of the ladder (Fig. 40), and is attached to the cutter shaft through a reduction gear, flexible coupling, and thrust bearing (Fig. 49). Cutter motor speeds are reduced to between five and 30 rpm by reduction gears and the power applied to the cutter may be as much as or more than 4000 horsepower.

Cutter motors are generally d-c and are controlled to provide smooth speed regulation. A-c motors are occasionally used with step-speed control. Hydraulic motors are becoming more popular for several reasons. One is that they are submersible and can therefore be mounted at the end of the ladder, thereby eliminating long cutter shafts and speed reducers (Fig. 50). Also, they can be banked to provide almost any power required. They do present a greater repair and maintenance problem than electric motors, however. As electric motor drives generally must be kept dry, they are usually at the top of the ladder, although some installations are now using submersible electric motors.

18. Motor Speed Controls. The need for speed control of motors, and the ability of the motors to maintain their speed under varying loads, is important in dredging. In soft materials it is often desirable to reduce the speed of the cutter motor. Also, where there is not much bank, *getting ahead* is important. Consequently, a high rope speed is needed and thusly a high winder-motor speed. On the other hand, when dredging in hard materials, a slower swing is necessary, and a slower rope speed is required.

Any change in speed involves horsepower or torque. *Horsepower* is the product of torque and speed. If the torque required by a cutter is held constant and the speed reduced, horsepower demand is increased. On the other hand, if horsepower is held constant and speed reduced, *torque* is increased. Therefore, in *constant horsepower* equipment, changes in speed are accompanied by opposite changes in torque. In *constant torque* equipment, changes in speed are accompanied by similar changes in horsepower. Most dredging equipment, particularly the cutter motor, requires constant torque.

Horsepower rating does not determine what is required to cut a certain material. What does is the amount of the force on the blades of the cutter. This force multiplied by the radius of the cutter determines the torque, not horsepower. Regardless of the peripheral speed of the cutter, the same torque will be required to cut the material. The cutter can be turning at 10 rpm or at 30 rpm, but the

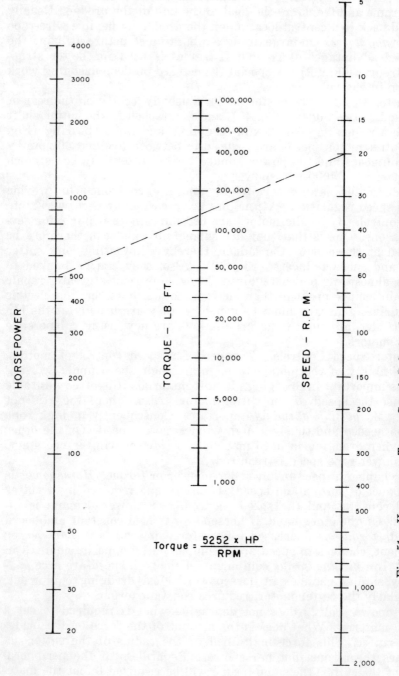

HORSEPOWER

TORQUE – LB. FT.

SPEED – R.P.M.

$$Torque = \frac{5252 \times HP}{RPM}$$

Fig. 51. Horsepower-Torque-Speed Relationship. Any straight line drawn through the three vertical scales will give equivalent values.

50

torque required will remain the same. Not so with horsepower. Horsepower, being the product of the torque and speed, varies with speed. For any required value of torque, a reduction in speed of, say, 50 per cent will result in a similar decrease in horsepower (Fig. 51). This fact is applicable to dredging when the cutter is operating in a material requiring high torque.

Suppose that a cutter motor is running at rated horsepower. Should stiffer material be encountered, three alternatives are possible, (1) a smaller diameter cutter can be substituted, thereby reducing the lever arm, (2) the motor can be overloaded, or (3) the peripheral speed of the cutter can be reduced. The third alternative is one reason for having cutter motor speed control.

A. MOTOR FUNDAMENTALS. The operation of an electric motor is based upon the fact that a conductor through which a current is flowing, if placed in a magnetic field, will be subjected to a force which tends to move the conductor (18). This force is created by the combined action of the *flux* (magnetic field—ϕ) and the current flowing in the armature (I_a). The speed at which this conductor is moved is dependent upon the voltage induced in it by the field and the current flowing through it.

The effective torque on the conductor is a product of the field flux (ϕ) and the armature current (I_a). As flux is generally a function of the field current (I_f), the torque is a product of I_a and I_f. The equation for torque on the conductor is then $T = I_a\phi = I_aI_f$, where torque is in *pound-feet*; I_a = armature current, in amperes and I_f = field current, in amperes.

In *shunt-field motors* (constant field) the I_f will be a constant and therefore torque will be proportional to armature current. If the field is variable, I_f will vary, and torque will be proportional to both armature and field current.

The output torque that a motor can produce, everything else being equal, is limited by the amount of current it can commutate. Motors may be able to use as much as five times rated current, but it usually is not practical because of the impossibility of commutating the high current.

For most applications the speed-torque curve of a motor is a straight line up to normal load. As long as a shunt motor has a constant field its torque is directly proportional to I_a, and consequently it produces *constant torque*—inasmuch as the I_f and applied voltage is constant, I_a is constant.

As horsepower is a function of the voltage, current, and efficiency, and is also directly proportional to the product of the current and the speed, a constant field condition will give variable horsepower up to rated load (18).

Speed of a shunt motor is determined from

$$N = 60 \left(\frac{V - I_aR_a}{(Z)(\phi)} \right) K \times 10^8 \qquad (1)$$

where N = motor speed, in rpm; V = applied voltage, in volts; R_a = resistance of the field, in ohms; Z = number of conductors in the armature; ϕ = field flux, in maxwells and K = a constant of the machine determined by the number of poles and paths. From this equation it can be seen that to change the speed of the motor, the only two possible variables are the applied voltage and the field flux or field current.

So, if a shunt motor is to be run at a speed different from design, flux or field current, or both, must be varied. If the field is weakened (ϕ or I_f reduced), the speed will increase. However, as shown by the equation for torque ($T = K_1\phi\, I_a\, K_2\, 10^8$), changing the flux or armature current will change the torque. Consequently, for speeds above design, torque is variable. As horsepower is the product of torque and speed, the machine will develop *constant horsepower*.

All motors are commercially rated in terms of full-load horsepower and speed. Using these values, the full-load torque can be determined from,

$$T = \frac{(5252)\ (HP)}{rpm} \qquad (2)$$

where T = torque, in pound-feet.

B. SERIES MOTORS. The simplest motor for speed control is a d-c series motor. It has a high torque at zero speed, but a sharply drooping characteristic, which unfortunately gives it poor speed regulation under changing loads. Consequently, it is not suitable for constant speed applications.

C. SHUNT MOTORS. D-c shunt motors have their fields connected in parallel with the armature. Since the field current is constant and independent of the load, torque is proportional to armature current and speed will be constant. Speed can be changed, however, by varying the shunt-field current.

The d-c shunt motor is not as suitable for starting heavy loads as the series motor, but its speed varies considerably less under load. As speed is inversely proportional to the field strength, at speeds above design speed the product of torque and speed will be a constant, and the d-c shunt motor will produce constant horsepower. As long as it is operated at full field (no speed control), the torque is directly proportional to armature current and the motor produces constant torque.

In adjustable-voltage systems the flux of the motor is held constant and the armature voltage is varied, producing constant torque. With constant field excitation, speed is proportional to the voltage applied to the armature, less the $I_a R_a$ drop. Speed can therefore be changed by reducing the applied voltage to the armature. Speed control by this method is called *adjustable voltage* or *Ward Leonard* control.

In the Ward Leonard system a separately excited d-c generator supplies the armature voltage to the shunt motor (Fig. 52). By varying the field of the generator, its output voltage which is applied to the shunt motor, is changed and thus the shunt motor's speed is changed.' With such a system speed can be controlled to as low as 0.1 of the motor's design speed, and through a speed range of as much as 10 to 1. Thus a 40 to 1 speed control can be had.

D. A-C MOTORS.   Speed control of an a-c motor is no different from that of a d-c motor as both operate on the same principle that field and armature current are involved in developing torque, and voltage in developing speed.

The polyphase induction motor is the most widely used a-c motor for speed control. It may have a wound secondary, or one consisting merely of a number of short wires connected together at their ends— the latter is called a *squirrel-cage* motor. The squirrel-cage motor is not as suitable for speed control as the wound-rotor motor.

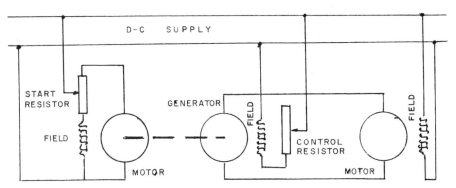

Fig. 52.   Ward-Leonard System.

If a resistance is inserted in the secondary of a wound-rotor motor a change in speed will be obtained. This procedure is impractical for speeds less than half rated speed, however, because variations in torque requirements generate high speed changes. But, if an external voltage is introduced into the rotor circuit, good regulation will be obtained. This method is used extensively in speed regulating sets. These sets have a high first cost and consequently are used only with large motors. But when speed ranges above two to one are needed, the speed-regulating set is usually more economical than other systems. One of such speed-regulating sets is the *Kraemer System.*

19. Kraemer Speed-regulating System.   The Kraemer system (Fig. 53) has a d-c motor coupled directly to a wound-rotor induction motor, which in turn is driven as an induction generator. A constant d-c supply furnishes excitation for a synchronous convertor and the d-c motor. The speed of the main motor is controlled by the excitation voltage of the d-c motor, which controls the voltage to the synchronous convertor. This in turn controls the voltage to the main motor. This system allows speed control below synchronous and produces constant torque. The speed range can be controlled down to zero if desirable (19).

Synchronous motors, per se, are strictly constant-speed motors and their speed can only be varied by frequency changes in the armature voltage. They are generally impractical for use as speed-controlled devices for dredges.

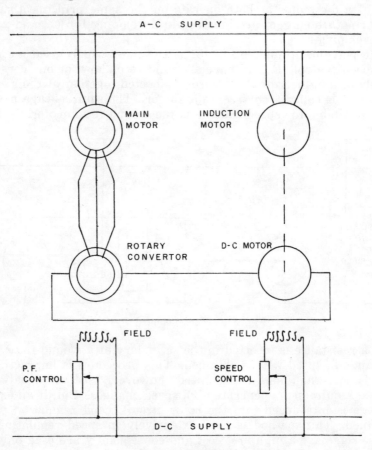

Fig. 53. Kraemer System.

20. Speed Reducers. Cutter motors are not connected directly to the cutter shaft. A reduction gear is used to reduce the speed to a 10- to 30-rpm cutter-shaft speed. There are some motors with integral reduction gears—called gearmotors—but their ratings are generally not more than 75 horsepower.

Most reduction gears are either *helical* or *herringbone*. *Herringbone gears* are so named because of the similarity of their teeth to the spine of the Herring fish. The teeth are arranged parallel to each other, but are in successive rows that slope in reverse direction. They come in single, double, and triple reduction combinations. Double reduction is most often used, as a single reduction usually does not have ratios high enough for dropping the speed to the cutter requirements. *Helical gears*, although easier to maintain, do not have the thrust-cancelling capabilities of the herringbone gears.

Fig. 54.   Eight-hundred Horsepower Speed Reducer (Farrel Corp.)

Double-reduction gears in commercial sizes usually have ratings less than 1,000 horsepower in the reduction ratios required. In selecting reduction gears it should be remembered that manufacturers assign torque ratings such that a 100 per cent overload can be permitted for starting or for occasional peak loads. Also, the equipment is usually rated for dredge service with a minimum service factor of two, and a Class H (heavy shock) load. In other words, a 1,000-horsepower gear should be selected for a 500-horsepower load. Figure 54 shows the exterior of an 800-horsepower reducer manufactured by Farrel-Birmingham Corporation of Rochester, New York, which at 600 rpm input has a 20-rpm output. Figure 55 shows the interior of the gear.

Fig. 55.   Interior of Speed Reducer of Fig. 54.   (Farrel Corp.)

Single-reduction gears come in much higher horsepower ratings than the double- or triple-reduction reducers. However, their reduction factors are usually limited to 1 to 10. With minimum driver input speeds of 600 rpm these gears are not satisfactory for cutter drives. Reduction gears for high-power cutter drives are usually built to the requirements of the particular service.

21. Cutter Shaft. The cutter shaft is supported by bearings mounted on top of the ladder directly above the suction pipe (Figs. 40 and 41). At its aft or upper end it is connected to the reduction gear through a thrust bearing and a flexible coupling (Fig. 49). These two take up the thrust and compensate for any misalinement, respectively. Shafts are generally not one integral piece, but are made up of flange-coupled sections. Diameters vary from four inches on the smaller dredges to as much as 20 inches on large ones, the diameter being determined by the torque requirements of the cutter.

22. Shafts. In determining the proper size shaft for a cutter motor, or for any other power transmitting system for that matter, there are certain fundamentals to be considered before a decision of size can be made (20).

In the broad category of forces that act on shafts there are two main classifications: (1) external forces, called *loads* (F), and (2) internal forces, called *stresses* (S). The internal forces resist the external forces. Any physical change in the body being affected by a force is called a *strain* (e).

Loads on shafts are of three types: (1) static, (2) repeated, and (3) impact. They all can show up either as axial, bending, or torsional loads. Torsional loads are the principal loads on shafts. This type of load multiplied by the angular velocity of the shaft gives what is called the twisting moment or torque (T). Torque is equated to horsepower as

$$T = \frac{(HP)\ (60)\ (550)\ (12)}{(2\pi)\ (rpm)} \tag{3}$$

where T = torque, in inch-pounds (one inch-pound of torque being the same as one pound pulling on a lever arm of one inch; in Fig. 56

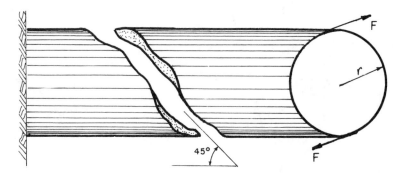

Fig. 56.   Forces on a Shaft and Resulting Plane of Failure in Torsion.

the torque on the shaft would be the force (F), in pounds, times the radius of the shaft, in inches) ; and HP = horsepower, defined as 550 foot-pounds of work per second (the same thing as lifting 550 pounds one foot in one second, or lifting one pound 550 feet in one second).

Stresses on shafts are either normal, causing compressive action (S_c), tensile, causing stretching action (S_t), or shearing, causing sliding or shearing action (S_s).

Strains in shafts show up as linear or torsional deflections. Linear deflection of a shaft is sometimes considered as the amount of vertical sag. Usually this is limited to 0.01 inches per linear foot of shaft between bearings. The maximum spacing of bearings to maintain this limit is generally determined by

$$L = 6.3\ (D^{0.66}) \tag{4}$$

where L = distance between bearings, in feet, and D = diameter of the shaft, in inches.

A shaft's torsional deflection is the amount of angular twist. According to some authorities the maximum amount of twist allowable should not be greater than 0.08° per linear foot of shaft (20). The diameter of the shaft required to maintain this limit is

$$D = 4.6\left(\frac{HP}{rpm}\right)^{0.25} \tag{5}$$

where D = diameter of the shaft, in inches.

A shaft's strength is attributed principally to its ability to withstand torsional, tensile, and shearing stress. The intensity of the stress is usually indicated in pounds. However, rather than say it has a stress of so many pounds, it is described as a stress of so many pounds per square inch.

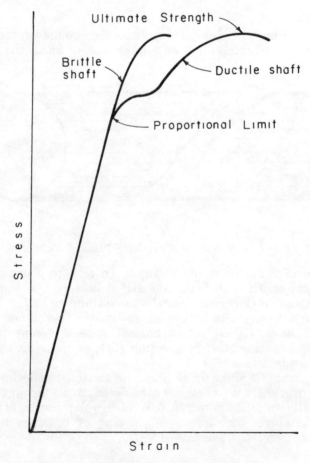

Fig. 57.   Stress-Strain Curve for Shafts.

A shaft's maximum strength limit is usually indicated by its *proportional limit* for a ductile material, and by the *ultimate strength* for a brittle material (Fig. 57).

Some of the steels used for cutter shafts are SAE (United States Society of Automotive Engineers) 4340, 4615, 4620, and 6150. Propeller shafts are generally SAE 2340, 2345, or 4140. The first numeral in each number represents the class of steel, that is, 1 represents carbon steel, 2 represents nickel steel, 3 represents nickel-chromium, 4 represents molybdenum, and so on. For the alloy steels, the second numeral indicates the approximate percentage of the predominant element. Usually the last two or three numerals indicate the percentage of carbon content. Thus, SAE 2340 would be a nickel steel of approximately three per cent nickel and 0.40 per cent carbon. AISI (American Iron and Steel Institute) classifications are usually the same as SAE classifications except the numbers are prefixed with the letter A.

Most small shafts with diameters up to three inches are usually cold-rolled steel. Shafts between three inches and five inches diameter are either cold-rolled or turned, but shafts above five inches in diameter are always turned.

The diameter of an ordinary shaft required to transmit a specified horsepower is generally considered as

$$D = \left[\frac{(321,000) \ (HP)}{(S_s) \ (rpm)}\right]^{0.33} \tag{6}$$

where D = diameter of the shaft, in inches, and S_s = allowable torsional shearing stress, in pounds per square inch.

For cutter shafts, however, a *fatigue factor* (K_t) should be added. This factor can vary between 1.0 for steady loads, 1.5 for suddenly-applied loads, to 2.0 or more for heavy shock loads. The diameter of the shaft when the fatigue factor is used is

$$D = \left[\frac{(321,000) \ (HP) \ (K_t)}{(S_s) \ (rpm)}\right]^{0.33} \tag{7}$$

where D and S_s are as defined above.

If it is desired to find the horsepower a certain diameter shaft will transmit, the equation would be

$$HP = \frac{(D^3) \ (rpm) \ (S_s)}{(321,000) \ (K_t)} \tag{8}$$

where D and S_s are as defined above. Figure 58 shows Equation 8 plotted as cutter horsepower versus cutter speed.

The allowable shaft torsional shearing stress (S_s) in Equations 6, 7 and 8 should be assumed to be not higher than 4,000 pounds per square inch, giving a safety factor of two. With the sudden shocks

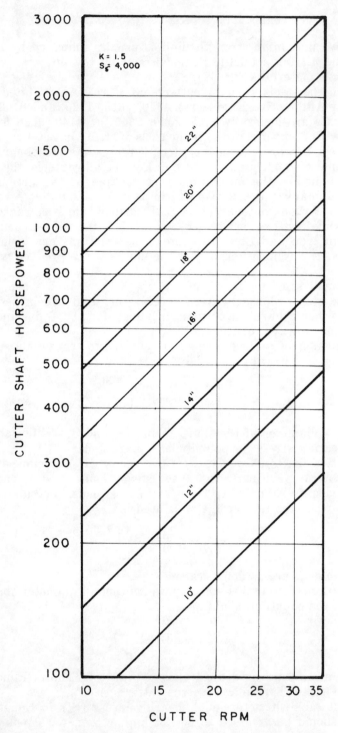

Fig. 58. Horsepower Capacity of Shafts at Different Speeds.

60

to which cutter shafts are subjected, even higher safety factors are often applied.

Most shaft failures occur because of low tensile strength, since shaft shearing stresses equal the tensile stresses. A brittle material, such as wrought iron, which is low in tension, usually will fail, as shown in Figs. 56 and 59. Note that a tension failure shows up on a 45° plane.

Fig. 59.   Tension Failure of a Cutter Shaft.

So far in this discussion it has been presupposed that the shafts are solid. An interesting aspect is presented when a hollow shaft is substituted for a solid one—such as the suction pipe being used for turning the cutter (Art. 14).

Suppose that a 10-inch solid shaft is to be replaced with a hollow shaft whose ratio of inside to outside diameter is 0.50. The diameter of the hollow shaft will be

$$D = (D_1) \left[\frac{1}{1 - (d/D)^4} \right]^{0.33} \tag{9}$$

where D = outside diameter of the hollow shaft, in inches; D_1 = diameter of the solid shaft, in inches and d = inside diameter of the hollow shaft, in inches.

Using Equation 9, the hollow shaft would have an outside diameter of only 10.219 inches. With an inside diameter of 5.109 inches, its rim thickness would be barely over 2.5 inches. The reason for these dimensions is that the stress decreases proportionately toward the center of the shaft, and resultingly the center material contributes less (Fig. 60). By using a hollow shaft the weight is not only reduced, but it is generally more reliable because of the probability that the core of a solid shaft will be less dense than its outer portions.

23. Couplings.   What size coupling should be used to couple shafts? If the coupling's bolt diameters are small in comparison with the radius of the bolt circle, as they usually are, the shearing strength of the bolts can be considered constant (Fig. 61). If this is so, the torque the coupling will transmit is

$$T = \frac{(M)\ (\pi)\ (D^2)\ (S_s)\ (R)}{4}$$ (10)

where T = torque, in inch-pounds; M = number of bolts; S_s = shearing stress, in pounds per square inch; R = radius of the bolt circle, in inches; $\pi = 3.1416$, and D = diameter of the bolts, in inches.

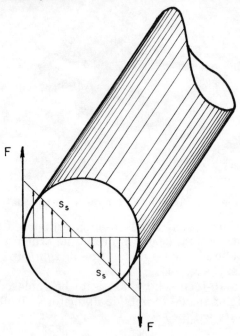

Fig. 60.   Stresses in a Shaft.

The horsepower transmittible by the coupling is

$$HP = \frac{(M)\ (\pi^2)\ (D^2)\ (rpm)\ (S_s)\ (R)}{792,000}$$ (11)

where M, D, S_s, and R are as defined above.

The amount of horsepower applied to the cutter will determine the force the cutter places on the material, and the force will be dependent upon the horsepower and the rotational speed and diameter of the cutter. For instance, suppose an eight-foot diameter cutter is turning at 15 rpm under a 150-horsepower load. The force each blade will apply to the material will be, from Equation 3,

$$F = \frac{(T)}{(S)} = \frac{(150)\ (60)\ (12)\ (550)}{(48)\ (6.28)\ (15)}$$
$$= 13,136 \text{ pounds}$$

where S = lever arm, in inches (48 inches in this instance).

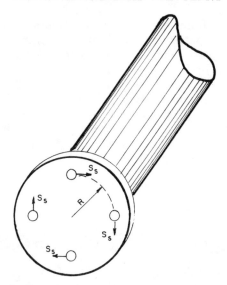

Fig. 61. Shearing Stresses in Coupling Bolts.

24. Hull. Using a dredging rule-of-thumb, the length of the hull is usually around four times its width, and its width is usually around three times its depth.

The American Bureau of Shipping allows a length-to-depth ratio of 14 to 1 for a dredge which is to be used *outside* (in the open sea), and 16 to 1 for *inside* dredges. In either instance though, there are several criteria which determine minimum and maximum dimensions. For instance, the depth of the hull must be sufficient to provide for flotation with an adequate freeboard. Although a dredge operating in calm water does not need as much freeboard as one operating in rough water, adequate freeboard is always an advantage, and there is a tendency among dredgemen to add more and heavier equipment as time passes. Inasmuch as the cost of hull construction is only about 10 to 15 per cent of the over-all cost of the dredge, adequate freeboard is good economy.

The width of the hull should be narrow enough that the dredge can pass through locks or narrow bridges—the breadth of inland dredges is usually limited to about 50 feet or less in the United States.

The length of the dredge will determine the maximum and minimum width of cut. A 60-foot long dredge cannot make as wide a cut as can one 100 feet long, but neither can a 100-foot long dredge make a cut as narrow as a 60-foot long one. Flotation requirements determine both length and breadth. A dredge's length and breadth must be such that the depth will give the minimum flotation required. Dredges designed to work in deep water do not necessarily have to be given this minimum consideration, but those which are to operate in shallow water do.

Hulls are usually fabricated with welded, mild steel. The plate used for most decking is generally too light. The minimum should be not less than $\frac{5}{16}$-inch plate, and $\frac{1}{2}$-inch or even $\frac{5}{8}$-inch plate is better.

Portable dredge hulls are built in sections that can be bolted together. Usually the sections consist of a center hull for the machinery, pump, and other equipment, and two or more pontoon side sections. Often large portable dredges have several sections making up the whole. For instance, one 30-inch dredge, whose hull was 130 feet long, 44 feet wide and 11 feet deep, was shipped in 20 sections, the conglomerate weighing 3,520,000 pounds.

Fig. 62.   Anchor Booms on a 12-inch Dredge.   (Ellicott Machine Corp.)

Hulls are usually built with two truss frames placed on either side of the ladder well and running the length of the hull. There is usually an adjacent frame on each side wall. This four-frame construction gives good longitudinal stiffening, and the addition of four to six cross-frames provides for transverse stiffening. A dredge hull is usually designed so that it is a structural frame capable of supporting itself out of water. In the water it should trim at the bow. With the ladder level, fuel tanks about half full, and one spud lifted, the dredge should float level.

25. House.   A house is usually built on top of the hull to enclose the machinery (Fig. 40). Normally it is a flat-topped, one- or two-deck structure, the upper story providing living quarters for the crew. On large dredges, 75 or more men are often accommodated. Older dredges usually have houses built of wood, but the modern dredges now use steel. Opposite the main pump, wide doors are often provided so that the pump or its parts can be removed easily from the dredge. On one-story houses an opening is sometimes made in the roof above the pump so that it or its parts can be lifted out by the derrick.

The house covers nearly the entire width and breadth of the hull except for space left along the sides and ends for walkways, the pump's discharge pipe, space at the rear for the stern connection and the spud frame, and space on the bow for the A-frame, gallows and other equipment.

26. Anchor Booms. Anchor booms are used for shifting anchors directly from the dredge. They eliminate the need for stopping the dredge so that the anchors can be shifted with a derrick and tug. (*See* Art. 51.) These booms are mounted on the forward portion of the hull ahead of the house (Figs. 62 and 63). Two hoisting drums are needed. Usually these drums are smaller than the swing drums— about one-half as wide and slightly larger in diameter. Booms may be as long as 100 feet or more, and have lifting ability of 40 to 50 tons (U.S.). They are most effective when dredging in soft material or a light bank where getting ahead is important.

Fig. 63.   Anchor Boom and Anchor.
(I. H. C. Holland, The Netherlands)

27. Lever Room. The lever room is on top of the house and near the bow so there can be a full view of operations. It houses the controls for operating the dredge. In the past these controls were heavy, long-handled, levers which were manually pulled by the leverman. Now these levers have been replaced almost exclusively by air or hydraulic controls (Fig. 64), but the names lever room and leverman remain.

Among the controls, gauges, and instruments in the lever room are those for controlling the cutter motor, anchor booms, swing wires, spuds, ladder, and sometimes the main engine. There are instantaneous and recording vacuum and pressure gauges for the pump, voltage and current meters for the cutter and hoist motors, often a pump-speed indicator, rpm meters for the pump and cutter motor, occasionally Radar, now and then a gyro compass, and sometimes underwater television.

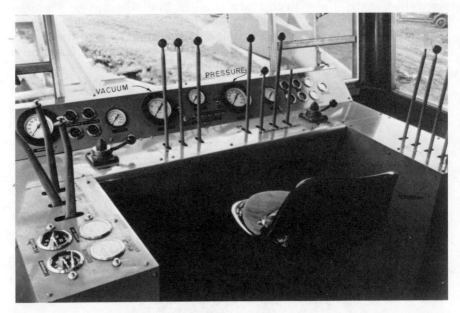

Fig. 64.   Lever Room on a 20-inch Dredge.   (American Marine & Machinery Co.)

28. Lever Room Instruments.   The instantaneous vacuum and pressure gauges give the leverman an indication of the production of the pump and help him maintain a steady output.   Additional discussion of the use of these two instruments is given in Arts. 123 and 128.

Ammeters for the cutter and hoist motors give an indication of the hardness of the material being cut.   A rise in cutter- or hoist-motor current is an indication that the material is becoming harder.   The meters also indicate when their respective motors are reaching maximum or overload ratings.

The dredge pump speed indicator and recorder present the leverman with information that helps him keep the pump at optimum speed.   As required he can signal the engine room for more or less speed.

The ladder depth gauge indicates the depth to which the dredge is cutting.   The leverman uses it to determine how much he drops the ladder for each successive cut, and at what depth the cutter is located at any particular time.   Often tide compensation is set into the gauge manually, but usually this correction is made mentally by the leverman.

Pipeline velocity and density meters, though still pretty much in an experimental stage, are becoming more refined. More detailed information is given about these instruments in Art. 128.

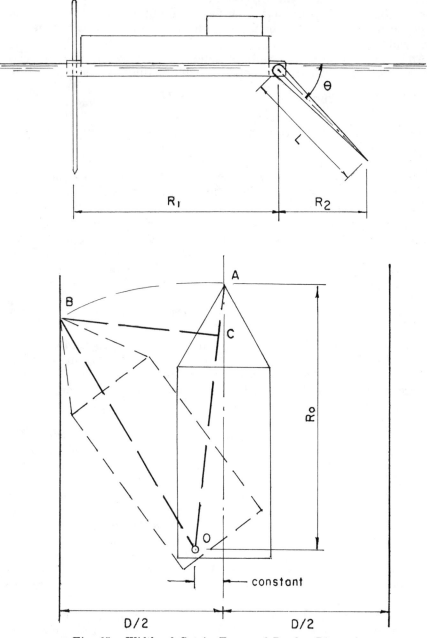

Fig. 65.   Width of Cut in Terms of Dredge Dimensions.

A gyro compass is occasionally installed on large dredges to provide accurate angular data for determining how much swing the dredge is making. Using *cut sheets* prepared by the civil engineer, the leverman can control his swing by watching the angular deflection of the gyro compass. In conjunction with a computer, the gyro compass could be made to signal when a specific width of cut was reached at any depth of the ladder.

An example of how this could be done is as follows. In Fig. 65, (D) is the total width of cut. Considering that the digging spud is at (O), the angle the dredge must swing will be A-O-B, or $Tan^{-1} \dfrac{D/2}{R_0}$, where R_0 = horizontal distance between the digging spud and the cutter, this being the distance from the spud to the ladder trunion (R_1) plus the distance from the trunion to the cutter (R_2).

The horizontal distance component of the length from the trunions to the cutter is $R_2 = L \, Cos \, \theta$, where L = actual length of ladder and θ = angle of inclination of the ladder with the horizontal. Consequently, $R_0 = R_1 + R_2$.

If a *Sin* potentiometer were introduced so that it would transmit a voltage proportional to the *Sin* of the angle A-O-B, and the ladder was provided with a similar potentiometer which would transmit a voltage proportional to the *Cos* of θ, a voltage V_d could be made proportional to the length thus

$$\frac{V_d}{2} = V_{Sin} \, (R_1 + V_{Cos} \, L) \qquad (12)$$

If this voltage was fed into a computer and the gyro compass supplied data of the actual angle being turned at any moment, a signal could be sounded when a prearranged angle was reached. This same system could be adapted to setting anchors with anchor booms, the computer and compass giving the indication when to drop the anchors at equal distances.

29. Hoisting Equipment. Hoisting equipment, commonly called the *winding gear*, is normally forward inside the hull house and generally set cross-deck (Fig. 66). It usually consists of two drums for hoisting the spuds, two for swinging the dredge, and one for raising and lowering the ladder. In most of the newer dredges, spud hoists are placed at the stern of the dredge. When anchor booms are used, two additional drums are added. *Swing wires* up to 1½ inches in diameter are common. Line pull of the drums varies depending upon the dredge. Average pulls might be 20,000 to 30,000 pounds. Wire speeds of 70 feet per minute are common. However, pulls can be as much as 150,000 pounds, and wire speeds of up to 180 feet per minute are used.

The dredge is swung from side to side by the winding gear. The swing wires, wound on the drums at opposite ends of the hoist assembly, run through the front bulkhead and out along the ladder.

At the end of the ladder, just behind the cutter, the wires feed through heavy sheaves and outward to the anchors (Figs. 40 and 50).

The hoist must also be capable of raising the spuds and ladder. It must develop a pull and speed in accordance with the equipment it controls. The spuds require high pull at slow speed; the ladder a medium pull at high speed. The *swinging swing* requires a low pull at high speed, and the *digging swing* either a high pull or high speed, depending upon the material being dredged. Twenty-five horsepower is about the minimum used for hoists; large dredges may have hoists with as much as 400 horsepower.

Fig. 66.   Hoisting Gear.   (Nashville Bridge Co.)

30. Wire Rope. The care, maintenance, and selection of wire rope is of primary importance in the operation of any dredge. Probably no other single item is used quite so extensively. The numbers, sizes, and grades of wire, and the ways in which it can be combined into rope, are so many that it is difficult for anyone to know exactly which type is best for any particular application.

Wire rope is available in five standard grades: iron, traction steel, mild plow steel, plow steel, and improved plow steel (21). The lowest grade of the five is iron. It has low tensile strength and low abrasion resistance. Mild plow steel is stronger and more abrasion resistant than iron, but it is still low grade. Plow steel and improved plow steel are the only two grades capable of withstanding the rigors of dredging. Plow steel is about 15 per cent stronger than mild plow steel and improved plow steel is about 30 per cent stronger than plow steel.

Ropes are built up by combinations of wires wound into strands, and strands wound into ropes. These windings are called *lays*. There

RIGHT *REGULAR* LAY: The wires in the strands are laid to the left and EACH STRAND is laid to the RIGHT as shown.

LEFT *REGULAR* LAY: The wires in the strand are laid to the right and EACH STRAND is laid to the LEFT as shown.

RIGHT *LANG* LAY: BOTH the wires in the strand and the strands in the rope are laid to the RIGHT as shown.

LEFT *LANG* LAY: BOTH the wires in the strand and the strands in the rope are laid to the LEFT as shown.

ALTERNATE (OR REVERSE) LAY: Alternate left and right lay strands as shown.

Fig. 67. Wire Rope Lays. (Wire Rope Institute)

are five basic lays in forming wire ropes (Fig. 67) : (1) *right regular lay*, where the wires are laid to the left and each strand to the right, (2) *left regular lay*, where the wires are laid to the right and each strand to the left, (3) *right lang lay*, where both wires and strands are laid to the right, (4) *left lang lay*, where both wires and strands are laid to the left, and (5) *alternate or reverse lay*, where there is an alternation of left and right lay.

Ropes generally suitable for dredging have the following combinations of strands to a rope and wires to a strand: 6 × 17, 8 × 17, 6 × 19, 8 × 19 and 6 × 24. The first numeral indicates the number of strands, and the second numeral the number of wires to a strand.

When a rope is wound on a drum, the proper lay should be used. Improper lays may cause the rope to foul and criss-cross when the load is released. Generally speaking, left lay rope should be favored, as it is usually more easily obtainable. Figure 68 shows proper lays for various drum windings.

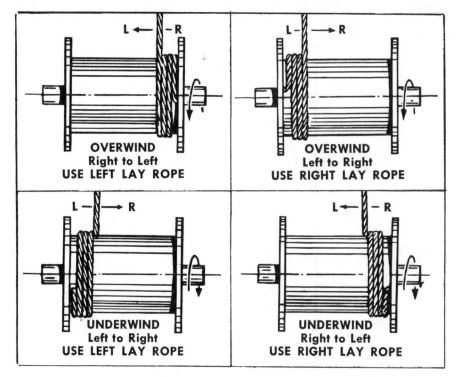

Fig. 68.   Recommended Lays for Drum Windings.   (Wire Rope Institute)

Another classification of wire rope is *standard* and *preformed*. Preformed rope's wires and strands are preshaped so that tension and torsion is removed, permitting them to be wound together easily. As a result, preformed rope can be taken apart strand by strand, wire by wire, and then put back together again. It lasts longer, is easier to handle, and is safer than the *standard* classification.

31. Ropes and Sheaves.   Some strength factors of wire rope are not too widely known. For instance, a high percentage of dredge wire rope installations expend from 50 to 75 per cent of the rope's strength in the sheaves alone. In most instances not more than 25 per cent of the rope's strength is ever used on the load itself (20).

Whenever a wire rope runs over a sheave, a number of stresses are

built up. Some of the stresses are attributable to the load being supported by the rope, and others occur from the bending of the rope
around the sheave. The largest of these stresses usually is caused by
bending, not the load. These bending stresses can be approximated by

$$S_b = 0.45 \; \frac{(E) \; (d)}{D} \tag{13}$$

where S_b = stress, in pounds per square inch; $E = 30 \times 10^6$ for steel
(usually(; d = effective diameter of the rope, in inches (0.063 times
the nominal diameter of 6×19 rope, or 0.050 times the nominal
diameter of 8×19 rope), and D = diameter of the sheave, in inches.

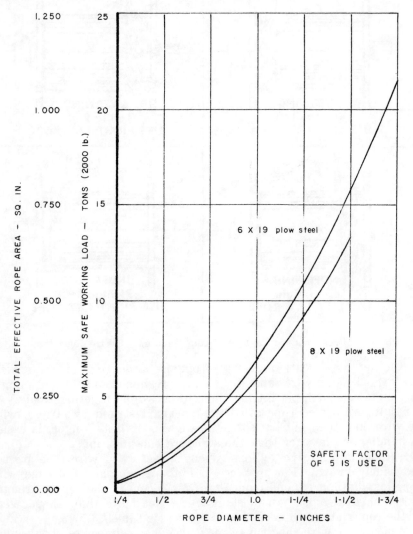

Fig. 69.   Dimensions and Strength of Wire Rope.

As an example of how much the working strength of a rope can be reduced by a sheave, consider a one-inch, 6 × 19, plow-steel rope running around a 30-inch sheave.
Then

$$S_b = \frac{(30)\ (10^6)\ (0.063)\ (1)\ (0.45)}{30} = 28,350 \text{ psi}$$

From Fig. 69 the area of the 6 × 19, one-inch rope is approximately 0.36 square inches. Hence the stress due to bending is (28,350) (0.36) = 10,206 pounds, or approximately 5.1 tons. Again from Fig. 67, the one-inch rope shows a safe working capacity of about 7.3 tons. From this it can be seen that nearly seven-tenths of the rope's capacity is being used up in the sheave. Only about 30 per cent is available for the load.

This example illustrates the need for sheaves with as large a diameter as possible. It also emphasizes why large safety factors are recommended for wire ropes.

In addition to having an adequate diameter sheave, the type of bending is also important. Reverse bends have a more detrimental effect than two bends in the same direction. Reverse bends can reduce a rope's life as much as one-half, as compared with two bends in one direction.

Load on a rope controlled by an electric motor can be calculated from

$$L = \frac{(HP)\ (T)\ (550)}{D} \qquad (14)$$

where L = load on rope, in pounds; T = time, in seconds, and D = distance travelled in T seconds, in feet. As it is reasonable to assume that the motor could be overloaded 50 per cent at times, the load determined from Equation 14 should be increased by 50 per cent when using it to select rope (21).

32. Chain Drives. Chain drives were developed primarily to transmit power at higher speeds than was possible with belts or gears. They are also generally used when the distance between the driving and driven shafts is too short for belts and too long for gears. Although their initial cost is higher than belting, they pay for themselves in service and reduction of down time (20, 22).

There are a number of different chain drives used, but the *silent chain drive* is the only one considered here, because of its general use in dredge power transmission (22). It is referred to as *silent* because the power is transmitted by all the teeth in the arc of contact (Fig. 70), so the links have no sliding action, either on or off the teeth, and this results in a smooth and practically noiseless action.

Ratios for silent chain drives vary between 6 to 1 and 10 to 1. Where higher reductions are required, double reduction is usually desirable. The angle between the bottom and top of the chain should not exceed 45°, as the arc of contact will be too small. Maximum speed is usually held to not more than 1,400 feet per minute. The preferable number of teeth in the sprockets is 17 to 75 for the driving sprockets, and 19 to 102 for the driven sprockets.

The *center distance*—the distance between sprocket centers (Fig. 70)—can be short, particularly if the ratio is small, and can be just enough to clear the teeth. Short center distances are used with ratios below 2 to 1, but on larger ratios the center distance is usually not less than the sum of the sprocket diameters.

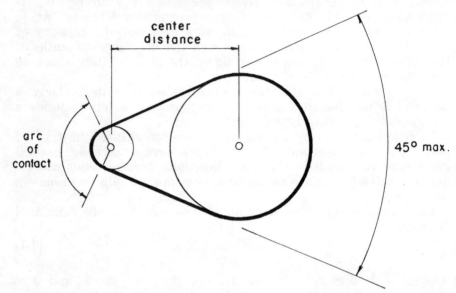

Fig. 70. Arc of Contact and Center-Distance.

The American Association of Roller and Silent Chain Manufacturers rate silent chain service factors for dredge pump drive as follows: electric motor, 1.8; steam turbine, 1.9; gasoline engine, 2.0; diesel, 2.5. To determine the horsepower per inch of width of silent chain, the standard rating should be divided by the service factor.

33. V-belt Drives. V-belt drives are used extensively for general speed reduction, and on small dredges they are used to couple diesel engines to the main pump.

A proper V-belt drive has only the angular sides of the belt contacting the sides of the pulley groove. The top of the belt should be nearly flush with the top of the pulley and the bottom of the belt should clear the bottom of the pulley groove by about 0.15 inches (20).

Pulley diameters should be as large as possible, but not so large as to exceed a belt speed of 7,000 feet per minute.

The center distance between sheaves can be short. For high speeds, short distances are desirable. Some dredgemen recommend the center distance be slightly larger than the diameter of the largest pulley and smaller than the sum of the diameters of both.

The amount of the arc of contact determines the power capacity of a V-belt. For instance, an arc reduction from 180° to 160° will reduce the power transmitting capacity about five per cent; reducing it to 145° will reduce the capacity about 10 per cent; for 130°, 15 per cent.

The arc of contact is determined by multiplying the difference in sheave diameters, in inches, by 60 and dividing this difference by the center distance, in inches, and then subtracting the quotient obtained from 180°. For instance, assume a V-belt on a 60-inch sheave and a 20-inch sheave, the ratio being 3 to 1. Assume a center distance of five feet. What will be the arc of contact?

$$180° - \frac{(40)\ (60)}{60} = 140°$$

This combination will give a power reduction of approximately 12 per cent.

V-belts are classified by the manufacturer at horsepower ratings depending upon their size and speed ratio. For instance, a 1.5-inch by 1.0-inch belt (the first value, 1.5, is the belt's top width; the second value, 1.0, is its depth) could have a 23.5-horsepower rating at a speed ratio of 1 to 1 on a 24-inch sheave, while it would have a 21.5-horsepower rating at a speed ratio of 3 to 1 on a 66-inch sheave. Suppose, for example, that the initial speed is 1,720 rpm. Then at a lower speed of, say 850 rpm, the horsepower rating of the belt would be reduced from 21.5 to 17 horsepower, on the 3 to 1 ratio.

34. Pulley Speeds. Speeds of pulleys are a function of diameters. If the circumference of a driving pulley is πD_1, one rotation will create D_1/D_2 rotations of the driven pulley. Whatever the speed (S_1) of the driving pulley, the speed of the driven pulley (S_2) will be $S_2 = (S_2)$ (D_2/D_1). The pulley diameter (D) is actually the calculated *pitch* or effective diameter—the outside diameter of the pulley minus the belt thickness plus about $\frac{1}{8}$ inch. On a pulley of 60-inches outside diameter with a 1.5-inch by 1.0-inch belt, the pitch diameter would be 60 inches minus one inch minus $\frac{1}{8}$ inch, or 58-$\frac{7}{8}$ inches.

The rim speed of a pulley is

$$\text{feet per minute} = \frac{(S)\ (\pi)\ (D)}{12} \tag{15}$$

where S = speed of pulley in rpm; π = 3.1416, and D = pitch diameter, in inches.

35. Anchors and Anchoring. The history of anchors is a long and interesting one. Many forms have been used throughout time, among them being the primitive Slave anchor, the East Indian Anchor, the Chinese, and the Old Fashioned or Kedge anchor (23).

The first real departure from these types was in 1821 when

Hawkins patented the *Stockless* or *Patent* anchor. This anchor is still used extensively on large ships, primarily because of its easy stowage in a hawser pipe. The *Plow* anchor was patented in 1933 and became quite popular in England. The *Danforth* anchor was patented a few years later (1939), and to date, for its size, it is the best for holding power (Fig. 71). It will hold 15 to 1,000 times its weight in small sizes, and 10 to 30 times its weight in larger sizes. A 5.5-ton Stockless anchor will drag with a 25,000 pound load, but a five-ton Danforth will stall a winch with a 120,000 pound load. Even concrete or granite blocks will only hold about one-half to two-thirds their air weight—about equal to their submerged weight.

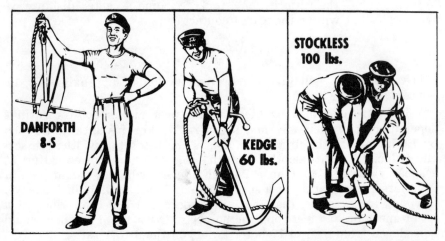

Fig. 71. Comparison of Holding Power to Relative Weight of Anchors.
(Danforth/White)

The actual force exerted by a vessel on its anchor is dependent upon both the vessel's physical characteristics and the existing wind and water conditions. In estimating the anchor load of a vessel it should be considered in three parts, (1) wind drag, (2) current drag, and (3) wave action (23).

Wind drag is determined by the sum of the effects of wind velocity, air density, and the shape of the vessel, or

$$D_1 = \frac{(C_d)\ (P)\ (V^2)\ (S)}{2} \tag{16}$$

where D_1 = wind drag, in pounds; P = density of the air, in per cent; V = wind velocity, in knots; S = cross-sectional area of the vessel presented to the wind, in square feet, and C_d = a coefficient varying with the vessel's profile. Table 2 gives values of C_d for various profiles, from which an estimate can be made for any particular craft. Generally speaking, 0.8 to 0.9 is satisfactory for a tugboat, and 1.3 to 1.5 for a dredge.

Drag of current or tide can be considerable. The same power is required to tow or propel a vessel through the water as it is to hold it against the same-speed current. Current drag can be approximated as

$$D_2 = (325.5) \ (H) \ \frac{(P) \ (rpm) - (1216) \ (V)}{(V) \ (P) \ (rpm)} \qquad (17)$$

where D_2 = current drag, in pounds; P = propeller pitch, in inches; rpm = propeller speed, in rpm; V = velocity of the vessel, in knots, and H = horsepower delivered to the propeller (23).

Allowing freedom of natural response on anchor wires will reduce wave-action drag considerably. Failure to allow this freedom will produce tremendous surge loads. Consequently, providing ample anchor line is the best way to reduce wave-action drag.

Table 2. Values of C_d for Equation 16
(Danforth/White)

Hollow hemisphere, concave to wind (like anemometer cup)	1.70
Flat rectangular plate	1.28
Flat circular disc	1.16
Wires, cylinders, masts	1.00
Cargo liner, wind dead ahead	.95
Oil tanker, wind dead ahead	.85
Streamlined passenger liner, wind dead ahead	.70
Pleasure boats, wind dead ahead	.70 - 1.00
Sphere	.47
Hollow hemisphere, convex to wind (like anemometer cup)	.38
Airplane	.09
Aircraft strut	.06
Streamlined cigar shape	.03

To determine the tension on cables under various conditions, the following formulae are useful when the wire is approximately horizontal

$$T = T_h + (W) \ (D) \qquad (18)$$

$$L = T_v / W \qquad (19)$$

$$T_v = (T^2 - T_h^2)^{0.5} \qquad (20)$$

where T = maximum pull on the wire, in pounds; T_h = horizontal load, in pounds; T_v = vertical load, in pounds; D = depth of water, in feet; W = weight of wire, in pounds per foot under water, and L = length of wire, in feet. For a wire leading upward from the bottom at 8° to 10° the horizontal load in the above four equations should be multiplied by 0.14. For any other angle, the *Sin* of the angle should be used (23).

The pull required to stop a boat or ship is approximately 100 times the displacement in long tons (2,200 pounds) times the speed in knots squared, divided by the distance in feet in which the ship is to be stopped. For instance, a 10-ton dredge surging at two knots would require 1,000 pounds to stop it in four feet. Figure 72 shows some suggested anchor sizes for various-sized boats, and Fig. 73 shows holding power of various anchors. Figure 74 shows the holding power of Danforth anchors.

SUGGESTED WORKING ANCHOR SIZES		
Boat Length	Danforth® Standard Anchor	Danforth® Hi-Tensile Anchor
0-9	2½-S	—
10-16	4-S / 4-SR	—
17-24	8-S / 9-SR	5-H
25-32	13-S / 16-SR	12-H
33-38	22-S	12-H
39-44	40-S	20-H
45-54	65-S	35-H
55-70	85-S	60-H
71-90	130-S	90-H
For storm anchor, use one anchor size larger. For lunch hook, one size smaller.		

This table of suggested working anchor sizes assumes fair holding ground, scope of at least 7 to 1 and winds of up to 30 knots. Suggested sizes for storm anchors assume the same conditions but with winds of up to 60 knots. However, many factors such as anchorage exposure, wind velocity, type of holding ground, scope, and hull form govern the size of anchor to be used in any individual situation. For good seamanship, a storm anchor should always be aboard as well as the working anchor.

Fig. 72.   Sizes of Danforth Anchors Recommended for Different Sizes of Boats.
(Danforth/White)

HORIZONTAL HOLDING POWER OF VARIOUS ANCHORS			
Weight of Anchor in Pounds	Concrete Block	Mushroom & Stockless	Yachtsman's Kedge
	HOLDING POWER IN POUNDS		
10	5	10	50
20	10	35	100
30	15	60	150
50	25	100	250
100	50	200	500
500	250	1,000	

Fig. 73.   Holding Power of Anchors.
(Danforth/White)

36. Main Pump. The main pump is located forward in the hull, its center near the loaded water line. On small- and medium-sized dredges the pump is generally turned by a diesel engine; on large dredges the pump is driven by a diesel engine, a diesel-electric motor, or a steam turbine. Gas turbines are being tried now, and will probably become more prevalent (Art. 167). Where commercial power is available and economical, the pump is often turned by an electric motor powered through a high-voltage cable from shore.

Electrically-powered pump drives have several advantages over other types of pump drives. The machinery is simpler, fewer crewmen are required, lay-up costs are less, and the motors can carry overloads up to 150 per cent. Where power is abundant, electrically-powered drives are probably the best investment. The main motor is usually excited by 2,300 or 4,400 volts, and the other motors through auxiliary transformers on the dredge. Some large dredges have drive motors for the pump with 13,200 volts excitation. Speed variation on the pump drive is generally around 20 per cent.

HORIZONTAL HOLDING POWER OF DANFORTH®ANCHORS IN POUNDS		
	Soft Mud	Hard Sand
5-H	400	2,700
12-H	900	6,000
20-H	1,250	8,750
35-H	1,600	11,000
60-H	2,400	17,000
90-H	2,900	20,000
200-H	5,000	35,000
500-H	7,500	50,000
3000-H	21,000	140,000
2½-S	140	800
4-S	230	1,600
8-S	480	3,200
13-S	720	4,900
22-S	1,200	8,000
40-S	1,500	10,000
65-S	2,300	15,000
85-S	2,700	19,000
130-S	3,100	21,000
180-S	3,500	23,000

Fig. 74. Holding Power of Danforth Anchors.
(Danforth/White)

More than 15,000 horsepower is applied to some of the large pumps. Small pumps have as little as 250 to 300 horsepower. Speed of dredge pumps is relatively slow—around 300 rpm on large ones and 800 to 900 rpm on small ones.

37. Pump Inboard Suction. The pump inboard-suction line extends from the dredge's front bulkhead, where it is flanged through the hull from the flexible coupling, to the eye of the pump. It is preferably straight from the bulkhead to the eye, but sometimes it has a slight upward slope. Just before it joins the suction eye, the suction line connects to a cleanout fitting often called a *stone box* (Fig. 75). This fitting has an opening cover in its top, side, or bottom, which when removed allows access to the eye and throat of the pump. Rocks, stumps, and other impediments which become stuck in the pump can often be removed manually through the box opening without dismantling the pump. A man can literally crawl through the stone box into the pump or suction pipe of large dredges.

It is important that the pump's suction line have no vertical bends.

In addition to introducing additional frictional losses, air trapped at the top of bends can seriously impede the pump's material-handling capacity.

Stone Box

Fig. 75. Stone Box. (Abex Corp.—AMSCO Division)

38. Spuds. The dredge is held in position or moved about with spuds. They are usually round, but there are still dredges using square spuds. Most spuds are made of cast steel or built-up plate, and some are as much or more than four feet in diameter. Wall-thickness varies, but on large dredges it is sometimes two-and-a-half to three inches. Spuds weigh as much as 30 tons and sometimes are over 100 feet long.

Located at the stern of the dredge opposite each other (Fig. 76), they are supported by a structure called a *gantry*. The gantry is generally the highest structure on the dredge—with the exception of possibly the smokestacks of steam-powered dredges. Its height is generally determined by the length of the spuds and the manner in which they are raised. Some gantrys are hinged so that they can be

Fig. 76. Spuds, Keepers and Gantry. (ARMCO Steel Corp.)

lowered to allow the dredge to pass under obstructions such as bridges or power lines that cross the channels.

There is another arrangement for supporting and lifting the spuds.

This is the *free-standing hydraulic cylinder* (Figs. 77 and 78). Used more often in Europe than in the United States, the free-standing cylinder method eliminates the need for a ponderous gantry and has the advantage of being easily dismantled when clearance is needed for passing under obstructions.

Fig. 77.   Hydraulic Cylinder Lifting System. (I. H. C. Holland, The Netherlands)

Fig. 78.   Close-up of Hydraulic Cylinder Spud-Lifter.   (I. H. C. Holland, The Netherlands)

The size and strength of a spud is determined by the displacement of the dredge, its digging depth, and the cutter power. In Fig. 79 the line pull of 20,000 pounds places a force of 15,300 pounds on the spud. A line pull of 10,000 pounds would decrease the force on the spud to 7,600 pounds.

Some dredgemen propose that a spud should have a *section modulus* equal to the depth of digging, in feet, times the discharge diameter, in inches. The depth of digging would be involved, of course, but how the discharge, per se, would have an effect is questionable.

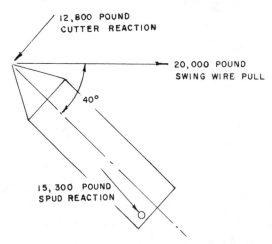

Fig. 79.   Reactions from Swing Wire and Cutter Forces.

As a matter of fact, this would not be dimensionally possible. The dimensional equation in this instance would be $L^3 = (L) (L) = L^2$, which would be an inequality—another length dimension would be needed on the right-hand side of the equation. This points up the advantage of verifying the correctness of equations. An equation must have the same dimensions on each side of the equal sign if it is to be correct. In dimensional analysis, length $= L$, mass $= M$ and time $= T$. Area, being a product of two lengths, will be L^2. Volume would be L^3, speed $V = s/t = LT^{-1}$, acceleration $= LT^{-2}$, force $F = MA = LMT^{-2}$. Other parameters are: head $= L$, output (quantity) $= L^3/T$, runner diameter $= L$, and acceleration of gravity $= L/T^2$. By using these fundamentals, any equation can be checked for correctness as in the above example (24).

Section modulus (I/C) is a function of the spud's diameter and its ability to resist bending. It can be determined by either of two formulas. For a solid spud the section modulus is

$$I/C = 0.098 \, (D^3) \tag{21}$$

for a hollow spud (the most common), it would be

$$I/C = 0.098 \, \frac{(D^4 - d^4)}{D} \tag{22}$$

where $D =$ outside diameter, in inches; $d =$ inside diameter, in inches; $I =$ moment of inertia, in inches to the fourth power, and $C =$ distance from the center to the outside of the spud, in inches.

Working
spud

Fig. 80. Walking Spud. Taller spud is the auxiliary; lower spud, the working
or walking one. (I. H. C. Holland, The Netherlands)

As an example of how the moment of inertia is indicative of a spud's strength, suppose a force of 10,000 pounds acts against a spud at the *keepers*. Say the spud has an outside diameter of 24 inches and an inside diameter of 20 inches.

The maximum moment acting on the spud will be at the point where it enters the bottom of the cut. It will be equal to

$$M = (S) \ (I/C) \qquad (23)$$

where S = tensile stress (commonly limited to 16,000 pounds per square inch, for steel spuds), M = moment, in pound-inches, and I/C = section modulus, in inches to the third power.

With a force of 10,000 pounds at 50 feet, the actual moment will be 50,000 pound-feet. Using Equations 22 and 23, the maximum safe moment on the spud will be 17,750,000 pound-inches, or about 1,480,000 pound-feet, indicating that the spud is adequate.

Spuds should be spaced not less than one-tenth the distance between the stern of the dredge and the cutter, so that getting ahead will not be limited. (*See* Art. 53.)

Spud rigging consists of hoisting sheaves, wires from the hoist drums, and the *spud wells* or *keepers* (Figs. 76 and 83). The wells carry the horizontal thrust created during dredging and keep the spuds alined as well. When weather conditions are bad or the cut too deep, three-wire mooring is often used instead of spuds.

Spud wells are usually under water, because having them as low as possible reduces the spud bending load, allows for a shorter spud, and requires a lower gantry and a smaller hoist. Some wells have been set as low as 40 feet below the dredge. However, the lower spud well is normally in line with the bottom of the hull. Practically all keepers have easy-opening releases to speed up spud removal.

39. The Walking Spud. Used extensively in Europe, a walking spud is a conventional spud placed in a groove in which it can move longitudinally along the centerline of the dredge (Fig. 80).

With the dredge alined in the center of the cut, the walking (working) spud down in the forward end of the carriage groove, and the stern (auxiliary) spud lifted, the dredge makes normal swings across the cut. When the required depth is reached, the working spud carriage is moved aft. As the spud is supported on the bottom, this effectively moves the dredge ahead. The carriage is moved backward a sufficient distance to give the required set. The dredge then again makes normal swings across the cut until proper depth is reached. This process is repeated until the working spud and its carriage are at the stern of the groove. The auxiliary spud is then dropped, the working spud lifted, and the carriage moved ahead. The working spud is then dropped, the auxiliary spud lifted, and the operation commences all over again.

The basic walking spud system was improved upon by Alfred Watkins who worked out a way to make the swing widths equal (7). He used two spuds, but one of them was placed in a tube set eccentrically in a tube set eccentrically in a rotor. It was called the *rotor spud*. The rotor had a worm gear on its circumference actuated by gearing. By turning the rotor, the center of the rotor spud could be moved into the line of advance without regard for the centerline of the dredge. The rotor spud could then be dropped and the fixed spud raised, thereby keeping the advance even. This invention was first used on a dredge built by the Tilbury Contracting and Dredging Co., Ltd., of England (7).

An improvement on this system was developed by Ir. F. Smit of Kinderdijk, Holland (7). He put both spuds in the rotor. The dredge swung around the circumference of the rotor (Fig. 81). At the end of each cut the stern spud was raised and the rotor turned 180°. The forward spud was dropped and the dredge commenced its swing again.

Fig. 81.   Rotor Spuds.
(I. H. C. Holland, The Netherlands)

40. Discharge Line.   The discharge line can be more easily described and located by considering it in three separate sections, (A) the pipe on the dredge, (B) the floating line, and (C) the shoreline.

A. THE PIPE ON THE DREDGE.   The pipe on the dredge runs from the discharge of the pump to the stern, preferably along the deck on the outside of the house (Fig. 47) the principal reason being to prevent flooding and possible sinking of the dredge should the pipe break. It has a thicker wall than other discharge pipe, the wall sometimes being as much as one inch thick.

Somewhere along the way to the stern, but as close to the pump discharge as practicable, a discharge *flap valve* is installed (Figs. 47 and 82). This valve is normally closed by gravity. When water or a

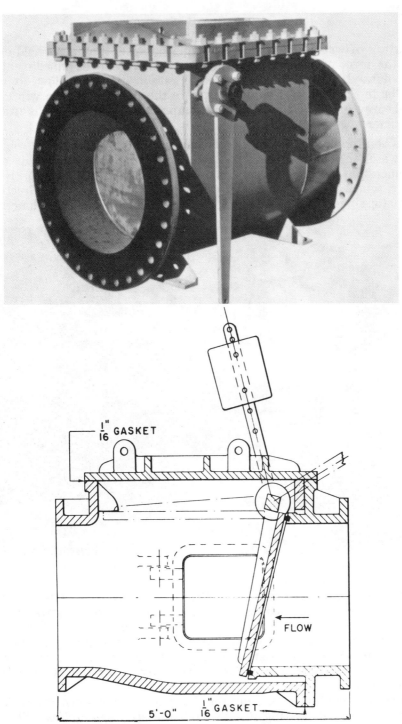

Fig. 82. (A, Top) Flap Valve. (PACECO) ; (B, Bottom)
Section of Flap Valve. (Corps of Engineers)

mixture of water and material is being pumped, the flap is held open by the force of the stream and offers relatively little impediment to the flow. However, should for some reason a reverse flow occur— water in the line start running back to the pump—the flap will close and prevent a reversal of the pump and possible serious water hammer.

When the flow in a long line is suddenly stopped, the long column of water in the line is free to continue moving ahead under its own momentum, thereby producing a reduced pressure at the pump. However, when the flow stops and begins to flow in a reverse direction, the stopping of this flow by the flap valve may cause water hammer.

Fig. 83.   Stern Swivel-joint Connection. (PACECO)

If the valve is built so that it will close before any appreciable reverse flow commences, the increase of pressure of the returning water will be negligible. If it does not work rapidly, however, the backward flow will set up a velocity flow in a reverse direction through the pump considerably greater than it initially had when the pump was operating normally. The closure of the valve after this reverse flow starts will cause very high pressures.

The pipe continues on from the flap valve to the stern where it is connected to the floating line through the *stern connection*. This is either a rubber hose (Fig. 77), a swivel elbow (Fig. 83), or one or more ball joints. Swivel elbows are preferred because of their wide-turn ability. Ball joints (Fig. 84) have a turning angle of approximately 10° to 15°, so the combination of enough ball joints to accumulate a suitable turning angle usually makes an unwieldly assembly.

B. THE FLOATING LINE.   The floating line extends from the rear of the dredge to shore. It is made up of sections of individual pipe from 30- to 50-feet long. Each section is supported by one or more floating pontoons (Fig. 85).

These pontoons are of various shapes, but usually on the larger dredges they are a circular, cylindrical type, sometimes with tapered ends. Generally there are two pontoons for one section of pipe, tied together with rigid, wooden, or sometimes steel (not recommended)

Fig. 84.   Ball Joint, Male and Female Sections.   (ARMCO Steel Corp.)

beams called *strongbacks*. The discharge pipe is supported on the pontoons by means of wood *saddles* rigidly fixed to the pontoons (Fig. 86). These composite sections are generally referred to as *pontoons*, and when placed in the floating line they are successively connected together by flanges, ball joints (Fig. 87), or rubber sleeves (Fig. 88). Rubber sleeves are not generally used except on small dredges for convenience and economy, but where high pressures occur in the larger pipelines, rubber sleeves are generally manditory, the main reason being that ball joints will freeze up under high pressures and then do not give the flexibility required.

A typical floating line (Fig. 31) might be made up of two or more pontoon sections connected together by flanges, several of these assemblies connected with ball joints, a 90° elbow pontoon, additional straight pontoon assemblies, and one special pontoon, often called a

Fig. 85.   Floating Pontoon Line.   (ARMCO Steel Corp.)

90

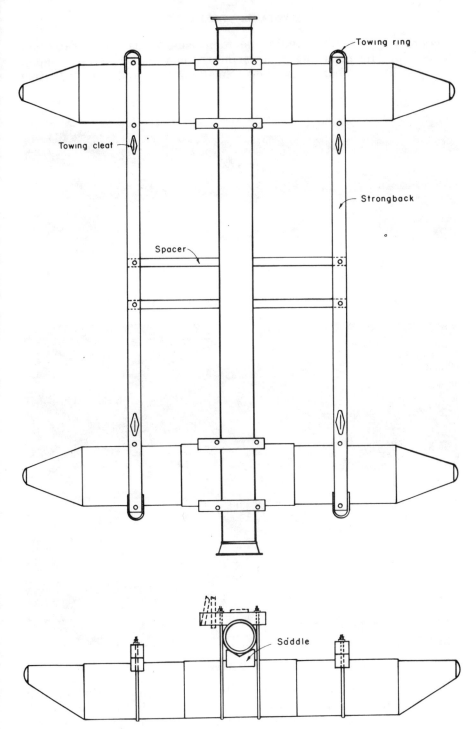

Fig. 86.   Typical Pontoon Construction.

91

landing pontoon. The landing pontoon usually has an A-frame and hand-winch for elevating or lowering the end of the pipe to compensate for different bank elevations. Small 0.5-ton hand-operated winch

Fig. 87. Making a Pontoon Connection with a Ball Joint. (ARMCO Steel Corp.)

Fig. 88. Pontoon Connection with Rubber Sleeve. (ARMCO Steel Corp.)

assemblies are usually placed permanently on some of the pontoon sections. These winches usually carry a ½-inch wire and a Danforth anchor which can be dropped on either side of the pipeline to stabilize or hold it in some particular position.

A walkway with a handrail is usually permanently attached to each pontoon section directly above the pipe (Figs. 86 and 89). When all sections of the floating line are connected there is a continuous walkway from the dredge to shore. On many small dredges no walkway is provided (even some of the large dredges do not have them). It is good practice, however, for all dredges to have walkways, not only for safety of the men walking the line, but for the ease and efficiency of getting to and from points on the line where work must be done.

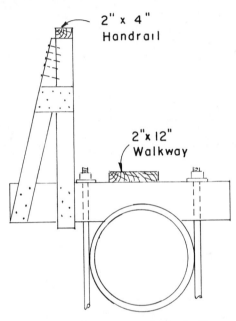

Fig. 89. Walkway and Handrail.

Sometimes two 90° elbow pontoons are placed in the line, the first to direct the floating line towards shore, the second to allow the line to run parallel with the shore to the landing pontoon. In heavily-traveled waterways this is a generally-accepted practice. Otherwise, the line floats in a wide arc from the dredge to shore so that the dredge can advance or move about without frequent stops to add additional pontoons.

C. THE SHORELINE. The shoreline consists of shorter and generally lighter sections of pipe than the floating line. Usually these sections are between 10 and 15 feet long with wall thicknesses of from 0.25 to 0.30 inches. They are connected to each other by ramming the tapered end of one into the straight, banded end of another. The tapered end is always on the downstream end (Fig. 90). (See Art. 143 for some discussion of this arrangement.)

Usually the connections are held together by wire wrapped around lugs which are welded to each side and end of the pipe. When con-

nections require a dry line (minimum leakage at the joints), burlap
sacks are often laid across the tapered end of the pipe before ramming. The burlap acts as a sealer around the inside periphery of the

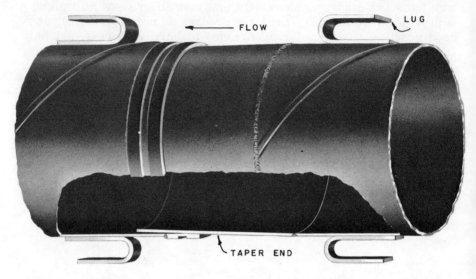

Fig. 90.　Shorepipe Connection.　(Naylor Pipe Co.)

Fig. 91.　Shoreline Laid on Cribbing.　(Naylor Pipe Co.)

joint. When leaks occur, wood shingles are often hammered into the
connection to seal the leak. When a dry line cannot be obtained in
this manner, the pipe are flanged together. Occasionally when the
line is under abnormally high pressure, the pipe are welded together.
The shoreline in contrast to the suction line can be run in any direc-

tion, vertically or horizontally, without serious impediment of the operation. Normally the pipe are laid on the ground, but in some instances they are placed on *cribbing* (Fig. 91).

At or near the discharge into the spoil disposal area a *Wye* is placed in the shoreline to provide two outlet possibilities (Fig. 92). When pipe are to be added, one leg of the Wye can be closed, stopping the flow in that leg, but allowing the flow to continue through the other leg. This arrangement saves time by not having to stop the dredge to add pipe, and it provides for two separate discharges that often give a better spoil distribution over a wider area.

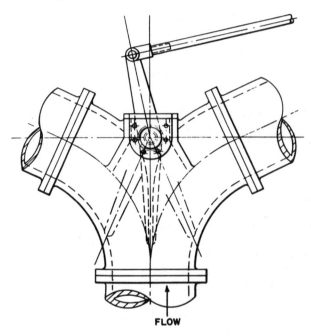

FLOW

Fig. 92. Discharge Pipe Wye. (Corps of Engineers)

41. Pipe. Off-the-shelf dredge pipe comes in several wall thicknesses and can be bought in standard lengths of 20, 30, or 40 feet.

Dredge pipe is subjected to considerable wear; consequently it needs to have abrasion resistance. This type of pipe often has specifications of 0.35 to 0.40 carbon and 0.6 to 0.9 manganese. Most dredging companies have their own pipe specifications and do not use off-the-shelf pipe.

The relative strength of pipe is generally indicated by its *schedule number*. This number is determined by the equality SN = (1,000) (P)/S, where SN = schedule number; P = internal pressure allowable, in pounds per square inch, and S = allowable fiber stress, in pounds per square inch (20). The higher the schedule number, the higher the relative strength. Schedule 10 pipe wall thickness is approximately 0.25 inches; schedule 20 pipe, 0.31 inches and schedule 40 pipe, 0.50 inches. These thickness values will change somewhat with the size of the pipe.

Pipe up to and including 12-inches diameter is referred to by its *nominal* or *inside* diameter. From 14 to 30 inches diameter the nominal and *outside* diameters are the same, and the pipe is usually referred to as *O.D. pipe.*

The weight of pipe can be determined by

$$W = (K) (D^2 - d^2) \qquad (24)$$

where W = weight per linear foot, in pounds; K = 2.67 for steel pipe; D = outside diameter, in feet, and d = inside diameter, in feet.

The breaking pressure can be determined by Barlow's formula

$$P = \frac{(2) \ (T) \ (S)}{D} \qquad (25)$$

where P = breaking pressure, in pounds per square inch; T = thickness of the wall, in inches; S = tensile stress of material, in pounds per square inch and D = outside diameter of the pipe, in inches. The value of (S) for dredge pipe can be approximated as 40,000 pounds per square inch. When determining working pressure however, use an (S) of 12,000 pounds per square inch—this gives a safety factor of about three.

42. Submerged Lines. Although most dredging operations only require floating and shorelines, it is often necessary to use a submerged line. When dredging in heavily-travelled waterways and a floating line has to cross the waterway to a spoil-disposal area, much time is lost in breaking the line every time a ship, barge, or boat needs to pass. Various methods have been devised to speed up the process of opening a floating line for traffic, but they all require the dredge to shut down. A submerged line eliminates this costly delay.

A submerged line is also an asset in bad weather. When the weather is not rough enough to stop dredging, but is too rough for a floating line, a submerged line is often the solution.

An essential of a submerged line is two stationary and substantial points where the ends of the line can be fixed as they come up out of the water. Usually when these cannot be shore-based points, they are well-moored barges.

There are different methods of installing submerged lines. Some are assembled on one shore and dragged into place by winches on the other shore. Some are, when conditions are right, assembled on shore and actually lifted by a large crane and placed in position. Each condition determines the procedure. One novel method of installation is floating the pipe into position and then allowing it to sink to the bottom. The details of this method follow.

To construct the line it is necessary to have an adequate air compression system. An air compressor supplying 100 to 200 cubic feet per minute at 100 pounds per square inch is adequate. The compressor is connected to an air valve installed at one end of the line. A sufficient number of tugs are made available to handle and tow the line.

The assembly operation usually begins from a barge. Sections of pontoon pipe are hoisted onto the barge and are flanged and gasketed securely together so there will be no leakage. Additional sections are connected to the sections on the barge. As the line becomes too long for the barge, the pipe is either lifted overboard by a derrick or slid off the end of the barge, allowing the pipe to submerge. The barge is then moved ahead to allow more pipe to be connected.

At intervals, ball joints are added to the line, the locations of the joints being determined from a profile prepared from cross-section information previously obtained at the site where the line is to be placed. The ball joints give the line flexibility and allow it to follow the cross-section of the channel. Successive pipe are flanged together and these sections connected with ball joints until the predetermined length of the line has been reached. Occasionally only one ball joint is used, as in the center of the line when the channel sides are relatively straight. If not already supported, the far end of the line is picked up by the derrick and lifted above the water's surface so the air valve is accessible. Through a similar air-valve connection at the other end, the air compressor is connected and air is forced into the line. Care is taken during air injection to have complete control of the amount of air being placed in the line and consequently the amount of water being displaced. Too much air can cause the line to bob up like a cork, damaging connections and anything in its way.

As the pipe fills with air, the line will become buoyant and the individual sections will begin to float. When the entire line is just about to float, the air compressor is slowed down and the floating carried on very carefully. Air is continually supplied at a reduced rate until all the pipe has risen to the surface and is floating. The air compressor is then shut down and the valve closed. The air compressor is not disconnected until it is determined that there are no leaks that would cause the line to sink during the tow to the site.

When the line's tightness is assured, the air compressor is disconnected, the line moved into position, and towing is begun. Upon reaching the site the line is moved into position directly above where it will eventually lie. A connection is made to one of the two previously-installed supporting connections on either side of the channel. When the line is in position, the air valve at one end is opened allowing the air to flow out and the water to flow in at the other end. This is done slowly inasmuch as too rapid a release would allow the pipe to drop too rapidly to the bottom. As the air is released, the pipe loses buoyancy and slowly sinks to the bottom.

Where the line can be assembled directly at the site the operation is similar, except that the line can be laid along the shore and then later floated to the surface and moved into the exact alinement. Occasionally, in critical dredging projects where a stoppage would be damaging, two lines are often laid—one for a spare in case of an emergency.

Chapter 3

Permits—Mobilization—Commencement of Dredging

43. Introduction. Operations may properly be said to have commenced when the plant arrives at the dredging area. However, there are several things that have to be completed before the dredge arrives on location.

44. Dredging in Navigable Waters. Whenever a navigable body of water in the United States is widened, controlled, modified, impounded, diverted, deepened, or changed, the Department of the Army must give approval prior to commencement of operations. The approval is usually represented by a permit being issued by the Corps of Engineers. The decision as to whether a permit will be issued rests primarily upon the effect of the work on navigation and conservation of wildlife.

Anyone contemplating work in navigable waters must therefore make application for a permit. Where work is to be for the United States government, the approval is understood and no permit is required. But where the work is to be done for private interests, either the owner, his representative, or the contractor must make application for a permit prior to the commencement of operations.

An application consists of a letter requesting a permit and sufficient plans to describe the proposed work. It should be addressed to the Corps of Engineers in charge of the locality in which the work is to be done (25).

45. Letter of Application. There is no prescribed form. The letter should include the address of the applicant, the date, the name of the waterway, the location and description of the work, and a statement as to whether the work is in the corporate limits of any municipality (Fig. 93).

The letter should give any supplementary explanation of the plans that might assist the Engineers in determining precisely what is proposed, such as the exact location of the work, the depth of the proposed dredging, the approximate amount of material to be removed, the definite location of the spoil-disposal area, and the names and addresses of the owners of the property adjoining the proposed work. If any of these data are clearly shown on the plans, it is not necessary that they be included in the letter.

The letter and plans must be complete without dependence upon other correspondence not included in the submission. The application should include any special authorization for the work, as for example, a copy of a State permit. The letter must be signed by the owner, his representative, or by the contractor who will do the work. It should be furnished in duplicate, and all attached papers should be furnished in quadruplicate!

4630 L. Street
------------, Texas
May 23, 1970

The District Engineer

Dear Sir:

We request a permit for dredging a slip as shown on the attached map alongside ------- Pier at ------------ Harbor. This is the second pier south of the City pier. The depth to be made is 15 feet at mean low water and we estimate that about 3000 yards will be removed. We desire to deposit the material on the public dumping ground off ---- ---- Harbor. We have closed an agreement with Mr. Want M. Land for this dredging. The adjacent property owners are Mr. I.C. Little, 4628 L. Street, and Mr. U.R. Wright, 4623 L. Street, --------, Texas.

Very truly yours,
SUNKEN DREDGING COMPANY

Ideal N. Mud
General Manager

Fig. 93. Letter of Application.

46. Preparation of Plans. Plans showing the location, extent, and character of the proposed work are an essential part of a permit application (Figs. 94 and 95).

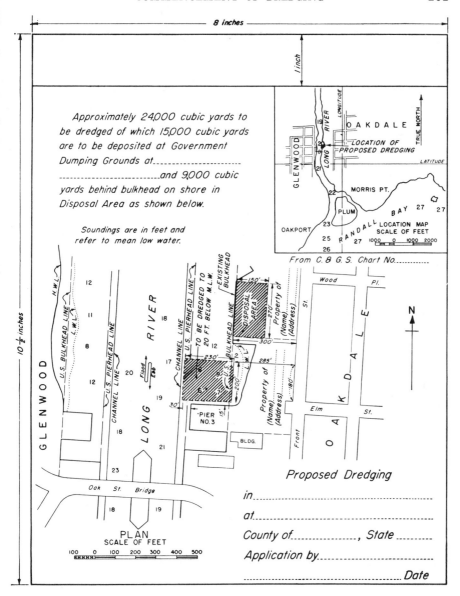

Fig. 94. Plans for Dredging Application. (Corps of Engineers)

They must be drawn on tracing linen, vellum, or heavy tracing paper, and four sets supplied. An exception may be made to this when a map or drawing is part of a printed map or plan which is sufficiently clear to permit reproduction. In ordinary applications for dredging, all four copies of the plans may be prints, and these may often be obtained from the Engineer.

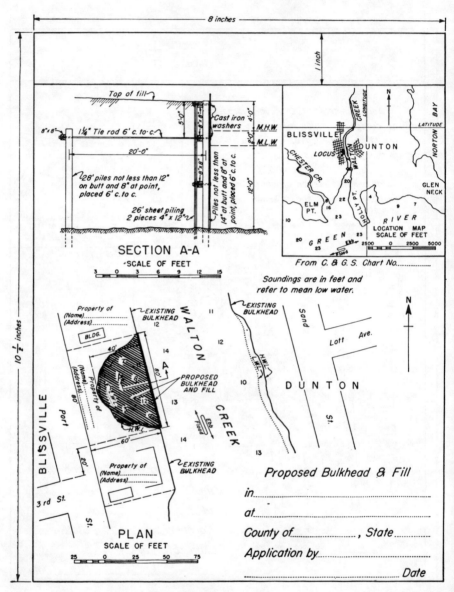

Fig. 95. Plans for Dredging Application. (Corps of Engineers)

In any case, four complete sets must be furnished. Plans must be on sheets eight by ten inches, measured from edge to edge. There must be a margin of one inch along the top for binding. All drawings must be drawn to scale and the scale shown graphically. They must have a meridian arrow showing North. When two drawings are shown on the same sheet they should be so drawn that their meridians are parallel. North must be at the top of the drawings. The direction of the current flow should be indicated for all rivers and streams, and in tidal waters the direction of the ebb and flood tides should be shown.

All soundings and elevations should be shown in feet, and they should be referenced to an established governmental datum plane in the locality. This plane in the United States is usually *mean low water* on the Gulf and Atlantic, *mean lower water* on the Pacific, *low water datum* or *mean lake level* on the Great Lakes, and *low water* on rivers.

Each drawing must have a simple title in the lower right-hand corner. A small-scale map showing the location of the proposed work is always required unless other plans submitted clearly show the general location. This location map may be on a separate sheet, or it may be drawn as an inset in a corner of the plans. It may be traced from a Coast Survey, Lake Survey, or Geological Survey chart, road map, or any other general map, and must bear a note stating the publication from which it was traced. The name of the waterway and the names of towns and prominent points should be placed on this map, and any lines of latitude or longitude should be included and identified. The location of the proposed work must be marked in red ink on all copies of this map.

The plans must show the area to be dredged, and unless the material is to be placed in an established dumping ground, the exact location for the disposal of the spoil must be shown. The boundaries of both these areas must be drawn in red ink on all copies. Existing depths of water in the vicinity of these areas should be indicated. If the deposit is to be behind a bulkhead, either in the waterway or on shore, the plans must be sufficiently detailed to show that the structure will be adequate to confine the material.

47. Notifications. Unless the application is for dredging of vessel berths and approach channels which do not adversely affect any interests, the Engineer will send notices to all parties thought to be interested, such as State and local harbor commissions, city authorities, adjoining property owners, and navigation interests. Copies of the notice will be posted in post offices or other public places near the site. Where the dumping of dredged material requires the exclusive time of government inspectors, the cost of same will be collected from the applicant. At the end of each month the amount chargeable for the cost of the inspection will be collected from the permittee.

48. Assembly and Tow. Generally the plant is at another location when a new contract is made. Consequently it is usually necessary to assemble and tow all the equipment to the new site. The dredge itself is usually towed stern-first to keep water from getting into the hull. The ladder is raised and blocked off, and in some instances the spud gantry is unhinged and laid back on the house, the spuds previously having been removed and loaded on a barge. Where tows must cross large bodies of water or the open sea, the sides of the dredge are usually boarded up as a protection against swells and waves. A skeleton crew normally rides the dredge to carry on maintenance, keep the equipment in operating condition, and to be on hand should trouble develop. In open water the larger dredges are towed by heavy tugs having 1,000 horsepower or more and tow lines of as much as two inches in diameter and 1,800 to 2,000 feet long. Added to the tow line is a bridle of 100 feet or more.

On the inland waterways, smaller tugs and lines are used. A small dredge can be loaded intact on a barge for towing on the open sea. One method of loading is to sink the barge, float the dredge over it, then pump out the barge. It rises and lifts the dredge with it. Portable dredges are also shipped in sections on barges and in the holds of ships.

Shore pipe are usually stacked on one or more barges, or if more economical or feasible, they may be trucked in to the site. Where dredges are large and steam is used, a water barge is usually available, and it can sometimes be used for stowage of pipe or other equipment. The floating line is towed in groups of several pontoons, the number depending upon the width of the waterway and the horizontal clearances along the way. The derrick barge is sometimes towed along with the shore pipe barges, but often separately.

49. Rules of the Road. All tows of dredge plants on the open sea or the inland waters of the United States must conform to certain traffic regulations or *rules of the road* (26). These rules were established primarily for the prevention of collisions. The United States Coast Guard is responsible for their enforcement.

A. DANGER SIGNAL. When two vessels are approaching each other and either fails to understand the course or intention of the other, the vessel in doubt should give several short rapid blasts of its whistle (usually not less than four) of about one second each.

B. VESSELS APPROACHING EACH OTHER—MEETING SIGNAL. If the vessels are approaching each other head-to-head, each should pass to the other's port (*port* is the left-hand side of a vessel when facing forward from the stern toward the bow; *starboard* is the right-hand side). Either vessel should give as a signal of intention of passing to port, one short (about one second) blast of its whistle. If the courses of the two are such that passing to starboard would be more practical, such as if they were both far on the starboard of each other, then either can give two short blasts. This signal should be answered by two short blasts from the other.

C. APPROACHING CURVE OR BEND. Whenever a vessel is approaching a curve or a bend where another oncoming vessel cannot be seen for half a mile, it should give one long blast when it is within one-half mile of the curve. This signal should be answered similarly by any vessel on the other side of the curve. Meeting signals should then be given immediately.

D. VESSELS OVERTAKING. When a vessel is running in the same direction and behind another and desires to pass on the starboard, it should give one short blast of its whistle. If the vessel ahead answers with one short blast, the astern vessel should pass on the starboard. Should the astern vessel want to pass on the port, it should give two short blasts. If the vessel ahead answers with two short blasts, then the astern vessel should pass on the port. However, if the vessel ahead does not think it safe for the astern vessel to pass at that time, it should give the danger signal. When the vessel ahead feels it safe for passing, it can signify its willingness to be passed by giving a passing signal, either to port or starboard.

E. VESSELS APPROACHING AT RIGHT ANGLES. A vessel having another on its own port should hold its course and speed. A vessel having another on its own starboard should keep out of the way of the other. Where practicable in narrow channels, all vessels should keep to the starboard side of the channel.

F. LIGHTS AND VISIBLE SIGNALS. During daylight hours, dredges not in operation must display two red balls—*day balls*—not less than two feet in diameter, mounted in a vertical line not less than three feet or more than six feet apart, and that are at least 15 feet above the lever room. At night a dredge must display a white light at each corner not less than six feet above the deck, and as well, two red lights in a vertical line located similarly as the day balls.

Dredges underway or engaged in dredging operations must display by day two black balls similarly sized and located as the day balls. If a dredge is anchored or moored, or engaged in laying submerged pipelines or levees, it must display day balls during the day. The upper ball must be painted with alternate black and white vertical stripes six inches wide, and the lower ball must be painted a solid bright red. By night the dredge must display three red lights in a vertical line, similarly spaced and located as the day balls.

Where there is a stringout of the plant, the three red lights must be at the channelward end of the stringout. If a stringout crossing a channel is to be opened for the passing of other vessels, the three red lights must be displayed at each side of the opening. Also, a horizontal row of amber lights not less than six feet off the deck or above the deckhouse must be displayed and spaced not more than 50 feet apart.

When attached to the dredge, the floating line must have one row of amber lights that are not less than eight feet and no more than 12 feet above the water and are equally spaced to adequately mark the entire floating line. If the floating line crosses a navigable channel, lights must not be spaced greater than 30 feet apart. If the discharge end of the line is in the water, two red lights must be displayed three feet apart in a vertical line, the lower light being at least eight feet off the water. If the line is to be opened at night for passage of vessels, a similar display of red lights must be placed each side opening.

Any vessel more than 65 feet in length at anchor in a channel should display during the day on the forward part of the vessel, one black ball not less than two feet in diameter.

G. PASSING SIGNALS FOR DREDGES. A vessel intending to pass a dredge or any of its plant should indicate its intention by giving one long blast of its whistle. The dredge should then direct it to the proper side for passing. If a floating line crosses the channel, the dredge should sound the danger signal. The line should then be opened, and when the channel is clear the dredge should sound the usual passing signal. The dredge should straighten out in the channel for passage of other vessels. When passing a dredge plant, all vessels with or without tows should pass at not more than five miles per hour when within 200 feet of the plant.

Anchors should be marked by day with a barrel or other suitable buoy. At night approaching vessels should be shown the locations of buoys by throwing a spotlight on them, or by having the buoys lighted by red lights.

The dredge must not obstruct the channel unnecessarily. When vessels are passing, swing or anchor lines on the passing side which may interfere should be slacked to the bottom. Where ample notice is given to a dredge in a narrow channel, it should move out of the way to allow clear passage.

Small motorboats of less than 16 feet in length must carry at night a white light visible for two miles around the horizon, and as well, a combination lantern in the fore part which is lower than the aft light and shows green to starboard and red to port.

H. NAVIGATION AIDS. As early as the American Revolution, navigation aids have assisted mariners. Some of these aids should be noted. It is standard in the Intracoastal Waterways of the United States for the black can buoys with odd numbers (Fig. 96) to be on the port side of the channel when entering from the north or east and traversed south or west, respectively. The red nun buoys with even numbers are on the starboard side of the channel when entering from the north or east and traversed south and west, respectively (34).

The *three R's* of boating (*red-right-returning*) applies throughout the waterways of the United States. This means that when going into port or upstream, keep the red buoys on the right. When leaving port or going downstream, keep the black buoys on the right.

50. **Arrival at the Dredging Site.** Generally the dredge is the last to arrive on location. Where shorelines have to be laid, the shore pipe and derrick barge usually arrive first, the floating line and other equipment later. In other instances, say where shore pipe can be trucked in, the shoreline may be laid some time ahead of the arrival of the other equipment.

Many contracts call for the dredging operation to commence by a certain date. Placing shore pipe, starting construction of spoil-disposal areas, or laying pipelines will usually satisfy this requirement.

Prior to the arrival of equipment, the location for a *landing* must be determined. A landing is some docking spot along the shore which is accessible by automobile or public transportation and as near the dredge site as possible. It is particularly necessary when the crews are not housed on the dredge. Some dredging jobs have landings so

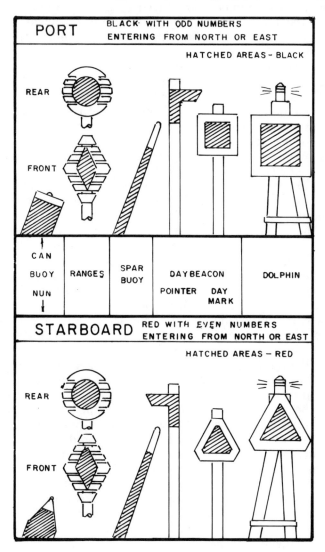

Fig. 96. Aids to Navigation.

far away from the job that a fast speedboat sometimes takes several hours to make the run. On such jobs it is often necessary to pay overtime for going and coming to the landing. It should be obvious that it is advantageous to select a landing as close to the job as possible.

Levees for spoil-disposal areas are usually started sometime before the arrival of the dredge plant, as they have to be completed before any dredging starts. On many jobs where spoil-disposal areas are small and a number are needed, levee building continues throughout the job, sometimes barely keeping ahead of the dredge. This is undesirable for it allows little or no time for the levees to settle or solidify.

51. Initial Operations. When the dredge arrives at location it is moved into position by the *dredge tender* (the tug assigned to the dredge), the alinement having been previously laid out by the civil engineer. One or both spuds are dropped, and the ladder is lowered. The floating line is taken out of tow and the pontoons are towed into place behind the dredge. The various configurations and combinations of pontoons are dictated by the deck captain, leverman or the superintendent. (*See* Art. 121 for dredge personnel categories.) The stern- and shore-connection are then made up. In some instances anchors from the winches on the floating line are set out, and their wires tightened to hold the line in place.

During these activities the leverman is on the dredge, usually in the lever room watching and directing the operations. As the work approaches completion, he sets out swing anchors.

Where anchor booms are not available, one of the dredge's swing wires is payed out to a derrick barge by the dredge tender. Here it is connected to one of the swing anchors. By radio, walkie-talkie, or by signals with the dredge whistle, the leverman directs the tender to tow the derrick barge to a suitable location. When satisfied, he signals for the anchor to be dropped. The derrick barge is then moved and the tender picks up the other swing wire from the dredge and takes it to the derrick barge. The second anchor is then set in a similar manner.

Placing the anchors is important. They must not be set too far ahead or behind the dredge to allow for an adequate swing, and they must also be sufficiently outward from the dredge to allow for an adequate advance. As the anchors are being set, the engine-room crew warms up the engines and prepares the equipment for dredging.

When the leverman feels everything is ready, he slacks off on the ladder hoist wire, allowing the suction to drop several feet below the water's surface—deep enough so that a vortex will not be formed and air drawn into the suction when the pump starts. He does not lower it into the material, however.

52. Pump Priming. Dredging cannot start until the pump is primed. Priming the pump is removing air that has collected in the volute and suction, and filling the space with water. Other pumps, such as positive-displacement types, do not need priming, inasmuch as they can pump out the air. The centrifugal dredge pump also pumps air for that matter, but only to the same amount of head as it can water. That is, if the pump can provide a head of 100 feet of water, it can also provide a head of 100 feet of air. One hundred feet of air, however, is only about 1.5 inches of vacuum—considerably less than the vacuum needed.

Should the center of the pump be below the water line, when the ladder is lowered and the pump started, water will come in and wash out the air in the volute. In such instances priming is easily accomplished without special equipment. In other instances though, particularly when the pump is above the water line, priming must be accomplished by some vacuum-producing device which will allow water to fill the pump. Exhausters operating on the venturi principle are often used, as are steam ejectors.

On dredges with gas removal systems (see Art. 127), separate priming systems are not required. The gas ejector's accumulation chamber, in connection with its exhauster, serves the same purpose. Gas ejector priming is generally faster because of its large air-handling capacity. The flap valve in the discharge line aids in the priming by blocking the discharge.

The usual method of priming with a gas ejector is to energize the exhauster and then turn the runner over slowly. Rotation causes what water is already in the pump to force the air in the pump toward the eye and thereby seal the discharge. The air in the suction then goes through the suction pipe to the exhauster and water takes its place. This system is often used when there is no flap valve in the discharge.

The leverman uses the vacuum and pressure gauges to determine how the pump is priming—both will rise as it primes. When the pump is primed and up to speed, the leverman checks all stations. If he is satisfied that all is ready, he starts the cutter rotating, lowers the ladder, and allows the cutter to eat into the material and begin feeding the suction. When he has dug to a sufficient depth to get a good cut, he starts the swing.

53. Swinging and Setting. Before the leverman starts the swing, he lifts the left spud, leaving the *digging* spud down. The digging spud is the one on which the dredge pivots when making a cutting swing. The other spud, *the setting spud,* is used principally for setting and swinging in the opposite direction. The digging spud is always the one nearest the stern connection. In this discussion the right spud is the digging spud, but the left could as well have been, depending upon which side of the hull the stern connection was assumed to be.

When the dredge is pivoting on the digging spud and making a swing, the cutter cuts into and under the material, lifting it up and into the cutter and the suction mouth, its conformation and rake making this possible. However, on the setting swing the lateral movement of the dredge is in opposition to the rotational movement and conformation of the cutter, and the cutter *overcuts* and tends to *walk* on the material. If the material is very hard, the cutter may tend to run away, and in such instances no digging can be done on the setting swing. Here a high rope speed is essential to get the dredge across the cut so that the cutting swing can recommence as quickly as possible.

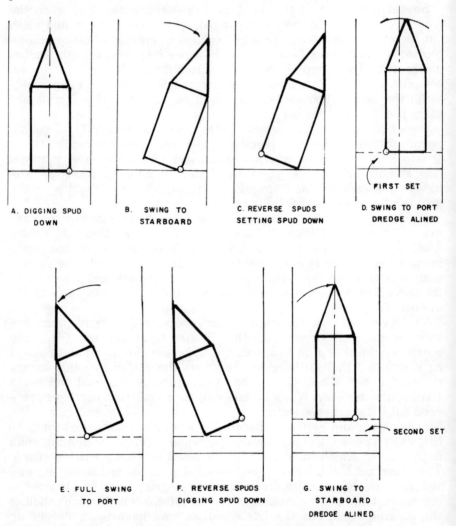

Fig. 97. Setting Dredge Ahead by Stabbing Method.

The leverman starts the swing by engaging the clutch of the drum of the right swing wire and slacking off the brake on the drum of the port. The dredge then starts to swing to starboard in an arc across the cut, pivoting on the digging spud (Fig. 97). At the limit of the swing the leverman drops the setting spud, raises the digging spud, reverses the swing wire action, and the dredge starts to swing to port. The leverman then lets the dredge swing across the entire cut, pivoting on the setting spud. At the port limit the spuds are again interchanged, the swing is reversed, and the operation repeated.

This combination of the interchange of the spuds and the swinging of the dredge causes a forward movement called *setting, upsetting,* or *stepping.* The particular method of spud interchange and swing just described is commonly called *stabbing,* the least complicated of the many variations used to step the dredge ahead. Figure 97 shows that the distance the dredge swings on its setting spud until the digging spud is dropped determines the amount of set the dredge will make. The same thing applies to the digging spud.

Various factors determine the amount of set the leverman may want to take. In soft digging the suction will pick up the material for a considerable distance in front and on both sides of the cutter. In hard or heavy material less spread of the pickup is possible. Consequently larger sets are taken in soft material than in hard.

In all setting and swinging operations, the leverman must keep the dredge alined with the center of the cut. It is obvious that if he makes a six-foot set on the port and only a three-foot set on the starboard, after a while he will have the dredge moved over to the right of the center of the cut. Should he keep this up, he would soon find himself aground on the starboard bank.

Inasmuch as sets are entirely dependent upon the amount of arc of the swing off centerline, the arcs are usually kept equal. However, in some situations it is necessary to make a shorter swing in one direction than another. In such instances a separate spud interchange may be necessary on the shorter swing.

When using the stabbing method of setting, not all of the bottom is covered by the cutter as the dredge makes each successive swing. When the setting spud is dropped at the end of the starboard swing and the dredge starts to port, the radius point of the arc of the new swing is changed. Moved not only forward by the amount of set, it is also moved to port a distance equal to the distance between the spuds multiplied by the *Cosine* of the angle of the port swing. The new arc will consequently be considerably ahead of the first arc, and, depending upon the amount of set, will skip part of the bottom. Obviously such a method is used only in soft material.

Consider the dredge in Fig. 65. Suppose the total length from the end of the cutter to the center of the spuds is 300 feet and that when the ladder is lowered to maximum digging depth, the overall length (R_0) is 272 feet. Also suppose the distance between the spud centers is 18 feet.

If this dredge were to use the stabbing method of setting where the set is to be made at the end of a 45° swing, the set would be $Y = 18$ *Sin* 45° $= (18) (0.707) = 12.73$ feet. This is an extremely large set and usable only in soft material. Additionally, the width of cut on

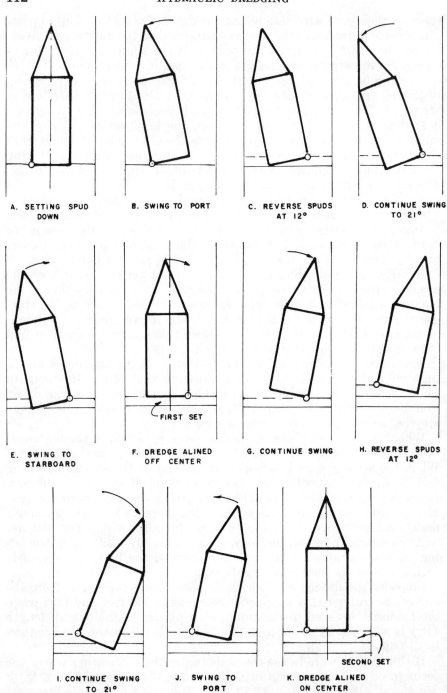

Fig. 98.   Variation of Setting Method of Fig. 97.

such a set at maximum depth would be 384 feet. Consequently, the stabbing method of setting here would be applicable on only a particular job.

Imagine that this dredge was to be used in a channel 200 feet wide. This would allow a swing at maximum depth of only $Sin^{-1} = 0.368$, or about 21°. If the set were made at the end of each swing, an upset of $(18)(0.368) - 6.6$ feet would be obtained.

Now consider that the material being dug was extremely tough, hard, clay, and that a single upset of 6.6 feet was too much for the cutter to handle. A set of four feet would be more desirable, say. The leverman could get a shorter upset by reducing his swing to $Sin^{-1} = 0.222$, or about 13°. However, this would give him a half-cut width of only 60 feet, or a total channel-cut of 120 feet, 80 feet shy of the required width.

What he can do to remedy this is use a variation of the stabbing method.

In Fig. 98 the dredge is alined in the center of the channel. A swing to port is started on the setting spud. When the angle of the swing has reached 13°, the digging spud is dropped and the setting spud is raised. The dredge is allowed to continue swinging to port until it is at an agle of 21° with the centerline. The swing is then reversed and the dredge swings back to the 13° angle with the centerline. Here a spud interchange is made again.

The dredge is now four feet advanced from its original position. The swing is then continued across the cut until the dredge makes an angle of 13° with the centerline on the starboard side. The spud interchange is made and the process repeated. The dredge proceeds up the cut in four-foot steps for each swing.

If this upset is still too great for the material being cut, the port or starboard set could be eliminated, giving a four-foot set for each cutting swing. Or the set could be reduced or increased as desired by making the set at different angles with the centerline.

It should be evident from the foregoing that the leverman has an almost infinite number of means to obtain proper set distances with various width cuts. For different length dredges these sets and swings will change proportionally with the overall length of the cutter-to-spud distance. For example, should a dredge have an effective horizontal length of 200 feet instead of 272 feet when digging at 45°, the set and swing would be reduced on the ratio of $200/272 = 0.735$.

Rate of swing varies with the consistency of the material. The main objective in dredging is to swing at the highest rate possible. In soft material the rate is often necessarily high to get adequate material. However, the rate of swing is generally slower in hard material, so as to not overload the cutter motor. Sometimes this does not always give an adequate supply. Whatever the rate though, it should be that which will provide the pump with adequate material without overloading the cutter or suction.

There are two limiting criteria controlling a dredge's production: the ability of the cutter to supply the pump and the ability of the pump to handle the material. On some jobs the material is soft and the bank small, and getting production depends upon the dredge's ability to get ahead rapidly to pick up enough material to supply the pump. Here high rope speeds are desirable. Some dredges have rope speeds of 180 feet a minute. On other jobs however, where the material is hard, high rope speed is not important, for there is plenty of material—it just has to be cut. A high line pull is usually necessary in such circumstances to get the cutter into the material. Some dredges have line pulls of 150,000 pounds and more.

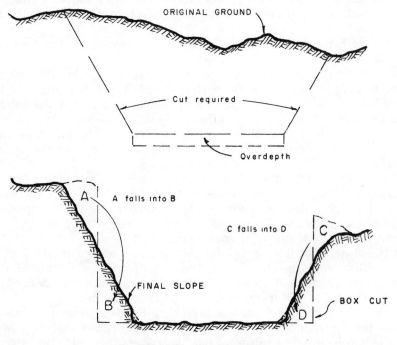

Fig. 99.   The Box Cut.

54. Box Cuts and Side Slopes.

Few channels have vertical sides, unless of course there is some form of wall, quay, or bulkhead. Most dredging contracts require side slopes, the slope specifications generally being predicated by the natural underwater repose of the material.

Generally speaking, side slopes are designed to be slightly flatter than the angle of repose of the earth in air. In very light, fine soils, slopes may be as great as 1 on 5, or more; in clayey loams or coarse soils they may be 1 on 1½ or 2; in firm clayey gravel or clay, 1 on 1¼ or 1. Experience with materials in any particular area is the best means of determining the angle of repose.

CUTTER AND SECTION OF SHAFT REMOVED

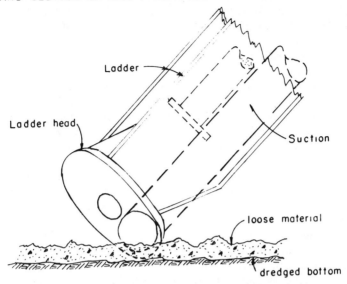

CUTTER AND SHAFT IN PLACE

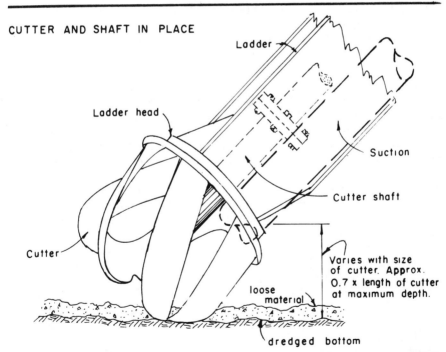

Fig. 100.   Suction Distance from Bottom, With and Without Cutter Attached.

It is difficult for a dredge to cut a side slope and although slopes are occasionally cut, most dredge cuts are boxed. A *box cut* looks like the end of an open box—the sides are vertical and the bottom flat (Fig. 99). Cuts made in this manner have a bottom width wider than called for in the specifications so that when the sides cave in the final slope will equal that required.

Too wide a bottom will involve overdredging, and reduce the profit. Too narrow a bottom will cause the section to be short, and will require redredging, which will also reduce the profit. (*See* Art. 72 for the methods of determining the width of box cuts.)

Specifications usually allow a certain amount of overdredging (Fig. 99). On jobs where the material is soft, overdredging is often done to make sure that no material will remain within the theoretical prism, particularly at the toe of the slopes where it is most likely. In hard materials, overdredging is usually not done intentionally. It should be realized however, that where overdredging is to be paid for, as much of it should be dug as is economically possible.

Where exact slopes are specifically required they can be dredged in place. Although this is a time-consuming operation, it can most easily be accomplished by using a gyro compass. (*See* Art. 56.)

55. Cleaning Up.   Often when dredging at maximum depth it is difficult to get the bottom clean, particularly when working in heavy material. This is principally because of the distance of separation between the suction mouth and the material. The limit of separation of the invert of the suction mouth from the material for the most effective pickup is about the diameter of the suction mouth, half the distance being a more desirable limit. As the dredging depth increases with any one dredge, the separation of the suction mouth and the bottom increases. Consequently, where specifications call for a clean bottom at maximum depth, the cutter and its front shaft section are sometimes removed so that the suction mouth can be placed closer to the bottom (Fig. 100). Suction cutter-drives allow dredging a cleaner bottom, as the suction mouth can be placed nearer the end of the cutter.

56. Gyro Compass.   A gyro compass is often used for side-slope or box-cut dredging because it will give accurate swing-angle data. From measurements made on before-dredging cross sections superimposed upon specification cross sections, the angle of swing required at any depth of the cutter can be determined. These angles are listed on cut sheets and given to the leverman, who, with the aid of the gyro compass, can control the swing to the limits indicated.

The gyro compass (Fig. 101) operates on the principle of the gyroscope in indicating true north. It consists essentially of an electrically-powered rotor which spins at a rate of from 6,000 to 21,000 rpm. This rotor is suspended so that it automatically orients its axis in the direction of the geographic meridian.

Its advantages are that there are no declination adjustments required, for there is no dependence upon the earth's magnetic field for direction indication, it is not affected by the magnetism of the dredge, or other magnetic influences, and its force is much stronger than that of a magnetic compass. Its disadvantages are that its mechanism is delicate and complicated, it gets out of order easily, and it needs a constant source of electrical power.

The gyro compass is used extensively for automatic steering of ships. In conjunction with an electrical contact device it causes the rudder to respond instantly to slight variations of the vessel's head. This application could be applied to the dredge swing or setting anchors. (*See* Arts. 28 and 54.)

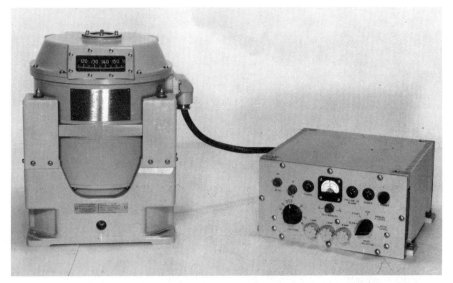

Fig. 101.   Sperry Rand Corporation Gyro Compass MK-27.

57. Spoil-disposal Areas.   Unlike other dredges which have hoppers or load the spoil on barges alongside, the pipeline dredge usually deposits its spoil ashore in spoil-disposal areas. These areas are located as near the dredge as possible. As time passes, however, and land is being reclaimed, they are becoming farther and farther away, particularly in populated areas. It is not uncommon now for dredges to pump material a mile or more, and longer distances are pumped quite regularly.

Silt, mud, and other soft materials which are more-or-less valueless for reclamation uses, are disposed of wherever possible. Sand, gravel, some clays, and other hard materials which make good fill material, are disposed of whenever possible in areas that can be reclaimed.

One of the criteria in determining the location of a shore-based spoil-disposal area is the capacity required. The area must not only be large enough to contain all the spoil, but it must be also large enough to allow for settling, and have levees strong enough to permanently confine the material.

Fig. 102.   Boom Discharge.   (J. S. Gissel Co.)

The location and capacity of spoil-disposal areas determine the effective progress of the work. For instance, where shore-based spoil-disposal areas adjoin the dredging site, shorelines can often be eliminated by using a specially-designed boom-discharge barge (Figs. 31 and 102). With such a discharge the material can be dumped directly over the levee and into the area, the barge being moved along with the dredge. When the material is light and the bank small, the dredge can move ahead rapidly. This operation provides for greater efficiency than when using a shoreline with all the subsequent stops that must be made to add pipe.

When areas are small, numerous shorelines have to be built. For some large areas, however, several shorelines will also be built for one individual area, the dredge hooking on to each as it advances, thereby keeping the overall discharge line as short as possible. This has much to do with the location of the shorelines and the shore connections.

When a certain spoil elevation is required in a spoil-disposal area, stakes are usually set throughout the area with crossarms nailed on at the required elevation. For night operation, lanterns or battery-powered lights are hung on the stakes with the globes or bulbs at the correct elevation. The night crews sight along the lights to determine the proper height of fill.

Spoil-disposal areas located in the water usually are not nearer than 1,000 feet to the dredged channel. This distance depends, of course, upon the anticipated rate of settlement of the spoil. For such areas it is not usually possible or necessary to build retaining levees, so the area is usually made quite large, and its outer limits normally not defined.

Sometimes when spoil is being dumped in water adjoining a cut, a *baffle plate* is attached to the end of the discharge. The plate is built so that when struck by the discharge, a force is created which pushes the plate and floating line ahead (Fig. 103). This arrangement is particularly advantageous in not having to move the discharge ahead or not having to add pipe each time the dredge moves ahead.

The force acting on such a plate upon which a stream of water is impinging is

$$F = V \frac{W}{g} \tag{26}$$

where F = force, in pounds; W = weight of mixture hitting the plate, in pounds per second; V = velocity of the mixture, in feet per second, and g = acceleration of gravity, in feet per second per second (27).

Assume a 20-inch discharge, with a mixture weight of 70 pounds per cubic foot, hits a flat baffle plate normal to its surface at 20 feet per second. The force acting on the plate, from Equation 26 is

$$F = \frac{20 \ (70) \ (\pi) \ (100) \ (20)}{(32.2) \ (144)} = 1,897 \text{ pounds}$$

Fig. 103. Baffle Plate Effect. (ARMCO Steel Corp.)

120

Should the plate now be turned sideward so that it is no longer normal to the stream flow, but at some angle (ϕ), the force acting on it would be a vector quantity (F_v) with two components (F_x) and (F_y), (27), where

$$F_x = V\frac{W}{g} - \frac{W}{g}(V \cos \phi) \tag{27}$$

$$F_y = \frac{W}{g}(V \sin \phi) \tag{28}$$

$$F_v = (F_x^2 + F_y^2)^{0.5} \tag{29}$$

These forces would be $F_x = (94.88)(20) - (94.88)(20)(0.866) = 254.28$ pounds, and $F_y = (94.88)(20)(0.500) = 948.50$ pounds. F_v will then be 982 pounds pushing against the plate at an angle of 30° with the centerline of the discharge. If the plate were fastened to the line with a proper anchor attached, the line could be made to move perpendicular to itself.

The same effect can be obtained with a curved pipe on the end of the discharge. Here the two components are

$$F_x = p_1A_1 - p_2A_2 \cos \phi + \frac{W}{g}(V_1 - V_2 \cos \phi)$$

$$F_y = p_2A_2 \sin \phi + \frac{W}{g} V_2 \sin \phi$$

If the curved pipe was a constant diameter, as it would be with dredge pipe, $p_1A_1 = p_2A_2$ and $V_1 = V_2$, so the equations would become

$$F_x = pA - pA \cos \phi + \frac{W}{g}(V - V \cos \phi) \tag{30}$$

$$F_y = pA \sin \phi + \frac{W}{g}(V \sin \phi) \tag{31}$$

where p = unit pressure on the water, in pounds per square inch; A = area of pipe, in square inches; ϕ = degree of bend of pipe, in degrees, and W, g and V as defined above.

Using the same discharge as before, (p) would equal the pressure due to the velocity only, as that developed for friction would have been used up at the end of the line, so (pA) would be $V^2/2g$ (0.4331) (314.16) = $400/64.4$ (0.4331) (314.16) = 845.11 pounds, and

$$F_x = (845.11)(1 - 0.866) + 94.88(20)(1 - 0.866)$$
$$= 367.52$$
$$F_y = (845.11)(0.500) + (94.88)(20)(0.500)$$
$$= 1371.35$$

so
$$F_v = 1419.95 \text{ pounds}$$

This force would tend to move the line similarly as the angled baffle plate. If this curved pipe were placed on a swivel, the line could be moved ahead, stopped, and then moved ahead again by merely rotating the pipe sideward or upward.

These relationships can also be used to calculate the forces acting on an elbow in the line. In such a problem (p) would be the actual pressure in pounds per square inch in the line at the elbow, for in addition to the velocity head, the overall friction head would not be all used up by the time the flow got to the elbow—some would be left for the rest of the line. The force at the elbow would be considerably greater than at the end of the line, because of the increased pressure on the water in the line.

A. LEVEES. When spoil-disposal areas are large enough that the spoil can be easily retained, spoil and water are allowed to run free, or only low levees are built. But with the continuation of dredging over the years, and the increasing value of land, spoil-disposal areas are becoming smaller and smaller. Consequently, the need for higher levees is increasing.

A considerable amount of work goes into constructing a levee. The dragline is the main tool for affecting this work. It can reach out and get material from the borrow pit or ditch within the spoil-disposal area and still leave an adequate berm. Borrow ditches are usually limited in width to the reach of the dragline's boom. Consequently, the size of the levee determines the size of the dragline that will be necessary.

The borrow ditch inside the area is not made continuous. At intervals of 200 to 500 feet, depending upon the length of the levee, 20- to 30-foot wide cross-dams are left (Fig. 104). The reason for the cross-dams is to prevent *channelling*. A continuous borrow ditch would allow the discharge water to flow along the ditch and not only cause the water to eat away at the levee, but it would not give the material time to settle out.

The base upon which a levee is built must be cleared of all grass, weeds, and other growth, and it should be thoroughly scarified. A levee built on grass can slide when only part of the area is filled with spoil.

A levee must have adequate freeboard. The minimum requirement is usually two feet above the projected surface of the area when filled. The freeboard height depends upon several variables. For instance, in large disposal areas, windblown waves can make-up across the surface. By the time they reach the other side they can sometimes broach a levee which has insufficient freeboard. (*See* Art. 71 for wave make-up calculations.)

When heavy sands, gravels, or rocks, and some balling clays are spoiled, they settle out rapidly. The water clears quickly and can be released rapidly. Silts, muds, and dissolved clays, however, do not settle out rapidly. The water from this kind of discharge cannot be released as soon and so a larger freeboard is needed.

Levees are a constant headache. They have to be continuously patrolled. Animals, snakes, and other rodents, and sometimes small boys, often burrow into them. The holes they make sometimes cause leaks. Once a leak starts it can enlarge rapidly and the entire levee can be broached in a matter of seconds. Voids left in a levee when it

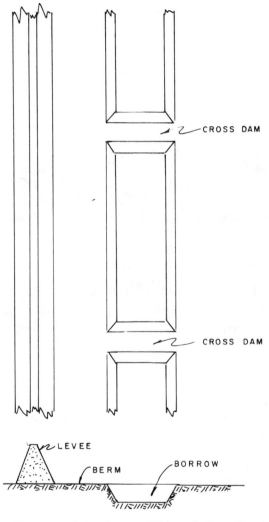

Fig. 104.   Levee Borrow Pits with Cross-Dams.

is being built often allow seepage. A soaked levee loses strength quickly. Seepage under a levee is also hazardous. When proper foundation procedure has not been followed, or when the levee is built on porous sub-bases, seepage under the levee can cause the base to soften and a levee to settle or a section slide out in a mass.

Occasionally a dredge is used to build a levee. The discharge end of the line is usually placed at the near end of the proposed levee aline-ment and spoil is allowed to build up. When the required height is reached, the line is lengthened and the levee continued. *Bleeder pipe* are often used to build levees (Fig. 105). The discharge line is laid along the centerline of the proposed levee on elevated H- or X-crib-bing or piling. Holes, varying in size from two by two inches to six by six inches, are cut in the underside of the pipe. When the dredge is pumping, the heavier materials drop out as they come to the holes, but the silts and muds which are in solution, flow on past and out the line to a waste-disposal area. This system is used extensively when graded fill materials are required, such as for a dam base, or the revitalization of sand beaches.

Fig. 105. Bleeder Pipe for Levee Construction.
(Naylor Pipe Co.)

B. SPILLWAYS. Water pumped into the spoil-disposal area along with the spoil is discharged from the area through a *spillway.* In small spoil areas the spillway is often merely one or more pipes in the levee near its top. The water from which the spoil has settled escapes directly through the pipes. This system of spilling can be used for water discharge when sands, gravels, and sometimes heavy clays are being pumped, as these materials separate out rapidly. It is not satisfactory, however, for muds, silts, or suspended clays, for these lighter materials require longer ponding, and a special type of spillway is therefore needed to control the height of the water. Figure 106 shows two types of spillways.

Spillways are preferably located as far from the discharge as pos-sible, as this will allow more time for the spoil to settle. On large projects the spillway can often be a major structure costing as much as $5,000. Some spillways are built of wood while others are made of

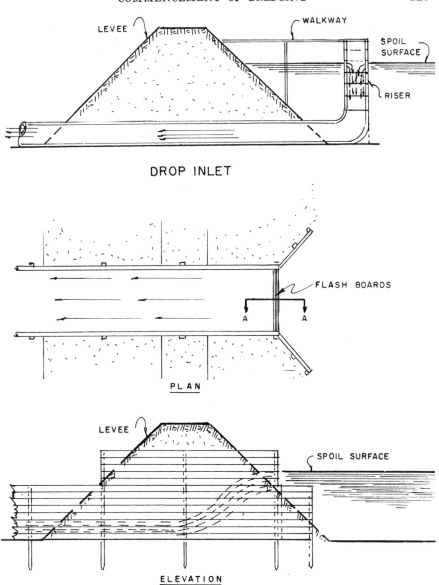

LEVEE

WALKWAY

SPOIL SURFACE

RISER

DROP INLET

FLASH BOARDS

A   A

PLAN

LEVEE

SPOIL SURFACE

ELEVATION

FLUME

Fig. 106. Two Types of Spillways.

steel and concrete. Most are designed to regulate the amount of water flowing through them. Both operate on the principle of regulating the water outflow by adding or subtracting *flash boards* over which the water spills. Flash boards are added or removed to regulate the height of the ponded water, and thereby control the turbidity of the overflow (Fig. 107).

C. TURBIDITY. With many dredging operations, particularly where the effluent from the spoil-disposal area is discharged into waters where there is marine life or conservation interests are active, there are conditions of turbidity to be considered. Usually the flash boards on the spillways are kept sufficiently high so that the effluent can be maintained clear. However, in many operations there is a require-

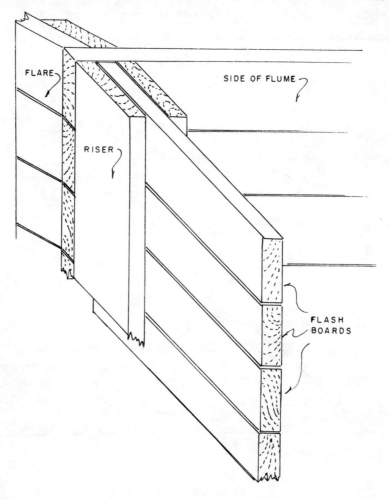

Fig. 107.   Flash Board Installation.

ment by the specifications for a certain specific clearness of the water flowing over the spillway, and, sometimes, a considerable amount of public dissention about the turbidity of the area surrounding the dredge itself.

It is admitted that the water around an active dredge becomes turbid, the degree of turbidity depending upon the consistency of the material being dredged. This turbidity, and the possibility of it having an effect on fish, oysters, and other marine life, has been given considerable attention (28, 29, 30).

Some investigators have gone so far as to stipulate a safe turbidity limit. In some instances it has been placed as low as 6,500 parts per million (ppm). Others give values such as 18,000 ppm. Some say 38,000 ppm. These stipulations, broadly speaking, are ridiculous. Fish have been found thriving in rivers with turbidities of greater than 70,000 ppm. Tests made under laboratory conditions have shown fish could survive in turbidities of 100,000 ppm.

It is obvious from these differing findings that there is no one, acceptable value of turbidity. Several variables must be considered.

There is, for instance, the consideration of the fishes' natural environment. Some fish have become adapted to survival in extremely turbid conditions—say, in the Mississippi River or the Missouri River. On the other hand, some fish have a relatively silt-free environment—in the open sea, for example. It is apparent that a usable turbidity value must, for one thing, be based upon the fishes' environment.

Additionally, unlike shellfish, fish can easily move about. Where isolated conditions of high turbidity exist, such as around a dredge, fish can easily swim out of the area if silt concentration is too high. Turbidity caused by dredging is not harmful to fish.

Oysters also show no harmful effects from turbidity caused by dredging, even if they cannot move about. Tests have been made where oysters were placed in boxes hung directly over the side of the dredge—in turbidities far greater than would ever occur in the oyster beds. Left there for long periods, they suffered no harmful effects. As a matter of fact, oysters have been suspended directly in the discharge of a spoil-disposal area spillway and were not affected.

Commercial shrimping interests will substantiate that shrimp are not harmed by turbidity. In fact it seems that the shrimp thrive in turbid waters. Many dredgemen have observed shrimp trawlers near dredging operations, some of them making trawls within 200 feet of the dredge. It is believed that the muds stirred up by the dredge contain nutrients and food for the shrimp.

Chapter 4

Surveying—Job Layout— Volume Calculation

58. Introduction. There is a great amount of office and field work to be done before a dredging job can start. A *reference line* (RL) from which all parts of the work can be located must be established, cross sections must be taken and processed to determine if dredging will be proceeding properly, the channel must be adequately marked so that the dredge can excavate accurately, spoil-disposal areas must be located, and retaining levees must be built. All these activities must be planned, coordinated, and completed, and the data properly processed, before dredging commences. As a considerable amount of this work is dependent upon a knowledge of measurement and surveying, the following discusses some measuring and surveying principles.

59. Units of Measurement. In dredging-job layout there are two fundamental measurements—angular and linear. Generally, angular measurements are made in degrees, minutes and seconds. In dredging work, however, seconds are usually disregarded, as the nearest minute is usually adequate. For instance, an angular error of 30 seconds (30″) corresponds to a linear error of about 0.15 foot in 1,000 feet.

There are still a few countries throughout the world, including the United States, where the common unit of linear measurement is the British foot. In an increasing number of countries, however, the metric system of measurement is used, the common unit being the millimeter. The unit of area in the United States is the square foot and the acre, the acre being equal to 43,560 square feet. The unit of volume is the cubic foot and the cubic yard, the cubic yard being equal to 27 cubic feet. In the metric system the main units are the meter, the liter and the gram.

60. Consistency of Measurements. In laying out a reference line, a disposal area, or performing any other operation requiring both angular and linear measurements, all measurements should be consistent. That is, it would obviously be a waste of time to measure angles to seconds when linear measurements were only measured to the nearest foot.

Consider a hypothetical case of a line 1,000 feet long at an angle to another line (Fig. 108). The error allowed in the linear measurement is to be, say, one foot. This is an error ratio of 1/1,000. Therefore, to have both the linear and angular measurements consistent, the angle also must be measured so as to have only a possible one-foot error. Angular error, just as linear error, can be expressed in terms of a ratio. In Fig. 108 the allowable angular error will be approximately three minutes (3′) since one minute equals approximately

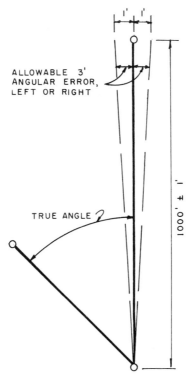

Fig. 108.   Angular Error in Transit Line.

Table 3. Angular Error Versus Linear Error and Resulting Ratio of Precision

Angular Error	Linear Error in 1,000 ft	Ratio of Precision
10′	2.9090 ft	1/344
5′	1.4540 ft	1/688
1′	0.2910 ft	1/3440
30″	0.1450 ft	1/6880

0.3-foot error in 1,000 feet. Table 3 shows some comparisons between angular and linear error (31).

It is interesting to note that as angles approach 90° they become more precise when used in calculations involving the *Sin,* but they decrease in precision when the *Cosine* is used in calculations. They approach their most precise values at 45° when the *Tangent* is used. It would consequently appear that when computations are to be made with the *Sin, Cosine* and *Tangent,* angles should be kept as near 45° as possible. Furthermore, the precision of an angle of say, 10°, with

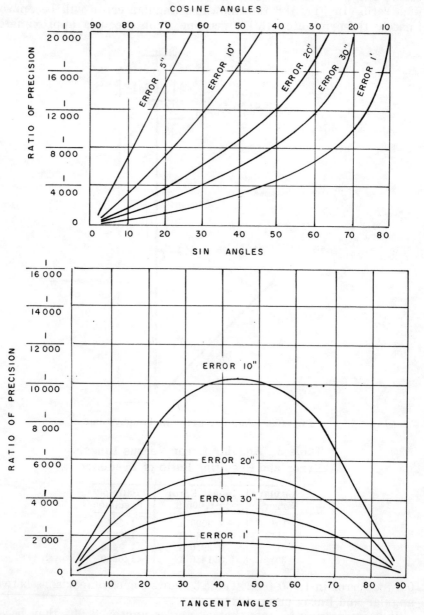

Fig. 109. Precision Obtainable When Using *Sin, Cosine,* and *Tangent* in Computations.

a possible error of one minute, would be 1/800 when using the *Sin* in calculations, while an angle of 45° with the same possible error, and using the *Sin*, would be 1/3,500! These relationships can be seen in Fig. 109.

61. Precision of Computations. While providing for the consistency of linear and angular measurements in the field, it should be realized that all this can be in vain unless consistency is also maintained in the office computations. In the addition and subtraction of quantities, precision depends upon the *number of places* in a number. In multiplication and division, however, precision is dependent upon the number of *significant figures* in the number. To differentiate between these two, suppose that a column of areas is to be added. Some of them are to even square feet, such as 2,025 square feet, while others are to tenths of square feet, such as 3,017.5 square feet. It is obvious that the sum cannot be expressed in tenths of square feet, because some of the areas are only to the nearest square foot. Consequently, the sum of the areas must be shown only to the least number of places in any individual area of the group, if precision is to be maintained.

In multiplication, the sum of the probable errors of the individual factors is equal to the relative error in the product. For example, suppose a turning basin was measured as 796.3 feet long and 436 feet wide. The product, square feet, would be precise only to the value of the three significant figures—the width has only three significant figures, although the length has four. Consequently, the area would be precise only to three significant figures, or 347,000 square feet—not to four significant figures (347,100 square feet), and certainly not to 347,186.8 square feet—as most persons would find it!

62. Field Measurements. There are three fundamental ways to measure distance in the field. They differ in the precision they will produce.

A. THE PACE. Pacing is used when a precision of not more than 1/200 is required. Each person should determine his own *pace* (one step), and should practice until he can hold it over any terrain. Ordinarily the pace is estimated as being 2.5 feet, having the advantage that 40 paces are equal to 100 feet.

B. STADIA. Under good conditions, stadia will yield a precision of about 1/1,000. The average, however, should be considered to be about 1/500 to 1/750. It is not as rapid as pacing, but it is more rapid than chaining. For distances up to 300 feet or so it is sufficiently accurate for most dredge layout work.

When making stadia measurements, the apparent distance between the two stadia hairs in the telescope on the stadia rod is observed. This apparent distance of separation on the rod is called the *stadia interval*. It is directly proportional to the distance from the transit to the rod. The stadia hairs are the horizontal hairs equally distant above and below the regular instrument center cross-hair.

Usually when reading stadia the lower stadia hair is placed on an even foot mark of the stadia rod, and a foot, tenths, and hundredths reading taken on the rod with the upper stadia hair. The point at which the lower hair is set is determined by whatever foot mark will cause the least inclination of the line of sight. Multiplying the stadia interval by the *stadia constant* will give the distance between the instrument and the rod.

The *stadia constant* is usually stamped on the instrument's serial number plate. Should it not be, it can be determined by measuring off several distances with a chain, observing the stadia interval for each, and then computing a constant for each. An average of several observed constants will give a suitable value. In modern instruments the stadia constant is usually 100.

For example, suppose that 100-, 200-, and 300-foot distances were marked off, and the stadia interval for each determined with the transit and rod. Suppose these stadia intervals were found to be, respectively, 1.145, 2.250 and 3.315. By dividing each of them into its respective distance, a separate stadia constant will be obtained—87.34, 88.89, and 90.50—the mean being 88.91. So, whenever that particular instrument is used, all stadia intervals would be multiplied by the stadia constant of 88.91 to determine the distance sighted. As just mentioned, most instruments have a stadia constant of 100, so the calculation is not as difficult as might be imagined from the foregoing exaggerated example.

C. CHAINING. Following stadia in increasing precision of measurement comes ordinary chaining. Precision can be obtained to 1/1,000 fairly easily. Very careful work can give 1/10,000. In the United States where a 100-foot steel tape (chain) is used, readings can very easily be made to one-tenth of a foot. A prime requisite is that the chain be kept straight, be supported throughout its length, and have an equal tension for each measurement—about 20 pounds pull is average for most chains.

63. Turning Right Angles. Often it is more convenient to turn a 90° angle with the chain than set up an instrument. This method is often used for setting *back stakes* or ranges for taking cross sections. One procedure is called the *3-4-5 method.* It is based upon the fact that a right triangle with one side three units long and another side four units long, will have the third side (the hypotenuse) five units long. The procedure to turn the right angle is as follows.

From a point on the RL where the 90° back stake is to be set, measure up or down the RL a distance of 18 feet, 21 feet, 24 feet, or any other distance that is a multiple of three, and set a chaining pin or stake. Then go back to the starting point on the RL, measure off approximately perpendicular to the RL a distance that is four times the multiple distance used for the first measurement. That is, if 24 feet were first measured along the RL, the multiple distance would have been 24/3 = 8. The distance measured perpendicular would then have to be (8) (4) = 32 feet. Set another chaining pin or stake.

Now, from the first pin or stake that was set on the RL, extend the chain a multiple of five times the original multiple distance, or in this instance where 8 was the multiple distance, 40 feet. If the distance between the two pins is exactly 40 feet, the second pin will be at an exact 90° angle to the RL at the original point on the RL. If the distance is not 40 feet, the second pin should be moved parallel with the RL until it is exactly 40 feet from the first pin, its distance from the starting point remaining 32 feet.

To determine an approximate right angle in setting the second pin, stand on the starting point, stretch the arms out sidewards, shoulder-high, pointing up and down the RL. With the eyes closed, bring the palms together in front. They will point approximately at a 90° angle to the RL.

A faster and probably as accurate method of laying off a 90° angle can be accomplished with a *right-angle glass*. This is a prism which reflects a light ray at a 90° angle. By sighting over the top of the prism down the RL, say, at a range pole set on the next station, a right angle can be made with the RL by moving another pole back and forth until its reflection is seen in the prism directly under the pole on the RL.

64. Levelling. There are several ways of levelling—that is, determining the elevations of a series of points. *Differential levelling* is the most useful to the dredgeman.

An instrument is set up and levelled at some arbitrary location, preferably equally distant from a bench mark or reference elevation and the point for which the first elevation is to be obtained. A level rod is then held on the bench mark by a rodman, and the feet, tenths and hundredths read on the rod. This value is added to the stated elevation of the bench mark to give the elevation of the instrument—called the *HI*, or *height of instrument*.

The instrument is then turned and pointed at the level rod which has now been set on the point for which the first elevation is to be obtained. A foot, tenths, and hundredths reading is again taken on the rod. This value, when subtracted from the *HI*, will give the elevation of the point.

The instrument is then moved ahead approximately halfway between the point just shot—called a *back-sight*—and the next point to be shot—called a *fore-sight*—and the procedure is repeated. This is continued until all points on the line or circuit have been determined.

The reason for keeping the back-sight and fore-sight distances as equal as possible is to balance out any errors that may exist in the instrument. When the back- and fore-sight distances are exactly equal, all instrument error is balanced out, and even if the instrument was out of adjustment, a correct reading would be obtained.

As an example of the proper method of entering levelling data in a field book (Fig. 110), consider the following hypothetical situation. The level is set up between BM-1 and station 1+00. The stated elevation for BM-1 is 27.96 feet. A rod reading taken on BM-1 is 4.76 feet. Consequently, the *HI* is 27.96 + 4.76 = 32.72 feet. The instrument is turned and a reading taken on station 1+00. The rod reading is 4.10 feet. Therefore, the elevation of station 1+00 is 32.72 − 4.10 = 28.62 feet. From the same instrument setting rod readings are taken on stations 2+00 and 3+00, and they are, respectively, 3.96 and 4.76. The elevations of these two stations are therefore 28.76 feet and 27.96 feet.

The instrument is then moved ahead to around station 4+50. A back-sight is taken on station 3+00 which gives 4.13 feet. As the

Grades for Levee of Spoil Area 6

October 5, 19--   ---------, Texas
Job 3567   Dredge "Digger"

BM-1 is a 4-in. brass plate set in concrete at USC & GS marker "Dog" El: 27. 964

Station	+	HI	-	El	
BM-1	4. 76	32. 72		27. 96	
1+00			4. 10	28. 62	
2+00			3. 96	28. 76	
3+00	4. 13	32. 09	4. 76	27. 96	TP-1
4+00			4. 12	27. 97	
5+00			9. 31	22. 78	
6+00			8. 72	23. 37	
7+00			7. 35	24. 74	
8+00	5. 35	31. 23	6. 21	25. 88	TP-2
9+00			5. 16	26. 07	
10+00			4. 12	27. 11	
11+00			2. 16	29. 07	
BM-1			3. 25	27. 98	Check

Note: These elevations on MSL datum—this is 0. 78 above MLW.

Fig. 110.   Levelling Data Entries in Field Book.

elevation of station 3+00 was determined to be 27.96 feet, a new *HI* will be 27.96 + 4.13 = 32.09 feet. A reading can then be taken on stations 4+00, 5+00, 6+00 and 7+00, and possibly 8+00, and the respective elevation of each determined.

The procedure is continued in this manner until all points are determined. As good practice requires a check of the work, the levelling is usually run backward to the bench mark to see if any errors have been introduced, or a check against some other recognized bench mark in the area can be made. On levee work the levelling usually involves a closed circuit, so a check can usually be made on the bench mark used in the beginning.

65. Adjustment of Levels.   The adjustment of levels is not commonly understood. As a result, a considerable amount of time, and sometimes money, is lost while an instrument is sent to the shop or the factory for adjustment—an operation that can be performed in the field in a matter of minutes. Furthermore, with an understanding of the fundamentals of level adjustment, the instrument can be kept in good adjustment, thereby preventing unnecessary waste of time when it is needed.

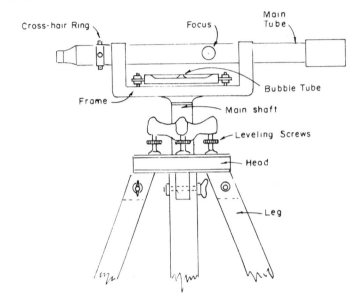

Main tube over one set of leveling screws

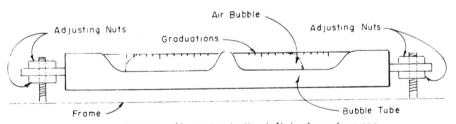

Bubble off center to the left by four divisions

Fig. 111. Instrument and Main Components.

The first thing to do when checking a level is to make sure the bubble tube is parallel with the main tube. Set the main tube across one set of levelling screws. Adjust the screws until the bubble is centered in the tube (Fig. 111). Now turn the main tube 90° until it is over the opposite set of levelling screws. Level it. Then turn the main tube back over the first set of screws and recenter the bubble.

Next, turn the main tube 180° (reversing direction of the tube, but being over the same set of screws). Does the bubble remain centered? If it does, proceed to *check for line of sight*. If not, *adjust for parallel.*

A. ADJUSTMENT FOR PARALLEL. With the instrument remaining as

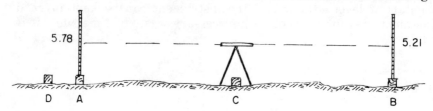

Reading "A$_1$" and "B$_1$" from "C"

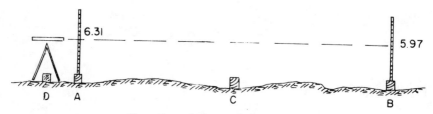

Reading "A$_2$" and "B$_2$" from "D"

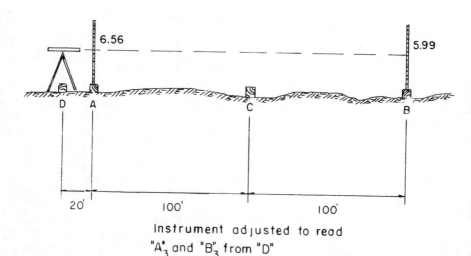

Instrument adjusted to read
"A$_3$" and "B$_3$" from "D"

Fig. 112. Construction of Layout for Instrument Adjustment.

it is—180° from the first position—bring the bubble back halfway (two graduations in Fig. 111) towards center by loosening the adjusting nuts on the side toward which the bubble should move (the right hand side in Fig. 111), and slowly turn the lower nut upwards. As the bubble moves towards the halfway mark, tighten the upper nut some and then bring the bubble back to the halfway mark by tightening the bottom one again. Do not tighten either too tight as they may need readjustment later.

Now turn the main tube 180°—back to its original position—and recenter the bubble with the levelling screws. Then turn 180° again—back to the second position—and check to see if the bubble centers.

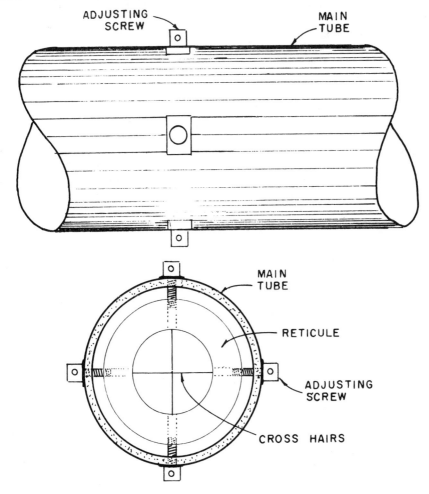

Fig. 113.   Instrument Reticule and Adjusting Screws.

If it does, tighten the nuts firmly while at the same time keeping the bubble centered, and proceed to *check for line of sight*. If it does not center, readjust the bubble halfway towards center again and continue this procedure until the bubble will center both ways. Check the instrument at 90°, 180°, 270° and 360° to make sure the main shaft is straight. Then proceed to check it for line of sight.

B. CHECK FOR LINE OF SIGHT. The first thing to do is to drive four
stakes in the ground in a fairly straight line. Select a spot where the
view between them will be unobstructed.

Drive two stakes (A) and (B), (Fig. 112), 200 feet apart. Midway
between these drive another stake (C). Then 20 feet back from stake
(A), drive stake (D). These stakes can be two-inch by two-inch hubs
or any other size that is handy. Leave them sticking above the ground
two or three inches.

Set up the instrument over stake (C). It does not have to be
exactly over it—within an inch or two is good. Set the tripod legs
so that one set of screws is fairly well in line with the four stakes.
Center the bubble across both sets of screws.

Have someone hold a level rod on stake (B). Point the instrument
at the rod and with the set of screws that are in line, adjust the
bubble until it is exactly centered. Read the height on the rod. In
Fig. 112 this is 5.21 feet. Call it (B_1). Now have the rodman move to
stake (A). Turn the level 180°, center the bubble exactly, and read
the level rod on (A). This is 5.78 feet in Fig. 112. Call it (A_1). If
the (A_1) reading is less than (B_1), drive stake (A) down enough to
make the (A_1) reading slightly less than (B_1) and then record the
last (A_1) reading, rather than the first.

Now move the level to stake (D). Have one set of levelling screws
in line. Center the bubble roughly all around. Point at the level rod,
which is still on (A), adjust the bubble until it is exactly centered,
and read the height on the rod at (A). This is 6.31 feet in Fig. 112.
Call it (A_2). Have the rodman move to stake (B). Check the bubble
for center and read the rod at (B). This is 5.97. Call it (B_2).
Write these values down as follows,

$$A_1 = 5.78 \qquad A_2 = 6.31$$
$$\underline{B_1 = 5.21} \qquad \underline{B_2 = 5.97}$$
$$C_1 = 0.57 \qquad C_2 = 0.34$$

subtract (B_1) from (A_1) and call the result (C_1). Subtract (B_2) from
(A_2) and call the result (C_2). If $(C_1) = (C_2)$, the instrument is exactly
level, and nothing more needs to be done to it. If (C_1) does not equal
(C_2), the level is not level. Proceed as follows to make it so.

C. ADJUST FOR LINE OF SIGHT. Subtract (C_2) from (C_1). Call the
result (C_3). Multiply (C_3) by 1.1 and call this product (C_4). Add
(C_4) to the original (A_2) reading.

$$C_1 - C_2 = 0.23 = C_3$$
$$C_3 \times 1.1 = 0.25 = C_4$$
$$C_4 + A_2 = 6.56$$

Now, sighting again at the rod on (A), the instrument still being at

(D), increase the reading (A₂) originally read, to $A_2 + C_4 = 6.56$ feet. To increase the reading it is necessary to adjust the cross-hair, or in effect, lower the reticule (Fig. 113). To do this loosen the top reticule screw and tighten the bottom one. If it is necessary to lower the reading, the bottom screw should be loosened and the top one tightened. To turn the screws, use a nail or a small punch that fits easily into the screws' adjusting holes. Do not use pliers.

Adjust the cross-hair until the rod reading at (A) is 6.56 feet. Make sure that the final adjustment of the reticule leaves both screws tight. It is best to bring the cross-hair to the correct reading, and then alternate in tightening both screws until they are both tight, keeping the correct reading all the time.

When the cross-hair is set to read 6.56 feet at (A), have the rodman go to (B). The rod reading should be 5.99 feet. This is because the difference in elevation of (A₁) and (B₁) was 0.57 feet, so, $6.56 - 0.57 = 5.99$. Inasmuch as the distance between (A) and (C) is equal to the distance between (B) and (C), 100 feet, the difference in elevation is exact regardless of the instrument's accuracy. If the reading at (B) is 5.99, the instrument is now level. As a check, go through the first two steps again to see if $(C_1) = (C_2)$.

66. The Meridian. A meridian is a fixed line of reference. It may be a line on the plans or it may be purely imaginary. Usually it is either true or magnetic north. A *true meridian* is a line running due north. Regardless of where on earth it is, it always runs due north, and it is usually determined by astronomical observation.

Occasionally it is necessary to establish a true meridian. Generally speaking this is considered a difficult task, and a lot of dredge engineers shy away from it. However, for dredging purposes, true north can be determined relatively easily by making a *Polaris* (North Star) observation. The method to be described is simple, and is paraphrased from a booklet published by Keuffel and Esser Co. of Hoboken, New Jersey (32). If normal care is taken, the true meridian can be established within ± 30 seconds (30″) of true north.

Polaris is not motionless. It travels in a continual counterclockwise direction around the true pole. When it is furthest west from the pole it is said to be at its *western elongation*. When furthest east it is at its *eastern elongation*. The approximate time of either elongation can be determined from Fig. 114. To adjust watch time to LCT (local civil time, which is used in Fig. 114), add to the watch time four minutes for every degree of longitude that the place of observation is east of the meridian from which watch time is reckoned. Subtract if west.

For example, if watch time is 10:00 Central Standard Time (90th meridian reckoning), and the observation is being made at 87° west longitude, add $3 \times 4 = 12$ minutes to the watch time—giving a LCT of 10:12.

Be at the location where the meridian is to be established some

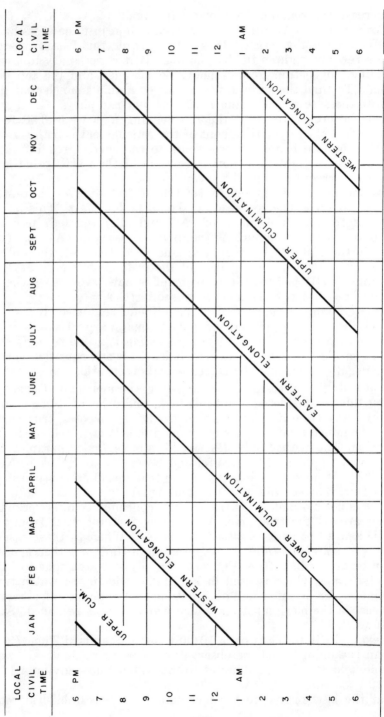

Fig. 114. Elongation and Culmination of *Polaris*. (Keuffel and Esser Co.)

140

time before elongation. Set up the instrument at some point (A). Set the horizontal vernier at zero, using the upper horizontal motion, and then clamp it. Sight a point (B) with the lower horizontal motion, making sure the vernier still reads zero. Unclamp the upper horizontal motion and with a clockwise motion point the instrument in the general direction of *Polaris*.

Before a western elongation *Polaris* will be moving down and toward the west. Before an eastern elongation it will be moving up and toward the east. A few minutes before elongation, sight *Polaris*

Table 4. Polar Distance of Polaris
(Keuffel and Esser Co.)

Polar Distance			Polar Distance		
	Angle	Cotan		Angle	Cotan
1968	° ′		1968	° ′	
Jan. 1	0 52.66	65.28	July 9	0 53.13	64.70
11	0 52.63	65.31	19	0 53.12	64.71
21	0 52.62	65.33	29	0 53.11	64.73
31	0 52.61	65.34			
			Aug. 8	0 53.08	64.75
Feb. 10	0 52.62	65.33	18	0 53.06	64.79
20	0 52.64	65.30	28	0 53.02	64.84
Mar. 1	0 52.66	65.27	Sept. 7	0 52.97	64.90
11	0 52.70	65.23	17	0 52.92	64.96
21	0 52.74	65.17	27	0 52.87	65.02
31	0 52.79	65.12			
			Oct. 7	0 52.80	65.10
Apr. 10	0 52.84	65.06	17	0 52.74	65.18
20	0 52.89	64.99	27	0 52.68	65.25
30	0 52.94	64.93			
			Nov. 6	0 52.62	65.33
May 10	0 52.99	64.88	16	0 52.55	65.41
20	0 53.03	64.83	26	0 52.49	65.49
30	0 53.06	64.78			
			Dec. 6	0 52.44	65.55
June 9	0 53.09	64.74	16	0 52.39	65.61
19	0 53.11	64.72	26	0 52.35	65.67
29	0 53.12	64.71			

and follow it until its eastward or westward movement ceases, and only vertical movement is observed. Read the horizontal vernier and record the angle. The motion east or west at elongation is nearly zero for about 10 minutes. It is recommended, therefore, that the angle between (B) and *Polaris* be repeated with the instrument's telescope inverted, thereby eliminating any instrument error, as well as verifying the first angle's value.

Suppose that an observation was made on October 17, 1968. The latitude, as taken from an available chart or map, was 40° 20′ and the angle turned clockwise from (B) to *Polaris* at elongation was 75° 20′.

From Table 4, determine the *polar distance* (90° minus the latitude)—in this example it is 0° 52.74'. Then from Table 5, determine the bearing of *Polaris*—1° 09.2' in this example.

Table 5. Bearing of Polaris at Elongation
(Keuffel and Esser Co.)

Polar Dist.	0° 52.50'	0° 52.70'	0° 52.90'	0° 53.10'	Polar Dist.	0° 52.50'	0° 52.70'	0° 52.90'	0° 53.10'
Lat.	Bearing at Elongation				Lat.	Bearing at Elongation			
°	° '	° '	° '	° '	°	° '	° '	° '	° '
10	0 53.3	0 53.5	0 53.7	0 53.9	40	1 08.5	1 08.8	1 09.1	1 09.3
11	0 53.5	0 53.7	0 53.9	0 54.1	41	1 09.6	1 09.8	1 10.1	1 10.4
12	0 53.7	0 53.9	0 54.1	0 54.3	42	1 10.6	1 10.9	1 11.2	1 11.5
13	0 53.9	0 54.1	0 54.3	0 54.5	43	1 11.8	1 12.1	1 12.3	1 12.6
14	0 54.1	0 54.3	0 54.5	0 54.7	44	1 13.0	1 13.3	1 13.5	1 13.8
15	0 54.4	0 54.6	0 54.8	0 55.0	45	1 14.2	1 14.5	1 14.8	1 15.1
16	0 54.6	0 54.8	0 55.0	0 55.2	46	1 15.6	1 15.9	1 16.2	1 16.4
17	0 54.9	0 55.1	0 55.3	0 55.5	47	1 17.0	1 17.3	1 17.6	1 17.9
18	0 55.2	0 55.4	0 55.6	0 55.8	48	1 18.5	1 18.8	1 19.1	1 19.4
19	0 55.5	0 55.7	0 55.9	0 56.2	49	1 20.0	1 20.3	1 20.6	1 20.9
20	0 55.9	0 56.1	0 56.3	0 56.5	50	1 21.7	1 22.0	1 22.3	1 22.6
21	0 56.2	0 56.4	0 56.7	0 56.9	51	1 23.4	1 23.7	1 24.1	1 24.4
22	0 56.6	0 56.8	0 57.1	0 57.3	52	1 25.3	1 25.6	1 25.9	1 26.3
23	0 57.0	0 57.3	0 57.5	0 57.7	53	1 27.2	1 27.6	1 27.9	1 28.2
24	0 57.5	0 57.7	0 57.9	0 58.1	54	1 29.3	1 29.7	1 30.0	1 30.3
25	0 57.9	0 58.1	0 58.4	0 58.6	55	1 31.5	1 31.9	1 32.2	1 32.6
26	0 58.4	0 58.6	0 58.9	0 59.1	56	1 33.9	1 34.3	1 34.6	1 35.0
27	0 58.9	0 59.1	0 59.4	0 59.6	57	1 36.4	1 36.8	1 37.1	1 37.5
28	0 59.5	0 59.7	0 59.9	1 00.1	58	1 39.1	1 39.5	1 39.8	1 40.2
29	1 00.0	1 00.3	1 00.5	1 00.7	59	1 41.9	1 42.3	1 42.7	1 43.1
30	1 00.6	1 00.9	1 01.1	1 01.3	60	1 45.0	1 45.4	1 45.8	1 46.2
31	1 01.2	1 01.5	1 01.7	1 01.9	61	1 48.3	1 48.7	1 49.1	1 49.5
32	1 01.9	1 02.1	1 02.4	1 02.6	62	1 51.8	1 52.3	1 52.7	1 53.1
33	1 02.6	1 02.8	1 03.1	1 03.3	63	1 55.7	1 56.1	1 56.5	1 57.0
34	1 03.3	1 03.6	1 03.8	1 04.1	64	1 59.8	2 00.2	2 00.7	2 01.2
35	1 04.1	1 04.3	1 04.6	1 04.8	65	2 04.2	2 04.7	2 05.2	2 05.7
36	1 04.9	1 05.1	1 05.4	1 05.6	66	2 09.1	2 09.6	2 10.1	2 10.6
37	1 05.7	1 06.0	1 06.2	1 06.5	67	2 14.4	2 14.9	2 15.4	2 15.9
38	1 06.6	1 06.9	1 07.1	1 07.4	68	2 20.2	2 20.7	2 21.2	2 21.8
39	1 07.6	1 07.8	1 08.1	1 08.3	69	2 26.5	2 27.1	2 27.7	2 28.2
40	1 08.5	1 08.8	1 09.1	1 09.3	70	2 33.5	2 34.1	2 34.7	2 35.3

To obtain the Bearing at any other declination compute:

$$\text{Bear. Polaris (in minutes)} = \frac{\text{Polar Dist. (in minutes)}}{\cos \text{Lat.}}$$

If the elongation was western, add the bearing of *Polaris* to the angle between (B) and *Polaris* (75° 20' + 1° 09.2' = 76° 29.2'); if it was eastern, subtract (75° 20′ − 1° 09.2′ = 74° 10.8′). In either instance the sum or difference will give the true bearing from (A) to (B), plus-or-minus about 30 seconds (30″).

Tables 4 and 5 and Fig. 114 are for the year 1968. Current-year tables can be obtained from a current Keuffel and Esser *Ephemeris,* copies of which can be obtained from Keuffel and Esser, or from a local supplier of engineering and surveying supplies.

A *magnetic meridian* is the direction that a magnetic needle or compass will point. The angle between the true and the magnetic meridian is called the *magnetic declination* of the location at which

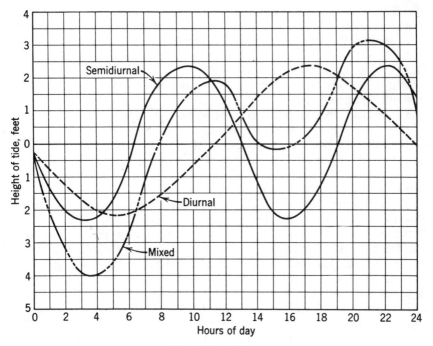

Fig. 115.   Tides.

the reading is taken. If the magnetic needle points to the east of the true meridian, the declination is east; if it points to the west of the true meridian, it is a west declination.

The *bearing* of a line is its direction with reference to a meridian.

Most dredging plans are referenced to the true meridian. Usually the bearing of the centerline of the cut is a true bearing, and in most instances is accurate to seconds. Thus, for a certain centerline the bearing might be N 38° 51′ 33″ W, meaning that the centerline is at an angle of 38° 51′ 33″ in a northwesterly direction from the meridian. On well-prepared plans it is easy to tell whether the true or magnetic meridian is being used—a half-head north arrow usually represents the magnetic meridian, while a full-head arrow represents the true meridian.

67. Tide. The rhythmic rise and fall of the surface of the sea is known as tide. It is caused by the gravitational attraction of the moon and sun on the rotating earth. The maximum height to which the sea rises is known as *high tide* or *high water*, and the minimum level is known as *low tide* or *low water*. The difference between high and low water is known as the *range of the tide*.

One high water per day is called a *durnal tide*. When there are two high and low waters per day, the tide is said to be *semi-durnal*. If one of the two high waters in a semi-durnal tide does not equal the height of the other, it is called a *mixed durnal tide* (Fig. 115).

68. Tide Gages. The simplest form of tide gage, and probably the most useful in dredging, is a board one or two inches thick and from four inches to six inches wide, fastened to a piling or some other suitable support. Normally it is white with black graduations. The U.S.C. & G.S. uses vitrified enamel graduations baked on sections of wrought iron plates which are then fastened to the wood board with wrought iron screws.

The main tide gage on a dredging job should be set near the middle of the job. Where the tide changes rapidly, additional gages should be installed at intervals throughout the work. They not only give the true tide at any point, but also make checking the tide easier.

69. Plane of Reference. The plane of reference for most dredging work is usually the mean of all low waters (Mean Low Water— MLW). Where tides along the Gulf coast and the south coast of Puerto Rico are chiefly durnal, MLW is based upon a mean of the lower of the daily low waters. Along the Pacific coast, Alaska, and the Hawaiian Islands, the reference is the mean of all lower low waters (Mean Lower Low Water—MLLW). In other countries other datums are used. For instance, in Great Britain the ordinance datum is approximately sea level (Mean Sea Level—MSL). In Ireland the ordinance datum is approximately the level of the low water spring tides in Dublin Bay. In Germany the datum is called *normalnull*, and is approximately the mean sea level of the North Sea on the German coast.

70. Reference Lines. A reference line (RL) is a survey line off-set some specified distance from the centerline of the cut (Fig. 116). Normally it is marked with wood stakes at intervals of 100 feet. At greater intervals, usually 1,000 feet, it is marked more permanently with markers of concrete, posts or piling.

Each interval marker is assigned a station number indicating the distance that particular marker is from a zero or starting point. On governmental work in the United States, the RL is usually laid out and maintained by the Corps of Engineers (COE). Most dredging work for the government is in waterways that have previously-established RLs. For instance, a contract might start at station 55+00.25— 5,500.25 feet from the RL's origin—and end at station 105+96.00. On private work, a RL may not have been established, so it must be laid out by the dredge civil engineer.

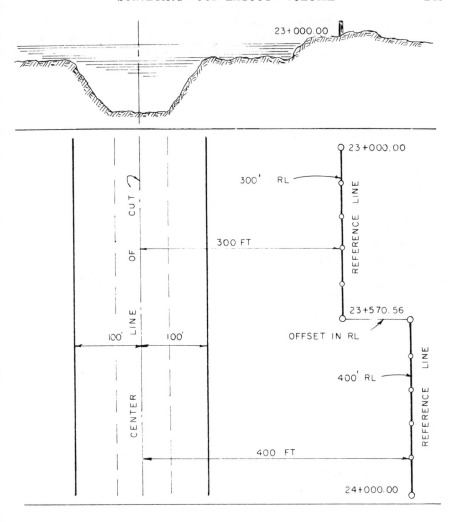

Fig. 116.   Reference Line and Offset.

Reference lines in the United States are usually tied to U.S.C. & G.S., COE, or Geological Survey (GS) control monuments. These monuments are usually permanent, four-inch diameter, brass plates set in concrete. They are accurately located horizontally, and often vertically (Fig. 117). COE monuments are numerous along waterways, usually having been set for the express purpose of establishing

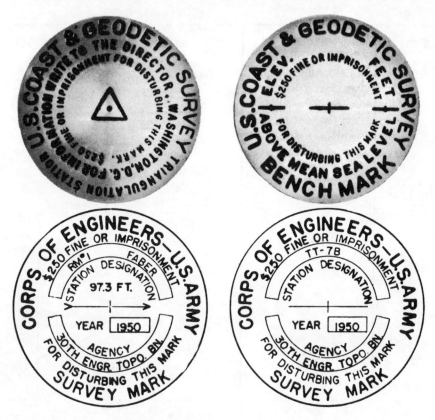

Fig. 117. Bench Marks and Monuments.

a RL, and consequently often are a part of a RL. U.S.C. & G.S. monuments are usually some distance from the RL, and also considerably fewer and farther between.

A. LAYING OUT REFERENCE LINES. Many contracts are with clients who have no facilities for laying out a RL. In these instances the civil engineer lays it out as one of his earliest activities.

A RL should be placed where it is accessible and convenient to use. A land-based RL is preferable, but often it must be in the water. It must be tied to some recognizable point shown on the plans, and preferably two recognizable points visible from each other and locatable on the ground. Where two reference points are not locatable, usually one reference point and a bearing must be shown. With these data the civil engineer can set up a line from the reference point, either by shooting *Polaris* (in the northern hemisphere), for accurate work, or by using the transit's compass for less-accurate work.

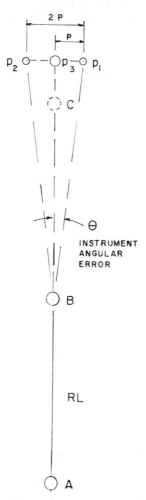

Fig. 118.   Prolonging a Line.

Once a starting point and a bearing are determined, it is a simple matter to establish the RL. Proceeding from the starting point, the civil engineer runs the RL parallel to the centerline of the channel and at some convenient off-set. At intervals of 1,000 feet he usually sets permanent markers. Temporary markers are interspaced at 100-foot intervals. It is often necessary to increase or decrease the off-set because of irregularities in the shore line (Fig. 116). The shortest off-set is always preferable, depending upon the difficulties involved in setting the line and using it later. It should be far enough from the cut that it will not be in the way of the dredge or other operating equipment, and at a location where it can be maintained at the off-set distance for as long a distance as possible. Although it is often necessary to change the off-set distance of a RL several times throughout a section of a job, these breaks should be kept as few as possible.

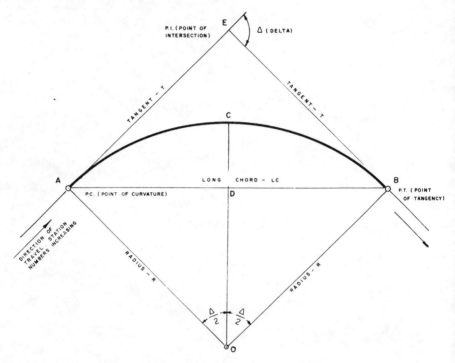

Fig. 119. The Circular Curve and Components.

When dredging is in open water, the RL obviously will have to be also. Where piling or channel markers are not available, temporary stakes, piling or buoys have to be set. Intermediate 100-foot stations are usually eliminated, and only one station per 1,000 feet is used. Such RLs are usually set back just far enough to be out of the way of operations.

B. EXTENDING REFERENCE LINES. When laying out a RL it is often necessary to extend it a distance greater than is possible from one instrument set-up. One thousand feet is about the maximum distance that can be sighted, this being greater or less, depending upon obstructions or atmospherics.

In Fig. 118 a RL has been run from station (A) to station (B). It must be extended to station (C). Proceed as follows. Set the instrument up at (B), take a back-sight on (A), or some other point on line. With both the upper and lower transit motions clamped, plunge the instrument's telescope and set a point (P_1) on line ahead towards (C). Rotate the transit about its vertical axis (loosen the lower clamp to do so), resight (A) and clamp the lower clamp. Re-plunge the telescope, and set a point (P_2) opposite (P_1). A point midway between (P_1) and (P_2), called (P_3), will be the true elongation of the line (AB). Sight the instrument at (P_3) and continue the line. The sequence of plunging the instrument twice is called *double centering* and it is used to eliminate errors in the instrument. Any unadjusted instrument that is not double centered will create, over a period of several extensions, a curved line rather than a straight one.

C. CURVES IN REFERENCE LINES. Figure 119 shows the important parts of a circular curve. Formulas for determining the most useful of these are,

$$
\begin{aligned}
\text{Tangent (T)} \quad &= \text{R Tan } \Delta/2 \\
\text{Long Chord (LC)} &= 2\text{R Sin } \Delta/2 \\
\text{Length (L)} \quad &= (0.0174533) \ (\ \Delta\ ) \ (\text{R}) \\
\text{Radius (R)} \quad &= 5,729.58/\text{D}
\end{aligned}
$$

where T = tangent length, in feet; R = radius, in feet; Δ = central angle, in degrees (in decimal degrees when used to form a product, but in degrees, minutes and seconds when used with the natural functions) and D = an angle subtending a 100-foot arc on the curve, in decimals.

The first operation in laying out a curve is to set up the transit over the beginning point, sight back along the straight part of the RL (called the tangent), plunge the instrument, sight along the forward tangent, and then turn an angle in the direction of the curve (right or left) equal to one-half (D). This half-angle (d) will be,

$$d = (0.30) \ (C) \ (D) \tag{32}$$

where C = arc length to the next station (usually 100 feet), in feet; d = one-half the angle subtended by the subchord of length C, in minutes and D as defined above. Sighting along the line created by the angle (d), measure 100 feet from the station beneath the instrument and set a stake (Fig. 120). This stake will mark the first 100-foot station on the curve. To continue the curve and to set the next station, turn twice the angle (d), and along this line measure another 100-foot chord from the stake at the station just set. At the intersection of this 100-foot chord and the line of sight, set another stake. This will be the second 100-foot station on the curve. Continue this procedure around the curve.

Should the curve not be an even multiple of 100-foot chords, the fraction coming either at the beginning or at the end, the following procedure should be followed.

Suppose that the start of the curve was at station 242+00 and its

end was at station 244+30. This would mean that stations 243+00
and 244+00 would be set as explained above, but that the distance
from 244+00 to the last station, 244+30, would be only 30 feet. After
setting station 244+00, add to the total angle already turned an angle

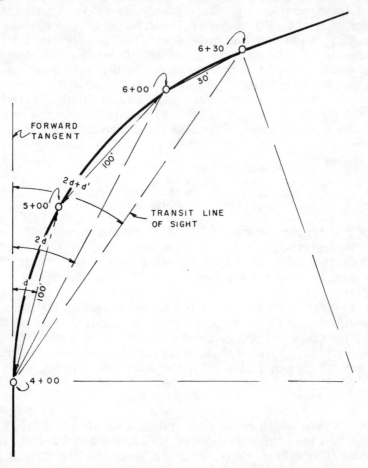

Fig. 120. Laying Out a Circular Curve.

equal to (0.30) (30) (D). Turn this total angle (from the original
forward tangent line), and sighting along this line, measure off 30
feet from station 244+00. Set a stake at the intersection for station
244+30. This *plus distance* could of course have come at the beginning just as well—the first angle to be turned then would have been
(0.30) (30) (D).

As an example, assume a curve starting at station 242+00 and
ending at 244+30, as in the preceding discussion. Also, suppose the
(D) of the curve was 5°.

The deflection angle from station 242+00 to 243+00 would be

D/2 = 2° 30', or, using equation 32, d = (0.30) (100) (5) = 150 minutes, or 2° 30'. The deflection angle from 243+00 to 244+00 would be also 2° 30'. The deflection angle from 244+00 to 244+30 would be d = (0.30) (30) (5) = 45 minutes. As a check, the deflection angle from 242+00 to 244+30 would be d_t = (0.30) (230) (5) = 345 minutes, or 5° 45'. It is noted that the total deflection angle for the entire curve is $\triangle/2$. That is, the sum of the deflection angles (in this case 5°45') should equal one-half the total enclosed angle of the curve. So from

$$\triangle = \frac{L}{(0.0174533)\ (R)} \tag{33}$$

where L = length of curve, in feet; $\triangle$ = total enclosed angle of curve, in decimal degrees and R = radius of curve, in feet (equal to 5,729/D). The total angle, $\triangle$, would be 230/(0.0174-533) (1,145.4) = 11.505 degrees. This checks the deflection angle, as $\triangle$ is twice d_t.

In this discussion and example the *arc definition* is being used, but chords are actually being substituted for measurement. The amount of error introduced is infinitesimal however, particularly for dredging-channel curves. For curves with degrees of curve up to around 10° the error introduced in the length of curve would be less than 0.15 feet. If 50-foot chords were used, the error would be less than 0.02 feet! Channel curves are seldom as sharp as 10°, being more commonly in the region of 5° and less. A 5° curve on which 100-foot chords were used would only have a curve-length error of 0.03 feet.

In laying out the RL curve, the radius used is different from that of the centerline of the cut. In Equation 33 the radius must be equal to the centerline radius plus or minus the RL offset, depending upon whether the RL is on the outside or inside of the cut.

71. Spoil-disposal Area Layout. One of the civil engineer's first duties is to lay out spoil-disposal areas. Some of them must be ready by the time the dredge is ready to start pumping. Laying them out consists primarily of marking line and grade.

If the area is an old spoil-disposal area there will probably be enough of the old levees left to determine line without much difficulty. Not so with new areas. The principal task in laying out levees for new areas is locating them as called for in the plans. Laths or poles set at 100-foot intervals are sufficient for line. Sometimes they can be eye-balled in, but other times a transit is needed. Plans and specifications usually determine the accuracy required—and no more accuracy should be used than necessary.

Whether the area is old or new, the elevation of the top of the levees must be correctly marked. This height, as well as the section-dimensions of the levee, is normally determined during the estimating period, as costs for building them depends upon the quantity of material they will require. New levees, and old ones that have to be raised, are marked by laths or longer pieces of wood with cross-arms attached at the required elevation. When the levees are being built, the dragline operator sights across the arms to determine the height required. If the specifications require a certain minimum or maximum elevation of fill, the civil engineer usually sets similar cross-armed stakes in the fill area while setting levee grades.

The main factor in determining the height of a levee is its ability to enclose and retain the discharged material. Excavated material usually requires more space in a fill than it does *in situ*. For instance, sand takes about the same space, sandy-clay about 1.25, clay about 1.45, and gravel and rocks about 1.75. Silt needs about twice the space of its *in situ* volume.

The top of the levee is normally made at least four feet wide. Less than this does not allow room for walking around the levee to inspect it. The height is determined by the minimum freeboard required. In addition to the calculated height needed to enclose the material, a minimum of two feet are usually added for safety. In addition to this, in large areas where wind-blown waves may increase the height of water against the levee, an additional amount is added. This extra height is

$$X = 0.17 \, (VF)^{0.5} + 2.5 - F^{0.25} \qquad (34)$$

where X = height of wave, in feet; F = fetch of the area's longest reach, in statute miles, and V = wind velocity, in statute miles per hour.

Levee side slopes depend somewhat upon the height of the levee and the material used to build it. Normally they are made as steep as possible to conserve the amount of material required. The levee's size is basically determined by having a section which will not give way under the pressure of the water and material pushing against it. On most levees the pressure against the side is $P = (SG) \, (A) \, (d_1 - d_2)$, where P = pressure, in pounds; SG = specific gravity of the spoil in the area; A = area of the section of the levee, in square feet, and d_1 and d_2 = distance from the top of the levee to original ground, and distance from the top of the levee to the spoil and water in the area at any time, respectively, in feet.

Unlike masonry and other construction materials, soils are extremely difficult to predict, particularly their shearing strength in fills and levees. However, some approximations can be made, which in conjunction with experience, can be helpful in estimating levee sizes.

The maximum force (N) which one body can exert upon another is its weight. The force (F) required to slide this body across the other is called the *frictional force* and it is proportional to a factor called the coefficient of friction (μ). In other words, the force which will cause one body to slide across another is

$$F = \mu N \qquad (35)$$

For soils, the coefficient of friction (μ) is extremely difficult to determine. For dry soils, earth on earth, the coefficient may vary between 0.25 and 1.0. Dry sandy clay may have a coefficient between 0.38 and 0.75. Damp clay may be 1.0, and wet clay 0.30. However, for general use, 0.30 is usually adopted.

To illustrate the use of these data in levee design, assume a levee with the dimensions shown in Fig. 121. Say the soil used in building the levee weighs 120 pounds per cubic foot. In a 100-foot length of levee there will be (20) $\dfrac{(20 + 4)}{2}$ $(100) = 24,000$ cubic feet, or 2,880,000 pounds. Call this weight (N).

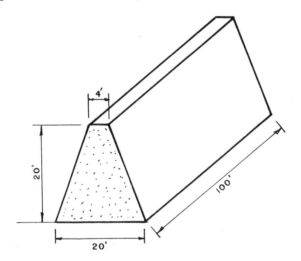

Fig. 121.   Section of a Levee.

With 18 feet of water and spoil inside the levee, the maximum capacity, the force against the levee would be $(18/2)$ $(64.4) = 579.6$ pounds per square foot. The 100-foot section of levee has (100) $(18) = 1800$ square feet of area. Therefore, against the 100-foot section there would be a force of (1800) $(579.6) = 1,045,000$ pounds. If damp clay were assumed and the coefficient of 0.3 used, the limiting force of friction would be (0.3) $(2,880,000) = 864,000$ pounds which, being less than the force against the levee, would not be sufficient to hold the levee in place, and it would probably fail. To make the levee substantial, it should be enlarged by a minimum of 1,045,000/864,000, or 1.20. By increasing the base to 30 feet, the cross-sectional area would be increased approximately 1.4. This would probably give a stable levee.

Generally speaking, levees are built with side slopes not steeper than 1 on 1, and bases generally equal to not less than 1.5 the height. Levees built of mud commonly found in swamps will require a large section and shrinkage will often be from 20 to 40 per cent. Clay and clayey-earths require the smallest sections and shrinkage will usually be from five to 15 per cent. Sandy soils require larger sections than clay and shrinkage may be from five to 10 per cent.

The amount of material required in a levee is determined by

$$Q = \frac{(H)\ (W_t + W_b)}{54}\ (1 + k) \tag{36}$$

where Q = quantity of material, in cubic yards; H = height of levee, in feet; W_t = top width of levee, in feet; W_b = bottom width of levee, in feet, and k = shrinkage, in per cent as a decimal.

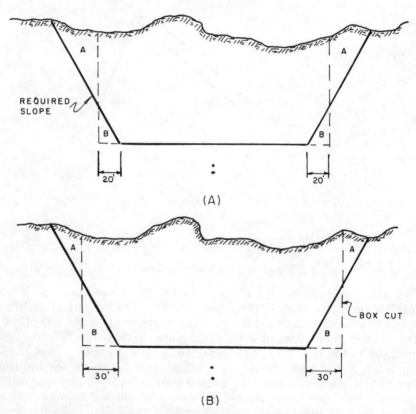

Fig. 122. Proportioning a Box Cut for Cut Stakes.

72. Laying Out Cuts. Another predredging activity is staking and marking the channel or cut so that the dredge will be able to keep alined. Setting centerline stakes is not sufficient in most instances. *Cut stakes* or *ranges* are required so that the leverman will know how much of a swing to make. Where the cut stakes or ranges are set depends upon the slope of the sides of the cut.

The dredge contractor is not generally responsible for determining the slope of natural repose of the material—the specifications usually state the required slope—however dredgemen do have to determine how wide to cut the bottom so that neither too much nor too little will be dredged, and that proper side slopes will be obtained.

Generally, the dredge makes a *box cut* and depends upon the vertical sides to cave in later, and thereby form the required slope (Art. 54). As shown in Fig. 99, the top portion (A) that will later cave in is expected to just fill up the over-excavated portion (B). It is up to the civil engineer to decide just how wide the bottom of the box should be to make the two areas equal. Generally, he proceeds as follows.

Prior to commencement of work, a set of predredging cross sections is usually supplied by the client, or a set has been made by the civil engineer. Superimposed on these cross sections are the specification cuts to be made. Depending upon the profile of the before-dredging section and the dimensions of the specification section, the civil engineer determines, by proportion, the bottom over-cut that will be required to make area (A) equal to area (B).

In Fig. 122(A) the bottom over-cut is shown as 20 feet. It can be seen that area (A) will be greater than area (B), and consequently when area (A) caves in some additional material will fall into the specified section and the section will not be clear. Redredging will be required. In Fig. 122(B) the bottom over-cut is 30 feet. Area (A) is slightly less than area (B), and will not quite fill up the space left by (B) so the specification section will be obtained. Using this proportion method the civil engineer can plot out the bottom over-cut distances for each section of the job and calculate the distance from the RL to each over-cut point. These distances are tabulated and used in setting the cut-stakes or ranges.

After-dredging cross sections are taken daily directly behind the dredge to determine if the cut stakes are effectively placed. From observing the after-dredging cross sections, the stake locations can be adjusted to obtain the best section. As an additional check, soundings are taken continuously off the front of the dredge. As the dredge swings into the toe of the cut on either side of the channel, a deckhand with a lead weight sounds the bottom. This gives instantaneous data on whether the dredge is *making water*.

If the water is not too deep, the cut-stakes are set directly in the water ahead of the dredge. If the water is too deep, or if the current is too strong for stakes to remain in position, buoys are usually used. Should it be possible to set ranges on land ahead of the dredge, or even behind it, this is often done. When these methods are not practical, other means of alinement are used. For instance, the Laser light is a relatively new electronic device being used quite extensively for alinement. (*See* Art. 75.)

73. Setting Cut-Stakes and Buoys. A *tag line* and survey boat are usually used to set cut-stakes and buoys. The tag line is normally a thin, stainless-steel or anti-corrosive, alloy wire, ⅛-inch or less in diameter. It is marked off every 10 feet and wound on a reel which is usually powered by a gasoline motor. The reel and motor normally are mounted near the rear of the survey craft. Generally the motor has a slip-clutch and brake, so that as the wire is payed out it can be kept taut, but at the same time allowed to pay out slowly.

To set the cut-stakes or buoys, the free end of the tag line is attached to a station on the RL and the craft motored out into the channel perpendicular to the RL, the tag line being payed out as the survey craft moves outward. The operator keeps the course perpendicular to the RL by lining on the station and a *back stake*.

When the tag line has been payed out the required distance to the first cut-stake's or buoy's location, the brake is set and the tag line made as taut as possible with the motor. The stake, usually two inches by two inches and up to 20-feet long is lifted overboard, and jogged down or driven in with a maul at the exact distance from the RL. The stake for the opposite side of the channel is then set in a similar manner.

The tag line must be kept taut when setting the stakes. Sag, under certain circumstances, can produce considerable error. A sagging tag line produces what is called a catenary, and the length of the line becomes greater than the straight-line distance from the RL. A sagging tag line will pull the cut over to the side on which the RL is located. The error introduced by a sagging tag line is

$$C = \frac{(W^2)\ (L)}{(24)\ (P^2)} \tag{37}$$

where C = linear error, in feet; W = total weight of tag line extended, in pounds; L = length of tag line extended, in feet, and P = tension, in pounds. To determine the error when the tension is not known, the following is approximate,

$$L = (A) \left[1 + \frac{(8)\ (F^2)}{(3)\ (A^2)} \right] \tag{38}$$

where L = actual length of tag line payed out, in feet; F = greatest amount of sag, in feet, and A = the span, in feet.

For distances less than 500 feet, the tag line must be kept taut enough to limit the sag to less than 10 feet. Usually a 15-horsepower outboard motor will be sufficient to keep the tag line taut enough for distances up to 500 feet.

Buoy setting is accomplished in exactly the same manner as setting cut-stakes. A barrel buoy often used is shown in Fig. 123. Note that the heavy weight is for setting on the bottom at the correct distance, the lighter weight being a tide or swell counter balance.

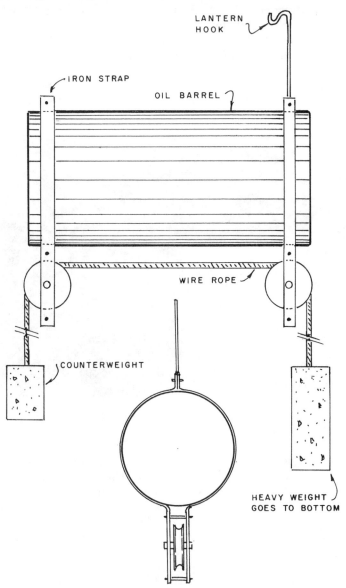

Fig. 123. Barrel Buoy.

Cut-stakes should be set to give the leverman a good alinement. On a straight-of-way, stakes can often be spaced at 200-foot or as much as 500-foot intervals. On curves, however, 100-foot intervals are usually required. Buoys are difficult to handle and usually a minimum of three in line are set out. Two would give a line, but if one was off there would be no way of knowing it.

74. Setting Ranges. Ranges can often be used effectively when there is land ahead or behind the dredge—as in basins or harbors. Ranges can also be two-inch by two-inch stakes with flags attached, or large four-foot by four-foot squares and triangles on towers. Large squares and triangles are used when the sight-distance is long. The triangle is placed in front, and the square in back, but set so that when viewed from the dredge the top of the triangle is just below the top of the square.

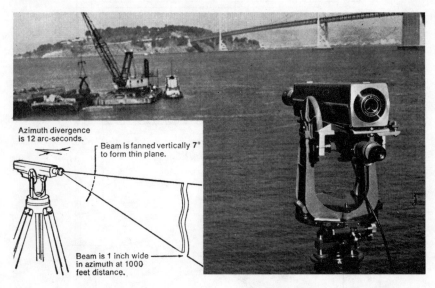

Azimuth divergence
is 12 arc-seconds.

Beam is fanned vertically 7°
to form thin plane.

Beam is 1 inch wide
in azimuth at 1000
feet distance.

TRANSIT-LITE
LASER BEAM CONFIGURATION

Fig. 124.   The Laser Light.
(Spectra-Physics)

75. Laser Light. A new instrument has recently been developed which is adaptable to dredge alinement. Called a Laser light, it produces a pencil-thin, perfectly straight beam of red light which is visible at a distance of several miles. It is small, being attachable to a surveying instrument (Fig. 124). The beam diameter is extremely narrow. At 100 feet it can be made only 0.08 inches wide and proportionately narrow for greater distances—at 10,000 feet it would be only eight inches wide.

A fan lens can be attached to the Laser light to produce a thin, flat plane. The plane created is as thin as the beam and fans out 40 feet for every 100 feet of range. It can provide an extremely accurate vertical or horizontal plane which is useful in dredge work. Personnel on the dredge can have a constant and accurate measurement of elevation by comparing some reference point on the dredge to this plane and therefore have a continuous measurement of tidal changes throughout the work.

76. Hydrography. Hydrography is the measurement of submerged land. Taking soundings before- and after-dredging is the major hydrographic work in dredging. Although usually supplied with before- and after-soundings by the client—particularly in governmental work—the civil engineer makes similar soundings to be assured that the ones given him are correct and that the dredge is doing what is specified.

Fig. 125. The Sutcliff Sounding Machine.
(Charles Griffin & Co., Ltd., England)

Several cross sections should be taken just ahead of the dredge daily. These provide up-to-date information of what is ahead, and when compared with daily after-dredging cross sections taken directly behind the dredge, give a true picture of how well dredging is progressing. From data of these cross sections the leverman and the civil engineer can also determine if there is need to adjust the locations of the cut-stakes or buoys. Data are also provided with which to calculate daily production.

Several types of sounding gear are used, from a hand-held pole to a fancy affair which was patented by Fielden Sutcliffe of Liverpool, England. This was a rather novel arrangement (Fig. 125) and was described as follows (33).

"The sounding equipment consists of a wheel, with a concave rim similar to a bicycle wheel on which is wound a fine steel wire having the lead attached to its free end. The wheel is mounted on a frame clamped to the gunwale of the survey skiff. The skiff is also equipped with a sheave supported at the bow. On the back of the wheel there is a reel on which a second line, called a preventer, is wound. The free end of this line is passed through the sheave and attached to the sounding lead, and together with the sounding line, forms a right triangle, the length of the base being the distance from the sheave to the center of the sounding wheel. The preventer line restrains the sounding line from trailing astern, thereby eliminating the need of casting the lead forward for each sounding. It also allows the sounding lead to be near the bottom, so that frequent soundings may be taken.

"The wheel and the reel are so proportioned relative to each other and to the horizontal distance from the sounding line to the sheave, that they pay out or take in the necessary amount of their respective lengths, thereby keeping the sounding vertical at all depths.

"The sounding wheel in this arrangement is 10 feet in circumference and 3.2 feet in diameter at the bottom of its groove. Consequently, the length of sounding line paid out per revolution is 10 feet, plus or minus a small amount.

"At the front of the wheel there is a scale, along which a pointer travels at a rate proportional to the vertical travel of the sounding lead, indicating the depth below the surface of the water.

"In taking soundings with this equipment, the operator first sets the lead at the surface of the water and the pointer at zero. He then grabs the rim of the wheel with his left hand, releases a catch with his right hand, and allows the wheel to revolve until the lead strikes bottom. Then, reversing the motion of the wheel he reads the depth indicated by the pointer at the instant he feels the sounding line become taut. He then raises the lead clear of the bottom in readiness for the next sounding. The operator is assisted in lifting the lead by a coil spring on the wheel axle."

Most sounding gear is not as complicated as the one just described, but the principles are the same, particularly in maintaining a vertical sounding line. In a moving boat the line tends to drag, and in tide or stream-flow the line tends to follow the flow. Consequently, methods are devised to prevent this, just as in the example above. In the simplest sounding method where the line is hand-held, it is usually held ahead of the sounding point and then straightened just as the sounding is taken. For soundings taken only periodically, as those from the decks of ships and tugs, the line is thrown ahead of the boat so that it has time to sink to the bottom before the boat comes up to it.

77. Electronic Depth Sounding. Depth of water can be determined by measuring the time a sound wave takes to leave the surface of the water, hit the bottom, and bounce back. By dividing this time interval by two, and multiplying by the velocity of sound in the water, the distance is determined. Today this principle is used in equipment called echo depth sounders.

Figure 126 shows a modern sounder manufactured by the Raytheon Company of San Francisco, California. In simplification there is a transmitter, a receiver and a recorder, enclosed in a case. They are

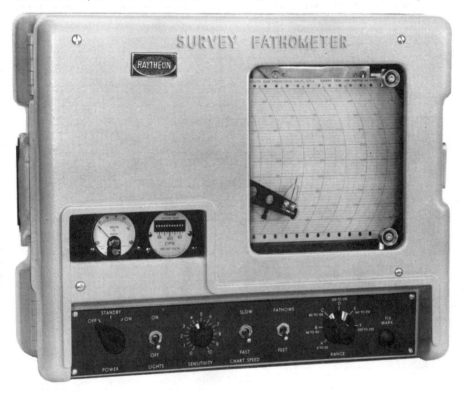

Fig. 126.   Fathometer, Transmitter, Receiver and Recorder All in One Unit.
(Raytheon Co.)

electrically connected to a transducer, which is effectively the same thing in water as an antenna is in air—similar to the microphone-speaker unit in an intercommunication system.

The transmitter provides very short bursts or pulses of high-frequency electrical energy at predetermined intervals. These signals are sent to the transducer which changes them into sound energy and radiates them downward in a very narrow beam toward the bottom. Hitting the bottom, they bounce, return, and are picked up by the transducer which changes them back again into electrical energy, and passes them on to the receiver.

At the same time, a mechanism in the recorder turns a pulley-supported belt to which is attached a pen. For approximately one-half of the pen's rotation it glides across a slowly-moving roll of chemically-treated chart paper. Whenever a pulse of electrical energy is applied to the pen, a mark will appear on the paper.

When the transmitter sends its first pulse of energy to the transducer for radiation, it also applies it to the pen and the pen makes a

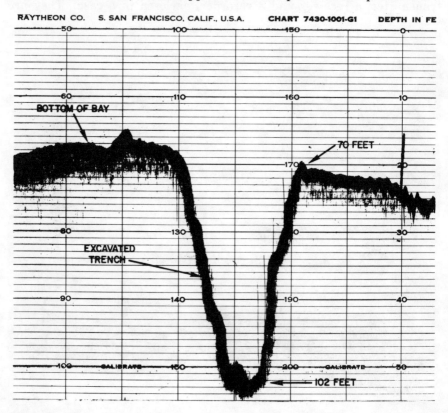

Fig. 127. Trace of Fathometer of Fig. 126. Submarine Subway. Trench being dug under San Francisco Bay for new Bay Area Transit system presented this profile to Raytheon Company electronic engineers testing new Fathometer depth sounder. The echo sounder was operating in second mode so that scale at left applies: uppermost horizontal line is a depth of 50 feet, bay floor is approximately 70 feet below the surface and trench at this point is 52 feet deep or 102 feet under water. (Raytheon Co.)

mark on the paper. This is called the zero mark. As the pulse time is extremely short (about 0.000005 of a second), the mark is not very long. By the time the signal has bounced back, been picked up by the transducer, and fed to the receiver and the pen, the pen has moved downward on the chart paper. The returned signal is applied to the pen and another mark is made on the paper. As the paper is cali-

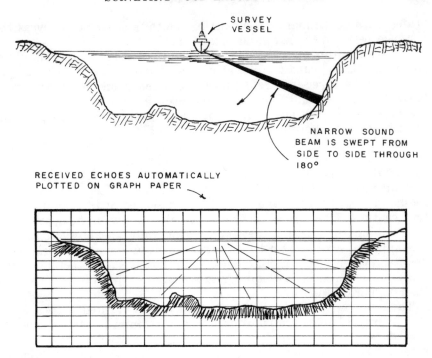

Fig. 128. How the Profiler Operates.

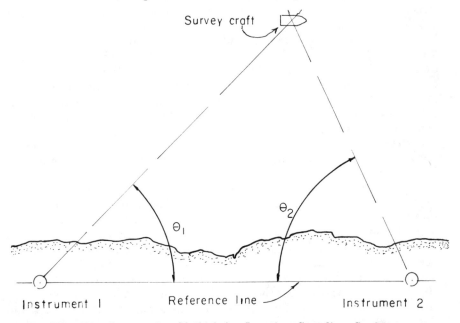

Fig. 129. Intersection Method for Locating Sounding Craft.

brated with depth marks, the existing depth is shown directly as the distance between the zero and second mark.

The transmitter pulses at a rate of about 500 per minute. The chart paper can be adjusted to turn at a rate of from three to 15 feet per hour. At the three-foot rate this gives a mark on the paper every 0.0012 inches—actually a continuous trace for both the zero mark and the depth mark. A clear and continuous graphic recording of the bottom depth is therefore obtained (Fig. 127).

In measuring the time it takes for the signal to leave and return to the transducer, two factors must be considered. First, sound travels at varying rates in water, depending upon the water's temperature and salinity. Its speed will vary between 4,550 feet per second in fresh water at freezing and 5,050 feet per second at high salinity and temperature. Pressure affects the speed also, but with the depths used in dredging the effect is negligible. Generally speaking there is a possibility of about five per cent error involved when operating in all possible water combinations. Normally however, the actual conditions encountered in most dredging operations will not produce more than 0.5 per cent error.

The equipment can be easily checked and calibrated with a *check bar*. A metal bar or rod is lowered in a horizontal position below the transducer. The sensitivity of the receiver is turned up and an echo received from the bar. The percentage difference between the recorded depth of the check bar and the actual measured distance between the transducer and the check bar is the correction factor to be applied to the soundings in that water.

78. Other Uses of Echo Sounders. Hard bottoms reflect more strongly than soft ones. The harder the bottom, the sharper and more dense is the trace on the chart. On soft bottoms the trace broadens out and becomes lighter, so a very broad trace will indicate a soft, muddy bottom; a narrow, dark trace will indicate a hard bottom. The thickness of the mud on the bottom can often be determined by the characteristic of the trace.

79. Profilers. A profiler presents a picture of the channel's cross section. Honeywell of Seattle, Washington, manufactures such a unit. It is portable, and is designed especially for underwater survey work and for control of dredging operations. The viewer can be installed in the lever room. It has a motor-driven transducer which scans from side to side, directing the sonar beam through an arc in the vertical plane below the dredge (Fig. 128). Each sweep of the beam gives a complete profile of the channel's cross section. A new profile of the channel can be obtained every 15 seconds. When installed on a vessel moving at, say five knots, a profile would be obtained every 120 feet.

80. Position Locating Methods. When the distance from shore or from the RL is too far for tag line use, location of survey craft and the subsequent soundings can be accomplished by the *intersection method*. Here two transits are set up on the RL at known stations and separated so that the angle between the RL and their line of sight to the survey craft is in the neighborhood of 45° (Fig. 129). Each transitman records the angle to the survey craft each time a sounding is taken, the instant of each sounding being indicated by a signal from the craft. The angles are later laid off on the chart of the area, their line intersections giving the location of each sounding. The probable error is suprisingly small, for as was previously brought out, 30 seconds (30″) of transit-angle error will introduce an error of only 0.15 feet per 1,000 feet. By using a standard 30-second transit this method can be extremely accurate.

Fig. 130.   The Autotape.
(Cubic Corp.)

When dredging is exceptionally far from shore, such conventional locating methods cannot always be used. Electronic equipment increases the range of visibility. One such electronic device manufactured by the Cubic Corporation of San Diego, California, is called the *Autotape*. This system employs microwaves to establish distances to fixed or moving objects along a radio line of sight. The system is automatic. Once on station, the system provides a distance reading at one-second intervals.

The *Autotape* can be used in the intersection method of locating a sounding vessel. It will give accurate locations even in fog (Fig. 130). Its accuracy is about 20 feet + 1/100,000 times the distance.

81. The Sextant.   The sextant is one of the main instruments used by a marine surveyor (Fig. 131). It is used extensively in dredging, principally because it needs no support and consequently can be used anywhere, ashore or afloat. Angles can be read either in the vertical or horizontal plane, which is an advantage it has over the transit or the theodolite.

Its operation is dependent upon two mirrors. Reflection between the mirrors allows the angle between two objects to be read directly on the scale of the instrument. The observer looks over the top of the horizon mirror at an object on his left and moves the index arm until the object on his right is reflected in the horizon mirror. Both objects are brought into coincidence with the sextant's tangent screw and the angle between them is then shown directly on the scale.

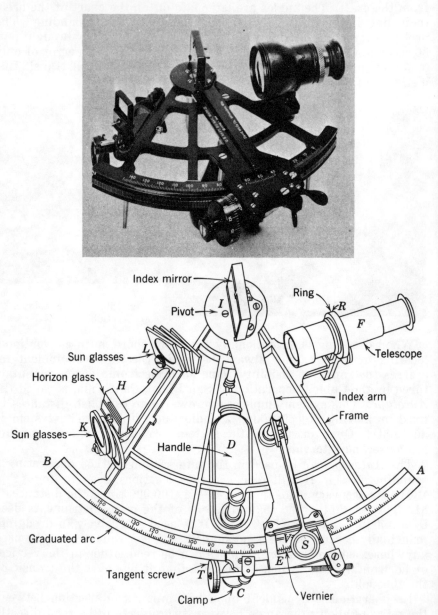

Fig. 131. The Sounding Sextant.

When objects are definite and readily visible, the sextant can be used without its telescope, especially if the angle is changing rapidly or the sounding vessel is unsteady. When objects are distant, indistinct, or indefinite, or the angles are changing slowly, and particularly where a small error in the angle will affect the position considerably, a telescope should always be used. Very little experience is required to measure sextant angles between prominent objects when the angle is changing slowly and the observer's platform is steady. However, in hydrographic surveying, angles usually change rapidly, objects are usually indistinct, and the survey vessel is usually far from steady. Under such conditions a great deal of practice is required to determine sextant angles quickly and accurately (79).

Fig. 132.   The Planimeter.   (Eugene Dietzen Co.)

Two types of sextants are available to the dredge surveyor: the *box sextant* and the *sounding sextant*. The box sextant has all its parts enclosed in a circular box and in this respect it is superior to the sounding sextant. The sounding sextant is quite similar to a navigational sextant, except it is more rugged, has a greater optical range, and has better light-gathering qualities.

82.   The Planimeter.   Planimetering is probably used more in dredging calculations than in any other field. Practically all cross section areas are determined with a planimeter. The planimeter (Fig. 132) is supported at three points, the anchor point (O), the roller point (R), and the tracing point (T). To determine an area, the point (O) is pressed into the paper at a location where the entire boundary can be reached with the tracing point (T). The tracing point is then set anywhere on the area's boundary, the roller's graduation set at 0.000, and the perimeter then traversed with the tracing point (T) around and back to the beginning point. Upon completion of the traverse, the graduation reading of the roller does not give the area, but when its reading is multiplied by the planimeter's constant, the product will be the area.

The best way to determine the *planimeter constant* is to trace an area of some small, known value and determine the constant therefrom. For instance, suppose the area to be determined is drawn to a scale such that one inch is equal to 25 feet horizontally and 10 feet vertically. A one-inch square would therefore be equal to 250 square feet. When this square is planimetered suppose the roller graduation shows a value of 0100. The planimeter constant would then be $250/0100 = 2.5$. Any area, with the same scale, that was planimetered thereafter would be determinable in square feet by multiplying the roller reading by 2.5. Square yards could be obtained by dividing the constant by nine, thereby obtaining a yardage constant of 0.278.

Planimeter readings are usually accurate to one per cent if carefully made. Large areas allow greater precision, accuracies of 0.1 to 0.2 per cent being obtainable.

83. Nautical Charts and Classifications. There were in the United States in the early 1800's only 16 states along the eastern seaboard and some interior territory. Although commerce between the States was mostly waterborne and foreign trade was entirely by sea, lack of nautical charts made navigation dangerous. Shipwrecks were common, insurance rates high, and products overpriced (34).

On February 10, 1807, an act was passed authorizing a national hydrographic survey. In 1839 the first nautical chart was printed; it showed Newark Bay but gave very little detail.

Today the U.S.C. & G.S. publishes nautical charts for over 2.5 million square miles of coastal waters of the United States and its possessions. Some of the information given on these charts which is of use to dredgemen is the location of spoil areas, rules of the road, bridge clearances, heights of overhead cable crossings, accurate bearings and meridians, and elevation of channel bottoms.

Side limits of improved channels are shown on the charts by dashed lines. Controlling depths in each quarter of channels 400 feet or more wide are usually given. Controlling depth for channels from 100 to 400 feet wide is given only for the middle half. Aids to navigation are also shown in their correct locations.

With few exceptions the charts are of the *Mercator projection*, where meridians of longitude and parallels of latitude are straight lines intersecting at right angles. Distances between meridians are equal, but distances between parallels increase progressively from the equator to the poles.

A Mercator projection has a number of advantages over others, the principle one being *conformality*—a straight line drawn in any direction on the chart will be a true track, and any vessel following it will pass all features along the line exactly as they are shown on the chart.

On practically all charts, one minute of latitude is approximately one nautical mile (6,080.2 feet).

Chart sizes are usually determined by the importance of the area, the purpose for which the chart is to be used, and the necessity for showing detail in the area. There are five main chart classifications: (1) harbor charts with scales larger than 1:50,000, (2) small-craft charts with scales of 1:80,000 and larger, (3) coast charts with scales from 1:50,000 to 1:100,000, (4) general charts with scales of 1:100,000 to 1:600,000 and (5) sailing charts with scales of 1:600,000 and smaller.

VOLUME CALCULATIONS

84. Average End Method. Calculating the amount of material to be dredged or the amount that has been dredged, is usually accomplished by the *average end method*. This procedure is explained in the following example.

(1) Station No.	(2) End Area sq ft	(3) Avg. End Area sq ft	(4) Dist. ft	(5) Volume cu ft
300+00	4001			
		4178	100	417,800
301+00	4356			
		4156	100	415,600
302+00	3956			
		4047	100	404,700
303+00	4139			
		3767	50	188,350
303+50	3396			
		3926	50	196,300
304+00	4456			
		4306	100	430,600
305+00	4156			
		4307	100	430,700
306+00	4459			
		4169	100	416,900
307+00	3879			
		3723	100	372,300
308+00	3567			
		4011	100	401,100
309+00	4456			
		4406	100	440,600
310+00	4356			
		4261	100	426,100
311+00	4167			
		4123	50	206,150
311+50	4078			
		3992	50	199,600
312+00	3906			
		4129	100	412,900
313+00	4353			
		4113	100	411,300
314+00	3873			

	5,771,000 cu ft
Divide by 27	213,740 cu yd
Divide by 35.314	163,420 cu mtr

Fig. 133. Quantity Calculation Tabulations.

Suppose that before-dredging cross sections are taken at 100-foot intervals from station 300+00 through 314+00, including intermediate stations 303+50 and 311+50. The cross-sectional area of the material within each of the specified sections is then determined by planimetering.

After all the end areas are planimetered (the end area being the cross section at each station), the area of each end area is tabulated opposite its respective station number (Fig. 133, Col. 2). Then, beginning at the top of the column, the first two areas (at stations 300+00 and 301+00) are added, and their sum divided by two. This will give the average area over the interval between the two stations. This average area is then tabulated in Column 3, and the procedure is continued for all station end areas. The area of an even section just prior to the plus station is added to the plus-station area and the sum divided by two, giving the average area over the 50-foot interval between the two stations. The same thing applies for the other intermediate sections.

Tabulated in Column 4 opposite the average end areas is the distance which the average area represents. In this example these distances would each equal 100 feet, with the exception of the four 50-foot intervals. Note that the two intermediate sections create four 50-foot intervals.

When these tabulations are completed, each average end area (Col. 3) is multiplied by its respective distance (Col. 4), and the product, which is cubic feet, is tabulated in Column 5. All the quantities in Column 5 are then added and the sum placed at the bottom. This sum is the cubic feet of material required to be dredged, or as the case may be, already dredged. Dividing this by 27 will give total cubic yards. Dividing by 35.314 will give the total cubic meters.

These data are useful in obtaining other information. For instance, the *average bank*—height of material to be cut—can be determined by dividing the average area (average of Col. 3) by the average width of cut—the distance between cut stakes. The number of cubic yards per foot for any section can be determined by dividing the average end area of the section by 27.

Chapter 5

Plans—Specifications—Contracts
Investigations—Estimating—Bidding

85. Introduction. When a dredging job is advertised by the government or by private interests, plans and specifications are provided contractors. In some instances however, there may not be any plans. The contract may be for the rental of the dredge for work which the client will dictate as work progresses. However, these instances are few, and most work is contracted on a *per-unit* basis. Examples of per-unit and rental specifications are given in the Appendix.

86. Plans. Dredging plans show the location of the general area of operation, the dredging site location, and the detailed alinement and dimensions of the cut. Generally, pre-dredging cross sections are included in the plans with the required theoretical sections superimposed. Sufficient additional information must be available for the dredging company to completely locate, and if necessary, lay out the work.

Good plans usually have boring logs and the location of the borings that have been made. Logs are not always supplied, however, and even when they are they often have been made by persons not familiar with dredging. Consequently, the material classifications are not always suitable for dredging estimating. Regardless of the source of the logs provided, before bidding, the dredging company should verify them by making borings of their own.

87. Specifications. Specifications should include all the requirements of the work—not just the technical, but the general, legal and operational. In addition, specifications should state what the work is to be, of what it consists, what is to be allowed in over-dredging, and the amount of material to be dredged. The specifications usually include a starting date, a time limit, and liquidated damages clauses.

In the preliminary perusal of the specifications one of the first things to do is to estimate the time required to do the work. In determining this the contractor must first decide what type of job it will be—a *get-ahead job* (light sweeping or maintenance), a *cutting job* (heavy, tough material), or a *pumping job* (soft, large quantity, or long-distance disposal). Dredges designed for get-ahead work are usually not as suitable for cutting or pumping jobs, and conversely, a cutting or pumping dredge is usually not adaptable to get-ahead work.

By dividing total yards in the job by its length and width, an estimate can be made of the height of bank. The height of bank will indicate whether or not it is a get-ahead job. For instance, say that past experience shows the dredge's production in the material is 700 cubic yards per hour and that the average height of bank is one foot. With a bottom-width cut of, say 135 feet, this would give a cubic yards per foot cut of (1) (135) (1)/27 = 5. To supply the pump with adequate material the dredge would have to get ahead 140 feet an hour. Obviously this would be a get-ahead job, not a cutting or pumping one.

With these preliminary data the contractor can decide whether he has the equipment available to do the work under the conditions and schedules specified, and consequently whether he may be interested in bidding.

Specifications should be studied carefully for any clauses that might later bring on a controversy. There are a number of standard clauses usually written into specifications that, although they seem innocuous on the surface, can be damaging when considered carefully (35). One of the most common clauses is ". . . failure to acquaint himself with all the available information concerning conditions affecting the work will not relieve the contractor of the responsibility for estimating the difficulties and cost of the work, and successfully performing and completing the work as required." This clause has been the downfall of many contractors. Three other standard clauses often found in specifications are: (1) ". . . does not guarantee that other materials will not be found, nor that the proportions of the several materials will not vary from those indicated"; (2) ". . . bidders must visit the site and inform themselves as to the conditions and difficulties of the work, and no allowance will be made for failure to correctly estimate the difficulties"; and (3) ". . . if materials, structures, or obstacles of a substantially different character are encountered in the execution of the work, and the cost of their removal obviously would be, in the opinion of the Engineer, either in excess or less than the contract price . . ."

The courts have repeatedly decided that contractors cannot recover under such statements as these. It is therefore up to the contractor to assure himself that he has fully protected himself when similar clauses are found in the specifications.

Other factors which should be considered in reviewing specifications are conditions that may not be covered. For instance, if a fill is required, no mention may be made of the possibility of subsidence. On some jobs a contractor could be ruined if he did not plan for subsidence or was not paid for it. Another example would be a requirement for "suitable materials" to be placed in a fill. Such wording might imply that the contractor was responsible for deciding what were suitable materials. Generally speaking, a contractor is not qualified to judge what is suitable. What he might think suitable could turn out not to be. Furthermore, it is possible that no available material could be termed suitable.

88. Contracts. A contract is an agreement enforceable by law, and only those connected with it are bound by its terms. It must contain the following essential parts to make it binding: (1) there must be lawful work, and some payment must be made for the services; (2) the parties must be competent, and both or all must agree to what the work is to be; and (3) it must comply with the provisions of the law (35, 36).

A. LAWFUL WORK. If there is a violation of statute or common law, or if there is an opposition to public policy, a contract may be considered illegal.

B. CONSIDERATION. One party, in return for the services of the other, must provide some act or service in return to make a contract valid. Payment of money is one form of act. If something other than money is offered as consideration, a dollar is usually added to establish consideration.

C. COMPETENT PARTIES. Anyone, except a minor, an insane person, or a drunk, can enter into a contract. A corporation can enter into a contract only to the extent allowed it by law. Municipal, state, county, and federal agencies can contract only within the authority of the contracting officers representing them. No recourse is available to a contractor who enters into a contract where the contracting officer acts outside his legal authority.

D. AGREEMENT. The wording of a contract should be clear. Both parties must be able to definitely determine what is intended. Usually their agreement is indicated by their signatures on the contract.

E. LIQUIDATED DAMAGES. When time is *of the essence* it means that time is an important consideration of the contract, and failure by the contractor to comply with any time limitations may create liability for damages. To preclude legal proceedings in such instances, liquidated damages are usually stipulated in the contract. Where they are, a starting date is usually given along with the amount of time allowed for completion. Usually the time for completion is a stated number of days—either *calendar* or *working* days. There is a considerable distinction between the two. A calendar day is a definite quantity and can be accurately determined; on the other hand, a working day is often indefinite.

When a contractor runs over his time on a working-day contract, controversy sometimes ensues concerning what days were working days. A high wind could create what a contractor might consider a non-working day, while the client might think otherwise. Calendar-day contracts are preferable.

F. PENALTIES AND BONUSES. Bonus payments are sometimes provided as compensation for early completion of the work, and penalty deductions are often made for delays. Bonus payments are few and far between on dredging contracts.

G. TERMINATION OF CONTRACTS. A contract is normally terminated when the obligations of both parties have been completed. Sometimes just substantial performance will terminate a contract. Agreement by both parties will allow termination. When one party fails to complete his obligations there is a breach of contract, and a termination. Impossibility of performance will also terminate a contract. Where conditions are found that would make the work impossible, the contract is terminated.

H. DISPUTES OF CONTRACTS. Usually contracts stipulate that the Engineer, acting for the Owner, will decide all controversies and disputes. This applies only so long as both parties go along with it. Either party can submit a dispute to the courts regardless of the Engineer's decision.

I. TYPES OF CONTRACTS. Most contracts fall into three general categories, (1) competitive-bid contracts, (2) negotiated contracts, and (3) rental contracts.

1. *Competitive-bid Contracts.* These contracts are divided into *lump-sum* and *unit-price* contracts. The lump-sum contract provides for a certain amount to cover all work. The unit-price contract provides for a breakdown of the units of work, and an individual price for each unit. In determining the low bidder in such a contract, the total amount, as in the lump-sum contract, usually decides.

2. *Negotiated Contracts.* Occasionally work must be done immediately, and often there is no time to advertise for bids and go through the normal contract-letting procedure. In such instances contracts are often negotiated. An example would be where a flash flood filled up a navigational canal and stopped all traffic. The government might negotiate a dredging contract so that the way could be cleared immediately.

3. *Rental Contracts.* Rental contracts can fall under either of the above two types of contracts. When in the opinion of the owner the work may be too varied for a per-unit type contract, or work requirements such that conditions could change as the work progresses, a rental-type contract is often made. The contractor may be asked to furnish his plant *bare boat* (without a crew) or he may provide all plant and personnel to do the work as prescribed by the owner.

J. RESPONSIBILITY. Unless the contract specifically states the contrary, the owner is responsible for the accuracy of information supplied to bidders. Understandably, most contracts will provide that the owner assumes no responsibility for the interpretation or accuracy of the information—thereby attempting to make the contractor responsible. This practice is questionable. However, the contractor should make a thorough investigation, and he should not rely on furnished information until he has checked it. More litigation has arisen over this one item than any other in the entire field of contractural agreements, and they are usually decided against the contractor!

ADVERTISEMENTS AND BIDS

89. **Advertisements.** An advertisement or notice to contractors in-

forms prospective bidders that work is to be done and that a contract is anticipated. It usually includes the name and address of the owner and of the person who will receive the bids. It also should include the time, place, and hour of the opening of the bids, and any other information necessary to advise the contractors that work is imminent.

90. Instructions to Bidders. These instructions give detailed information to the contractors for making their bids, and describe special features of the work.

91. Bid Form. This form is used in submitting a bid. Each item of work is usually broken down into bidding units (on per-unit contracts), such as the cubic yard for United States dredging work. Sometimes the bid will require a statement as to whether the unit is *in place* or *in the fill*—a considerable difference.

92. Opening Bids. Usually bids can be submitted, withdrawn, or resubmitted any time prior to the time stated for opening them. After opening starts, however, changes are not permitted. On most governmental and public work, bid openings are *open*—the contractors and the public can be in attendance. On some private work, bid openings are *closed*—the owner and his engineer open the bids privately. For the good of all concerned, all openings should be open.

93. Analysis of Bids. Most dredging contracts require bids on a per-unit basis. For comparison purposes the per-unit prices are multiplied by the estimated bid quantities. When errors are detected, the unit price figure usually governs. The actual final cost of the dredging contract is seldom determined by the quantities shown on the bid. Payment generally ends up being the per-unit times the actual amount excavated—as determined by measurements made just before and after dredging. Often it is specifically stated in the contract that the quantities shown in the plans are for bidding purposes only.

Where the contract is a lump-sum type, the contractor must determine for himself how well the contract quantities represent the actual quantities. Lump-sum contracts in dredging are not common.

94. Unbalanced Bids. Several different classifications of materials are usually encountered in dredging. Where the materials differ substantially, such as rock in one section and silt in another, separate bid items might be requested for each.

In a *balanced bid* each item is bid to carry its share of the profit. However, contractors often modify their unit prices to change this distribution; this is called *unbalanced bidding*. Although generally frowned upon by owners, the unbalanced bid has justification. Two good reasons for submitting an unbalanced bid are (1) the contractor may feel some item will have more quantity than shown on the bid form, so he increases his unit price on it and reduces it on another item proportionally. If he is right, he gains, and he loses nothing if he is wrong, inasmuch as his total bid remains the same, and (2) he raises the unit price on items which will be finished first and thereby does not have to wait so long for most of his money.

INVESTIGATIONS

95. Introduction. Investigations cannot be classified under any one category. Some are in open water where all investigation must be done from floating equipment. Others are on land where the investigation can be covered with trucks or other land equipment. There are jobs that require deep dredging, and consequently borings must be deep—this usually requires mechanized equipment. On the other hand, some jobs have shallow cuts, and hand-boring equipment can often be used. Some maintenance or sweeping jobs need only to be probed.

In this broad field of investigation a description of all methods would be difficult. Consequently, only generalities will be considered. At the same time, however, principles applicable to all investigations will be pointed out as they apply to the work in particular.

Getting to the site may or may not present difficulties. If there are accessible roads it will not be difficult, but if it is necessary to travel across country, it may be. Probably a landing point will have to be established from which the remainder of the distance can be covered by water.

Arriving at the site, an inspection of spoil-disposal areas is made to determine what work will be required—such as brush cutting, clearing out old levees, determining spillway locations, estimating length of pipelines and their locations, and checking impediments, such as high or steep inclines, gulleys, or washes.

Sources for fuel, water, and supplies, as well as their costs, must be established. Prices in one locality may be higher or lower than in another. When large quantities are bought, a quarter- or a half-cent can make a measurable difference in overall costs.

The entire length of the project is inspected thoroughly. Sandbars and other obstructions are checked, as are clearances under, over, or through bridges, pipelines and aerial cables.

On projects where there may be need for getting around obstructions rather than over or under them, such as dams and railroad bridges, routes for the detours have to be investigated, and an estimate of the additional work and cost involved must be made. Locations for storage of dredge equipment must be predetermined and, if the work is in open water, safe harbors have to be located for future use in case of storms.

When these items and all others of particular nature to the job have been covered, an investigation of the subsurface material to be dredged is made. With a large enough party this could have been proceeding while the surface investigation was going on.

96. Borings. The number and spacing of borings is dependent upon what is needed to get a true picture of the material profile. It is obvious that borings would not be taken every 100 feet on a job 10 miles long; it would be neither feasible nor practical. By studying the plans' boring logs, a representative picture of material consistency can be obtained. From this an estimate can be made of what material changes are to be expected and about how far borings should be spaced. If the material between 500-foot spaced borings remains substantially the same, the distance between successive borings might be increased to 750 or 1,000 feet. The spacing distance, per se, is immaterial. Spacing of borings should be determined by the material.

If borings are taken on land and are not too deep, they can usually be obtained by two or three men with 1½- or 2-inch earth augers.

Fig. 134.   Kit for Hand Borings.   (Acker Drill Co.)

The auger is attached to a section of standard ¾-inch galvanized water pipe four to five feet long, with additional sections being added as the hole is deepened. The auger is rotated and downward pressure applied by holding the pipe with wrenches, two- or three-way tillers, or other specially-designed devices. When the auger penetrates its length, it is pulled up, the material stripped off for testing, and the depth of the boring noted. In obtaining samples of the material for testing, undisturbed samples are preferable. However, to even ap-

Fig. 135. Mechanized Boring Machine. (Acker Drill Co.)

proach obtaining these would usually require special equipment, which for the great majority of dredging jobs is not warranted. The common hand-operated ship auger obtains samples quite satisfactory for most dredging work (Fig. 134). For more difficult work, mechanical boring machines are often used (Fig. 135).

When borings are made on land, a place to stand is no problem. On water it is. Usually a barge is used in conjunction with an attendant boat, or a platform provides a place upon which men can stand (Fig. 136).

When boring over water or in loose material, a *casing* is often necessary to maintain a hole. The casing is extended down through

Fig. 136.   Making Borings over Water.   (Acker Drill Co.)

the water and below the submerged-ground surface sufficiently to assure that the hole will stay open.

Casing pipe is usually four-inch diameter, extra-heavy steel. Common steel pipe is usually less expensive than galvanized pipe.

As the hole is deepened the casing is extended by screwing together the sections. The threading of the sections should be done by machine so that all threads will be the same. Some investigators prefer the pipe ends to come together in the couplings, believing that it relieves the threads. Others prefer threads that leave the ends of the pipe separated about a quarter of an inch or so within the couplings.

In deep borings or stiff clays, pulling equipment is usually required for retrieving the casing and auger. This pulling equipment is also

Fig. 137.   Driving Casing.   (Acker Drill Co.)

used to lift a heavy weight for driving casing in some instances. It is usually an A-frame outfitted with a block on top and some kind of motive power for pulling and driving (Fig. 137).

Sometimes it is impossible to penetrate material with an auger.

Substances such as silt, fine hard-packed sand, shell, gravel, or loose rock, block or defy augers to pick up anything. In such instances

Fig. 138. Wash Boring Rig. (Acker Drill Co.)

wash borings are made.

A. WASH BORINGS. Although they do not provide samples as representative as regular borings, wash borings sometimes are the only method of getting down through a material.

Most wash borings require a casing. Should the only purpose of the boring be to just reach a prescribed depth, no casing is needed. The wash pipe is jogged up and down and allowed to jet its way downward. In areas where sand is the only material presumed present, this type of jog-boring is used to assure there are no other layers or other material interspaced above grade.

Wash borings taken to obtain samples however, must have a continuous casing. The casing is usually made up in the same manner as described in the preceding paragraph, using four-inch by four- or five-foot sections of pipe successively screwed together. The wash pipe, usually a ½-inch or ¾-inch diameter pipe similar to the one used with the auger, is connected to a flexible hose which in turn is connected to a high-pressure pump that is either hand- or engine-operated. The wash pipe is inserted in the casing, lowered to the bottom surface, and jogged up and down. The high-pressure water jet from the pump loosens the bottom material and forces it up and over the top of the casing, providing samples of the material. Figure 138 shows a modern wash-boring rig using mechanical power.

One piece of equipment used in deep or difficult borings is the *shell*. It is lowered into the casing to obtain samples of the bottom when boring in sands, gravels, soft silts, and noncohesive formations. It is merely a tube with a cutting edge and a retaining valve on its lower end, the cutting edge entering the soil and forcing it up into the body of the shell. When the shell is lifted out, the valve retains the sample. Extremely hard material is penetrated by using either percussive chisels, diamond bits, or a variety of other special-tipped tools.

97. Testing Samples. Although the ways to test boring samples vary from testing by hand to laboratory methods, the author's experience inclines him toward the hand and visual methods. However, this applies only when the results of this type of testing can be used in comparison with the results of other similar testing and in comparison with dredge production over a long period of time.

Materials can be given tests for shear, voids, ratio, grain size, compressibility, bearing capacity, weight—ad infinitum. However, the fundamental reason for obtaining the sample is to determine what the dredge will do in it. Any test that is not comparable with dredging results in material similarly tested is highly speculative, and actually is not worth much regardless of how it is made.

Each company usually has its own terminology for classifying soils, and usually in relation to what the dredge will do in them. One classification group might be (1) mud and silt, (2) sandy silt, (3) silty sand, (4) fine sand, (5) coarse sand, (6) clayey sand, (7) sandy clay, (8) soft clay, (9) medium clay, (10) stiff clay, and (11) hard clay.

Tests by feel and visual observation are used constantly. For instance, if a clay is so hard that only a fingernail will go into it (squeezing will not change it), it might be classified as hard clay.

Soils have different characteristics that can easily be determined by sight and feel. For instance, the following characteristics are usually consistent for the materials listed.

Gravel	Coarse particles larger than ⅛-inch diameter
Coarse sand	Smaller than gravel, but large enough that the individual grains can be felt when rubbed between thumb and forefinger
Fine sand	Particles too small to be felt when rubbed between thumb and forefinger, but distinguishable by sight
Silt	Particles so fine they cannot be distinguished by sight, but can be under a microscope
Clay	Particles finer than silt
Very soft	Exudes between the fingers when squeezed in the fist
Soft	Easily moulded in the fingers
Firm	Can be moulded in the fingers, but takes strong pressure
Stiff	Cannot be moulded in fingers
Very stiff	Brittle and tough

Clays are especially difficult to classify. They are all made up from shales, and they vary in water content. The clay particles themselves, not counting the water, generally weigh around 175 to 180 pounds per cubic foot. However, clay that is considered soft may have 40 per cent water content and weigh around 124 pounds per cubic foot (37). The porosity here is similar to that of average sand with 35 to 40 per cent water. Mud and silt containing around 60 per cent water will generally weigh 100 to 110 pounds per cubic foot.

Other than hand and visual testing, there are several field-testing devices that are quite advantageous. One of these is the *vane shear-testing device*. It was originally developed in Sweden, circa 1948 (38). It consisted of four metal vanes fixed at right angles to the end of a steel rod. The vanes were driven into the material by the rod and rotated by a lever at the top. The torque required was measured by spring balances. When the shearing strength was overcome, the readings dropped. The maximum readings, just before the drop, were applied to the equation

$$S = C (P_1 + P_2) \text{ Cos } \phi \qquad (39)$$

where S = shear, in pounds per square inch; $P_1 + P_2$ = critical spring balance readings, in pounds; and ϕ = angle read on the scale at the point of overcoming the shear, in degrees, and

$$C = \frac{a}{(\pi)(D^2)(H + D/3)} \qquad (40)$$

where a = distance of the lever arm from rod to lever, in feet; D = width of vane, in inches; and H = height of vane, in inches. Approximate dimensions of the vanes and rod normally used were D = two

Fig. 139.   Vane Shear Tester.   (Acker Drill Co.)

to three inches, H = 4.5 inches. Thickness of the vane was 3/32 inches, and the diameter of the rod, 0.5 inch (38).

A modern *Vane Shear Tester* has now been developed and is being manufactured by the Acker Drill Company of Scranton, Pennsylvania. It has been used extensively in dredging investigations giving accurate shear readings directly to depths of 100 feet (Fig. 139).

Other methods are used for testing. Some investigators use a penetration test where a ball or rod is dropped on a sample from a certain height, and the depth of penetration used as an indication of the material's consistency. Others rely upon commercial testing laboratories.

For those who favor the penetration or indentation method of testing, the *Pocket Penetrometer* is a useful device. Developed by the Acker Drill Company, it is widely used in dredging investigations (Fig. 140).

Fig. 140.   Pocket Penetrometer.
(Acker Drill Co.)

The reliability of any data becomes greater as the amount of it increases. For instance, determining the classification of clay by the fingernail method will not, it is believed by many, produce the same result time after time. They say a ball dropped from a certain height gives a truer and more consistent value. This may be so, but whether this kind of accuracy is any more valuable is debatable, particularly in dredging.

Whatever the method used, the important fact is that from investigation to investigation and job to job, the same method should be used to evaluate the material. If this is done, the records of an individual dredge's production in various materials will provide good data for estimating future work in similar materials by similar testing methods.

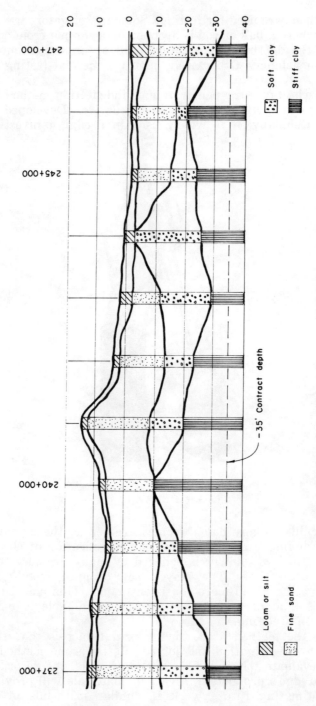

Fig. 141. Material Profile for Proposed Dredging Project.

186

98. Working Up Bids. In the most precise investigations, boring data are shown on logs and then superimposed on profile paper. The various strata are connected together from log to log and thereby a complete profile of the entire job is obtained (Fig. 141). From this profile and the theoretical width and slope of the average section, a calculation can be made to determine what percentage of the total quantity is represented by each of the various types of materials. Planimetering is used to determine the areas.

From these data a tabulation of the estimated cubic yards of each material can be obtained. With previous dredge production in identical materials known, a rate of production can be estimated, and subsequently, the amount of time required for excavation can be determined.

For example, suppose that planimetering the four strata of Fig. 141 gives the following classification distribution: silt and loam, 7 per cent; fine sand, 37 per cent; soft clay, 26 per cent; and stiff clay, 30 per cent. Should it have been determined from the specifications, or from calculations made using the cross sections, that there were 1,800,000 cubic yards in the total job, the proportional amounts of the different materials would be: silt and loam, 126,000 cu. yds.; fine sand, 666,000 cu. yds.; soft clay, 468,000; and stiff clay, 540,000 cu. yds.

Consider now, for this example, that the dredge being planned for the job has past production experience in similar materials as follows: silt and loam, 1,500 cu. yds. per hr.; fine sand, 1,000 cu. yds. per hr.; soft clay, 750 cu. yds, per hr.; and stiff clay, 500 cu. yds. per hr. The hours required to excavate each of the four materials would, therefore, be: silt and loam, 84 hours; fine sand, 666 hours; soft clay, 624 hours, and stiff clay, 1,080 hours. The total time required would then be 2,454 hours.

Now the estimated excavating time just determined is not the time to complete the job. *Production time* is considered good if 18 hours per 24-hour day can be averaged. Production time is the time actually spent on excavating materials (the time calculated in the preceding paragraph), as contrasted to (2) *non-production* time spent in moving, adding to or removing pipe from the line, cleaning out the pump, and other job-contributing activities, and (3) *shutdown time* spent in repairs, maintenance, or other non-contributing activities. On a monthly basis, 18 hours per day would be 540 hours. Consequently, the number of hours calculated for excavation (production time) would be divided by 18 to give the number of days, or by 540 to give the number of months. The job of this example would require 136 days or 4.54 months on an 18-hour day or 540-hour month basis.

Should the job require a large number of moves, setbacks, or pipe-line changes, the 18-hour average daily production time might be too high. Also, should the work have a great number of obstacles, such as stumps, trash, or submerged piling, production time would also be again reduced. Consequently, only in a very few instances should production time be figured greater than 18 hours per day when making an estimate unless there is substantial experience available that indicates reasons for doing so.

99. Cost Considerations and Pricing. With the time estimate completed, excavation costs can be calculated from known daily operating costs. (*See* Chapter 6.)

Dredge daily operating costs vary from job to job. If fuel and water costs fluctuate, daily costs will change accordingly. Furthermore, if large shore crews are necessary they cannot be considered part of the usual normal daily costs. This extra cost for labor can change considerably from job to job.

Normal labor costs can cause an appreciable change in daily costs. Where unions are active, labor costs may be higher than in areas where there is no union. In estimating foreign work, additional personnel costs have to be considered, such as housing, subsistence, medical care, and transportation.

Mobilization and demobilization costs must also be considered. Usually on local or medium-distance jobs, mobilization costs can be determined from other jobs. However, where long transports are necessary, such costs as towing and insurance must be investigated. Demobilization costs vary depending upon what can be done with the dredge after completion of the job—move it to another job, let it sit, or tow it back to the yard. If the dredge can be moved to a new job upon completion of the one being estimated, part of the demobilization may be charged off to the mobilization of the other, particularly if close-by. Even if the dredge is to lay up at the job site, some demobilization cost must still be added for the work involved in breaking up. If the dredge is to be towed back to the yard for lay-up, towing costs should be determined and charged to demobilization.

In many instances demobilization and mobilization are separate bid items on a contract. Consequently, these costs would not be added to the costs of operation when calculating overall cost for production time.

Overhead must also be added to the total costs. Usually this is a fixed value determined over a long period of time, and only the length of the job is needed to determine the cost of overhead. Some dredging contractors are never amazed at what goes in for overhead and office expense on some jobs. Many contractors support an excessive overhead and never realize it. This cost in many cases could be reduced substantially. Such items as prestigious offices and proliferation of executives often burden a contractor unnecessarily.

The contractor should, of course, not forget costs for insurance, depreciation, surety bonds, and the like. Some feel that depreciation is not applicable, inasmuch as they are continually repairing the equipment. This is a fallacy. Although the equipment may have been kept up, it still becomes more antiquated each year, and consequently is not as competitive as newer or more modern equipment would be.

In addition to all these costs there should be a contingency cost. A contingency cost is supposed to cover those unexpected but always-occurring happenings—a levee breaks, additional equipment is needed, the dredge has to shut down, or a line plugs and no other is available. The only way such costs can be determined is by *guestimation*—adding a certain percentage of the overall cost which the experienced dredgeman feels is adequate on that particular job.

Next to be added is profit. Most contractors know what they need per dredge-day to make their business profitable, or at least to break even. Depending upon experience, the conditions, and the amount of work available, a profit value is determined and added to the other costs.

Often a contract is let for a series of sections of a job and each progressive section must be completed before the next is commenced. In such instances separate amounts are bid for each individual section. It is often practical to put some of the costs of later sections into the bid of earlier sections. A contractor who depends upon his major cash return coming at the end of a job has to finance himself, and his client, just that much longer. Sometimes this is difficult.

Where there are items in a contract that are small in quantity or do not amount to much, it is wise to price them liberally. Often it happens that the client's estimates are shy on such items. Even if the quantity is not later increased, the contractor will still be ahead and the difference will not affect the overall price appreciably. (*See* Art. 94.)

When all the costs are added, a total initial bid price is obtained. By dividing this by the total material quantity of the contract, an initial per-unit price is determined. Most dredgers do not stop here, however. Looking at this final figure they sometimes say, "What will this job go for?" Then, depending upon their past experience, present conditions, pure intuition, number of bids expected, who will be bidding, and so on, they add to or subtract from the initial bid price.

Another price adjustment is also often made. If the estimated price comes out to, say, $1.00 per unit, a contractor might cut it to $0.9989, the idea being that other bidders might also come up with the $1.00 price.

Finally, the last change in a bid price is probably the lucky number change. Where a bid price comes out to, say, $0.2865 per unit, a particularly-favored numeral may be substituted for the last, or even last two, digits, such as 77 instead of the 65; thus the price would be $0.02777.

Bids are not always necessarily based upon the total costs and profits exclusively. Sometimes it is beneficial to bid at a low profit, or possibly none at all—particularly if it may place the dredge in position to be on the spot for a more lucrative, larger, or continuing job.

One last precaution; the dredging contractor must take into consideration the possibility of his not being paid. He should assure himself that money to pay for the work is available and that it will be disbursed. In some foreign work (and some state-side jobs) the possibility of getting paid is highly speculative. Sometimes in governmental work appropriations are lacking and the contractor might have a financing problem.

Before turning in a bid a contractor should check his prices thoroughly. It is good practice to have at least two persons check the prices independently, and it is not bad practice to have someone outside the company give them a final check. When these three separate checks are compared, any great discrepancies can be rechecked. The resulting consensus of the final price will be more realistic and dependable.

Chapter 6

Costs—Management—Personnel

100. Introduction. In Chapter 5, costs in relationship to bidding were reviewed generally. In this chapter costs are considered from a dollars-and-cents viewpoint, and different methods of obtaining them are discussed. Costs of labor and equipment are rising rapidly today. A fair estimate of the increase in both would be from 6 to 7 per cent per year. All prices of present-day equipment and labor shown herein are based upon quoted or published prices during the period 1967–1968. For any other period, fair estimates can be determined from the *Engineering News-Record Index* which is discussed in Section 110.

Although it is not practicable to develop a costing system that will be applicable to all dredging operations, the procedures presented here are those of acceptable use.

The cost of equipment is basically the cost of ownership plus the cost of operation. The cost of ownership includes *fixed costs*—such as delivery price, interest, taxes, insurance; *depreciation;* and variable or *operating costs*—such as supplies, fuels, oils, greases, repairs, and labor.

101. Delivery Price. Equipment delivery price is probably the first item to be considered in establishing fixed costs. Once established it remains constant, unlike other items in this category which may vary with time and conditions and have to be recalculated each time an estimate is made. The delivery price is nothing more than the number of dollars that were paid for the equipment plus freight charges (39). Freight charges are usually based upon weight and shipping distance and consequently may vary considerably, depending upon the destination of the equipment.

For example, the rate to ship a 16-inch dredge to some location in the United States might be, say $1.65 per hundred pounds. So,

$$\text{Freight Charge} = \$1.65 \ \frac{\text{weight of dredge}}{100}$$

$$= \$1.65 \ \frac{170,000}{100}$$

$$= \$2,805$$

With the factory price being, say $300,000, *delivery price* would therefore be $300,000 + $2,805 or a total of $302,805. With the delivery price computed, the average investment price can be calculated.

191

102. Average Investment Price. The average investment price is the value in dollars equal to 52.5 per cent of the delivery price, when a depreciation period of 20 years is used. Generally, 20 years is about the most applicable period for dredge depreciation.

With a 20-year depreciation period, the dredge is depreciated one-twentieth each year. The charge is against the original delivery price, as shown.

Value 1st year:	$302,805	=	100%
Value 2nd year:	$287,665	=	95%
Value 3rd year:	$272,525	=	90%
and so on			
Value 20th year:	$ 15,140	=	5%
			1,050%

Therefore, the average investment would be $1050/20 = 52.50$ per cent of the original delivery cost. In this instance the average investment would be,

$$(\$302,805)\ (0.525) = \$158,972$$

103. Interest, Taxes and Insurance. These costs are sometimes considered to equal 15 per cent of the average investment. This 15-per cent multiplier is used in the example here, but respective values of each can be determined individually—and there is precedent for doing so, particularly in these days of rapidly rising prices and interest. In this example these three would yield: interest, 7 per cent; taxes, 4 per cent; insurance, 4 per cent.

Therefore, the cost for interest, insurance, and taxes taken altogether would be,

$$(\$158,972)\ (0.15) = \$23,846 \quad \text{per year}$$

104. Depreciation. This cost, as explained in Section 102, is obtained by dividing the delivered price by the number of years used. Thus in this example the depreciation would be,

$$\frac{\$302,805}{20} = \$15,140 \quad \text{per year}$$

Using a 20-year depreciation period does not mean that in 10 years the dredge will be worth only one-half of its original delivery price. Some dredges will be worth more due to good repair and modernization, while others may be worth considerably less than half because of lack of same.

105. Repairs and Labor. There are numerous methods for determining costs of repairs and labor. The best method, of course, is maintaining records. Where these are available, no better data can be used in a cost determination.

However, when these data are not available, some empirical methods which have been established over the years can be used. They are as follows: For average working conditions the cost of repairs and labor per year is often considered as equal to the total delivered price multiplied by 15 per cent. The two can be evenly divided into 7.5 per cent for repairs and 7.5 per cent for labor. It should be understood, however, that these values are for average conditions. A job requiring a large shore crew would have a labor cost greater than 7.5 per cent. On the other hand, a major breakdown, where replacement parts would be considered capital investment rather than repair, would not be included in the 7.5 per cent.

106. Operating Costs. Operating costs include expenses for services, supplies, fuels, lubricants and other similar items resulting directly from operations and which are used up in every-day production. They do not include capital expenditures. Operating costs are difficult to determine precisely as they vary so much from job to job. Nevertheless, records of past operating costs can be as indicative as anything.

For those who have no previous data upon which to rely, the following are given as representative averages of a wide cross-section of dredging operations. These costs are for one year and are based upon the initial delivered cost.

| Maintenance | 7. 5% | Lubricants | 0. 8% |
| Fuel | 7. 5% | Supplies | 0. 7% |

In the example being used, the dollar costs would be,

Maintenance	(0. 075)	($302, 805)	= $22, 710
Fuel	(0. 075)	($302, 805)	= $22, 710
Lubricants	(0. 008)	($302, 805)	= $ 2, 420
Supplies	(0. 007)	($302, 805)	= $ 2, 120
		Total	$49, 960

107. Hourly Cost. As mentioned previously in Article 98, an 18-hour day or a 550-hour month is considered acceptable production time for most dredging operations. It is also generally accepted that six months overall cumulative operation per year is possible to live with. However, it is not logical to say that for only 4,380 hours of the year (one-half year) costs go on, and for the other 4,380 hours the costs stop. They go on continuously, although possibly not as heavily during the shutdown periods. On the other hand, when thinking in terms of contracts and bidding, it must be realized that all costs have to be paid for and the only way they can be paid is for the dredge to be operating. For instance, should costs be averaged on an hourly basis for the full 8,760 hours of the year, and the dredge operate only six months of the year, only one-half of the costs would be realized. This is the same thing as assuming daily costs can be broken down into hourly costs by dividing by 24. (It should be noted here that the total number of days per month are usually considered to be 30 when estimating and making up bids.)

The total costs developed herein are regarded as being returnable only by working time, and therefore should be rated on an 18-hour day basis. Taking the costs of the example, the total hourly costs would be,

$$\text{Investment} = \frac{\$158,972}{3,300} = \$48.17$$

$$\text{Interest, insurance and taxes} = \frac{\$ 23,846}{3,300} = \$ 7.26$$

$$\text{Depreciation} = \frac{\$ 15,140}{3,300} = \$ 4.59$$

$$\text{Repairs and labor} = \frac{\$ 45,420}{3,300} = \$13.76$$

$$\text{Operating} = \frac{\$ 49,960}{3,300} = \$15.14$$

Total hourly operating cost
(based upon a 550 HR month) $88.92

The total hourly operating cost multiplied by the number of production hours estimated for the job will give a total cost, which can be called the total job operating cost.

Obviously the 18-hour daily and six-month yearly estimated operating time may not apply to any one specific dredge operation. Where it does not, applicable values certainly should be used instead of those presented here.

108. Representative Cost Factors. In the preceding discussion of costs of equipment, various percentage values were used. These factors represent only average values determined over a long period and a great number of jobs. In addition to these there are still other proportionate values that can be used in determining other costs.

In addition to profit, a return on investment should be considered in any estimate. It is obvious that had the capital outlay for equipment been placed in banks, stocks, bonds, or other securities, a return would have been expected. Consequently, a return should be expected even though the capital is invested in equipment. The going rate for investment capital can be determined relatively easily at any particular time. However, in this example the amount of seven per cent of investment cost is used.

Overhead should of course be considered. As mentioned previously, many a contractor's overhead is unnecessarily high—only a few have too low overhead. A common figure used for overhead is 15 per cent of the operating cost, but this figure's validity is debated.

Profit is an elusive value. What price a contractor puts down for this is purely up to him. On a job in his own country it might be considerably lower than in a foreign country. In the United States today 10 to 20 per cent of the cost of operation should well cover the profit incentive of most contractors.

Some other rules of thumb for miscellaneous costs are: $225 to $300 a horsepower for dredge investment cost; $30 times brake horsepower for investment cost of large diesel engines; $35 times brake horsepower for small diesels; and 53 per cent of investment cost for total operating costs.

Data for computing fuel and lubrication costs are often helpful. The following amounts are average. Consumption of diesel fuels can be estimated as 0.4 pounds per hour per brake horsepower. To obtain the gallon (U.S.) consumption, brake horsepower divided by 20 is often used. Gasoline engine fuel consumption in gallons can be approximated by dividing the brake horsepower by 9.5. The U.S. gallon is the equivalent of 0.832 times the Imperial gallon.

Lubricating oils, though not a major item, do add to the costs. They can be approximated by dividing brake horsepower by 1,750 to obtain gallons per hour consumption. Some diesel engine manufacturers use brake horsepower divided by 12,000. Grease consumption can be approximated by roughly estimating 150 to 200 pounds per month for most dredges over 16 inches.

A breakdown of costs for maintenance and repair on dredges from six to 10 inches, in cents per cubic yard produced, is shown in the following tabulation. For larger dredges it will be higher—for instance, 12 to 14-inch dredges may require 125 per cent of the following values, and dredges 16 inches and over, as much as 135 per cent.

| Machinery | $0. 000168 | Pump | $0. 012123 |
| Cutter | $0. 000231 | All other | $0. 019867 |

109. Labor Costs. Representative minimum hourly rates for dredge labor vary considerably across the United States. For instance, in Alaska the United States Department of Labor (C.O.E.) specifies a leverman's base rate as $7.16 per hour with $0.25 for health and welfare, and $0.30 for pensions (1967). On the other hand, in Tennessee and Arkansas, the base rate is $3.06 (1967) with no fringes. Most rates include, along with the basic hourly rate, payments for health and welfare, pensions, and occasionally, vacations. The fringe benefits usually average around $0.10 to $0.20 per hour each. In connection with these labor costs it must be remembered that the contractor will be assessed additional costs, such as workman's compensation and unemployment.

Workman's compensation rates are fairly stable in the United States, although they are expected to rise in the next few years. For average dredging firms the costs for this item can be taken as 13 per cent of the employees' base salary per year (1968).

Unemployment payments, both state and national, are based upon a percentage rate of the base salary. This percentage rate depends generally upon the company's experience rate. This experience rate is a fairly difficult thing to determine, and even more difficult to understand. In essence it is a function of the amount of unemployment payments paid out by the Unemployment Commission to former employees of a company. When a company first comes under the program (it is mandatory where there are three or more employees), the rate is fixed at 2.7 per cent of base salary. This continues for at least 18 months, at which time an accounting is made by the government and a new rate assigned, based upon the company's experience. The best experience is obtained when no previous unemployment payments have been paid to previous employees. In such experience-rate situations the minimum rate of 0.10 per cent can be obtained. A low experience rate is quite an asset for larger companies, and there have been instances where a company was actually purchased by another just to obtain its low rate.

Social Security rates are easily determined, as they are fixed by the government at a certain percentage of the employees' salaries. At this writing (1967) the rate is 4.8 per cent (9.6 per cent total), but without a doubt it will go much higher.

Retirement and hospitalization will depend upon the individual company's own program, and the rates for these will vary with the company, number of employees, and amount of coverage afforded.

110. Cost Index. The *Engineering News-Record Construction Cost Index* was created in 1921 and is basically an index of the rise in basic United States construction and labor costs over the years (40). It is very useful in anticipating costs.

When the Index was first started, it was believed by many that steel prices controlled all other prices—if steel costs rose, so would material and labor costs. Conversely, if steel prices dropped, material and labor costs would decrease as well.

However, labor wages have become the controlling factor, and are indicative of all other prices. Although earlier it appeared that common labor set the scale, common labor began to climb at a much faster rate than skilled labor. Consequently, in 1938 *Engineering News-Record* established a *Building Cost Index* for predicting the cost of skilled labor.

One of the misconceptions about the Cost Indexes is the idea that they are based upon the quantity of material used in construction in 1913 (the base year for the Index) and that adjustments are needed occasionally. The base used, however, is much broader and the need for adjustments of the original weightings are not necessary.

The two Indexes, *Construction Cost* and *Building Cost,* measure the trends in basic costs of construction materials and labor. They do not take into account the ability of management or the ups and downs of fluctuating periods. The Index shows trends, not exact prices. However, between the extremes of high productivity and low productivity, the depression, the post-war periods, and periods of recession, the Indexes are very accurate and are useful in estimating.

Engineering News-Record reports an instance where a company plotted the Cost Index on a long sheet of cross-section paper for a considerable number of years. Opposite the date of each job they had bid they wrote the cubic-yard cost. By comparing the cost indexes of today with those of the former jobs, they could bring any job costs up to date immediately.

Cost indexes are used for a number of other purposes. For instance, *Engineering News-Record* reported that on one job the contractor and the owner agreed that when the job had to be shut down for a considerable period, the original per-unit prices would be adjusted automatically according to the Construction Cost Index change, over the period of inactivity.

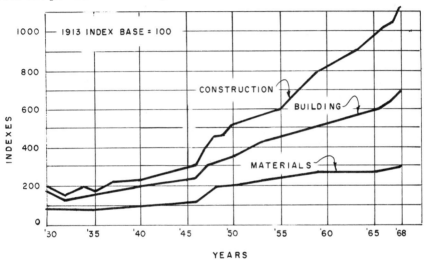

Fig. 142. *Engineering News-Record* Cost Index. (*Engineering News-Record*)

Table 6. Cost Indexes for February, 1969
(Engineering News-Record)

COST INDEXES ENR 20-Cities 1913=100	Feb. Index Value
Construction Cost · · · · · · ·	1,235.39
Building Cost · · · · · · · · ·	776.86
Common Labor (CC). · · · · ·	2,327.37
Skilled Labor (BC). · · · · · ·	1,122.16
Materials · · · · · · · · · · ·	566.11

Another use reported was where a contractor was allowed to tie his bid prices into the Construction Cost Index and any fluctuation in it. This arrangement would probably only be applicable in new construction or where there was a period of rapidly changing prices.

Shown in Fig. 142 is the *Engineering News-Record Index* of cost trends since 1930. It indicates the effects of wage rates and material price changes as trends, but is not adjusted for productivity, management efficiency, competitive conditions, automation, design changes, or other intangibles that affect the actual costs. In normal times the Indexes are quite accurate. Table 6 shows the February, 1969 indexes based upon a 1913 index of 100.

111. Early Dredge Costs. In 1905 a leverman was paid $150 a month—as was a civil engineer. By 1935 this had approximately doubled. Oilers in 1905 were paid $66 a month and deckhands around $50.

At that time a 20-inch dredge, complete with pipelines, cost approximately $100,000. A 12-inch dredge could be bought for $40,000.

Earlier, in the 1890's, a 30-inch dredge sold for $87,000. It had 300 horsepower on the pump. With a 20-foot head it discharged at 10 feet a second. Its daily operating cost was $97.00 and it averaged about 600 cubic yards per hour in sand (92).

Engineering News-Record reports that a 12-inch dredge in 1902 cost $40,000. It had 125 horsepower on the pump. With a static lift of 30 feet and 2,000 feet of pipeline, it averaged around 50 cubic yards per hour at a cost of approximately $0.085 per cubic yard.

In 1945 the following costs for complete dredges were reported,

10 to 16-inch portable, electric	$ 50,000 to $ 150,000
6 to 12-inch portable, self-powered	$ 200,000 to $ 600,000
14 to 24-inch self-powered	$ 200,000 to $ 600,000
20 to 30-inch electric	$ 300,000 to $ 750,000
27 to 30-inch self-powered	$1,000,000 to $2,000,000

An electric dredge generally costs about one-half the first cost of a self-powered dredge (67).

Table 7. Dredge Auxiliary Equipment Costs

Discharge Diameter	Pontoons Complete	Shore Pipe	Ball Joints	Rubber Sleeves	Dredge
ins	per ft	per ft	each	each	bare boat
10	$18.00	$ 7.00	$ 700	$100	$ 80,000 - 105,000
12	26.00	8.00	800	115	120,000 - 130,000
14	28.00	9.00	850	150	150,000 - 210,000
16	40.00	10.00	950	175	230,000 - 400,000
18	56.00	12.00	1200	200	420,000 - 470,000
20	60.00	13.00	1400	300	500,000 - 550,000
24	70.00	15.00	2000	-	680,000 - 930,000
27	80.00	17.00	2300	-	1,000,000 - Up

Note: Complete pontoon includes: Rubber sleeves through 14 inches, 0.250-inch wall thickness, two floats, ball joints 16 inches and above.
Bare boat price does not include stern discharge connection.

112. Present-day Equipment Costs. Equipment costs, although not fluctuating as rapidly as labor costs, are increasing at a rapid rate. Some estimates are from four to eight per cent per year. Shown in Table 7 are bare-boat and auxiliary-equipment costs for some typical off-the-shelf dredges.

These costs shown in Table 7 are not necessarily representative of all dredges. They are *off-the-shelf*—all design and construction completed. This type of dredge is satisfactory for particular types of work, but a *contractors' dredge* is usually needed for general work, and is built to specifications determined by the types of work anticipated by the contractor. As an example of specifications and costs for a contractors' dredge, see Table 8. Such a dredge would not generally be found on-the-shelf.

MANAGEMENT

113. Introduction. Although records of some kind are kept in most businesses, their quality and usefulness vary widely with dredging companies. It is sorrowfully evident that under present-day conditions, complete accounts and records are essential to staying in business no matter how much work is available. This is particularly true with the smaller firm operating with a smaller backlog of capital.

The typical dredgeman, particularly at the start of the business, has little knowledge of or familiarity with—or an interest in—financial statements, procedures, or economic principles. He is usually too preoccupied with the details of dredging operations and gives too little attention to his accounts and statements.

114. Records. Even in the very smallest concern the dredgeman-proprietor cannot be expected to have a detailed knowledge of all accounting and record keeping procedures (41). Usually the fledgling firms and sometimes the older ones as well, fail to utilize records which give a clear picture of the business. Without proper records the risk of failure is tremendous—the majority of business failures (nine out of ten) are due to the lack of proper records!

The basic statement of a business's condition at any specific time is its *balance sheet*. The basic statement of its operations for a certain period of time is its *profit and loss statement*. These two statements are the standard for reporting the condition of a business.

Many operators determine their financial condition merely by comparing cash income with cash outgo for a period. If anything is left over, the business is considered in the black. These methods, however, do not work in a modern dredging operation, and they certainly will not satisfy a banker when a loan is necessary.

115. Balance Sheet. The balance sheet is a list of the company's *assets* (property and money held for use in the business) and *liabilities* (debts). The difference between the two is the company's *net worth*. Assets and liabilities are grouped in order of their ease of convertibility into cash—they would be *current* if convertible in six

Table 8. Contractor's Dredge Costs

Description	Weight Crated for Export pounds	Cost dollars
12" Dredge. 54'×22'×5'. Portable Hull. 5 sections. 725 HP Pump Engine and Aux. Equipment.	233,200	200,000.
1000' Pontoon line. 12" I.D. × 1/4" wall. 20, 50' sections, 40 pontoons. 20, 12" ball joints	107,000	30,000.
3000' Shore line, 12" I.D. × 3/16" wall, 150, 20' sections, 2 shore valves, necessary fittings	83,000	15,100.
One Landing Pontoon Assembly: 3 pontoons, 2 pcs. 70', 12" I.D. × 1/4" wall, 2 strong backs, A-Frame, 2, 12" ball joints, 2 blocks, 1 hand hoist and necessary rigging	11,200	4,000.
One 90° Pontoon Elbow with fittings	6,900	2,900.
One Combination F.O. & Deck Pipe Barge 60'×26'×6' 40,000 Gal. F.O. capacity deck capacity to carry 3000' shore pipe & F.O. transfer pump on deck	77,000	23,500.
One Derrick Barge Hull, 50'×26'×5'	57,000	19,000.
One Derrick Barge Whirley Crane, 7.5 ton capacity. 5,500 lb single line pull 60 ft boom; 3 parts load tackle - 8 parts Hanger tackle - 54" Roller path Diesel engine driven - hoist & swinger 2800 lb	16,000	18,000.
Tugboat. 45' twin screw with 300 HP. GM-671 Engines	82,000	69,000.
Dredge Tender, 38' Twin screw, 200 SHP, GM-471 engines	27,000	34,300.
Tools, Machinery, Hull, Elec. & Mechanical spares	41,000	36,600.
	741,300	$452,400.

months, or *fixed* if convertible in more than six months. A person's opinion of the degree of convertibility of an asset is usually too optimistic—particularly at the price he expects.

Current assets include such items as cash, notes due, accounts receivable, inventories and prepaid expenses. *Fixed assets* are usually physical things, such as the dredge, pipelines, boats, buildings, machinery, and equipment used in the business. These are things not readily convertible into cash.

Some businesses require a higher capital investment in fixed assets than do others. For instance, a dredging company would certainly require more fixed assets than would a grocery store. However, in any business it is imperative that the fixed assets be as low as possible.

Current liabilities consist of short-term notes payable, accounts payable, and expenses payable. *Fixed liabilities* consist of mortgages and long-term notes.

The amount by which current assets exceed current liabilities is called *working capital*. Working capital keeps a business going, for no matter how much work there is, without money to pay salaries and expenses, the business will fail. A general rule is that working capital should equal current liabilities—that is, current assets should be at least twice current liabilities.

116. Profit and Loss Statement.   The profit and loss statement is a financial summary of the business for a certain period. It shows the total amount of business done, the income and the outgo, the profit or loss, and how it all occurred.

117. Failure or Success.   No one has derived a sure formula for success. Success is not just drive, energy, and lots of work—the world is full of broken businesses in this category. It is not a question of salesmanship, advertising, or luck. Most business successes occur through the combination of knowledge and skill in management.

The best indicators of a business's progress are its balance sheet and profit and loss statement. These can be used to determine the condition of a business by applying *ratio analysis* (42).

118. Ratio Analysis.   The most fundamental ratio in determining a business's condition is comparison of its current assets with its current liabilities. A general rule is that a business should have at least two dollars in current assets for each dollar in current liabilities. This is not always applicable, however. For instance, a seasonal business such as a lawnmower business with a normal 4 to 1 ratio might be down to 1 to 1 at the height of the season.

Although a 2 to 1 ratio is no guarantee of soundness, it is not a bad idea to have at least that much. Ratios of less than this are generally indicative of possible trouble.

A. LIABILITIES TO NET WORTH.   This ratio is one of the best indicators of top-heavy liabilities. Some analysts feel that a ratio of 0.75 or more is too high. When the ratio rises above this, liabilities should be reduced. There are only three ways to reduce liabilities: (1) invest more capital—not always available, (2) liquidate assets—not always practical, and (3) build up capital from earnings—cannot be done immediately.

B. NET PROFIT TO NET WORTH. A dredging contractor bought a dredge for $400,000 and within a year made a gross profit of $800,000. A 100 per cent profit in one year was pretty good! He took the $400,000 and bought another dredge. The next year he didn't get one job. He went broke. This is not a unique situation. The first year his net profit to net worth ratio was 1 to 1, which was good, but the second year he overextended his so-called net worth but made no profit. A profit must be made, and if one cannot earn at least seven per cent on his capital investment before taxes, he should get out of the dredging business. He could invest the capital in blue chip stocks or bonds and make nearly as much with practically no risk.

C. FIXED ASSETS TO NET WORTH. When jobs are plentiful and prices high, the general tendency is to get all the work possible. This brings on an urgency to buy more equipment so that these jobs can be done. The cycle frequently leads to extremes and money is often borrowed at overly-high interest rates. Then comes a slowdown and prices fall. Many a dredging contractor knows the answer to this. Money borrowed to buy fixed assets becomes a mortgage on future earnings—because bills cannot be paid with pipe or barges. If fixed assets exceed 75 per cent of net worth, there may be trouble ahead.

119. Average Collection Period. Doing a large volume of work for someone who does not pay is worse than doing a smaller volume with prompt payment. One thousand dollars overdue for six months costs $35.00 at today's rates. In other words, every month a customer delays payment he is automatically granting himself a 0.6 per cent discount.

PERSONNEL

120. Introduction. A dredge operation is not just a machine doing some work, such as a dragline or a scraper. It is a complete construction organization. The management, control and operation of the plant requires a comprehensive complement of personnel. On very small dredges the crew may consist of only one or two men. On somewhat larger dredges (eight to 10 inches, for instance) there may be as many as 15 to 20 men. Larger dredges may have from 50 to 100. These complements do not include special crews, such as shoreline gangs and dump crews.

121. Job Classifications. Dredge personnel are organized in categories depending upon their skills and positions. First there is the management, as in any other construction organization. Large dredging companies often have a chairman of the board, a board of directors, a president, and several vice-presidents. On the other hand, smaller dredging companies may have only three or four men carrying out these functions. Some small dredging firms have one man doing it all!

A. GENERAL SUPERINTENDENT.   Following the management team is the *general superintendent*. He has the responsibility of the overall field operation of a fleet of one or more dredges. In the largest dredging companies the general superintendent might be responsible for the dredges in a certain area, such as the eastern United States, or a foreign operation. These men are usually classified as being in the category of management.

B. DREDGE SUPERINTENDENT.   Under the executives and general superintendents are the actual dredge operating personnel. Probably on top of this pyramid is the *dredge superintendent,* or *captain,* as he is often called. This man has the direct responsibility for the overall operation of an individual dredge plant. Through intermediary employees he controls every activity of the plant, from moving it to a job to seeing that a sufficient amount of coffee is available in the galley. Of all the men in the dredging operation, he is probably the most important. Depending upon his ability, coupled with cooperation from above, is the success of any job.

Although he may or may not spend all of his time on the dredge, he is responsible for the plant 24 hours a day. Some superintendents are so organized that they spend only a portion of their time on the dredge. Others, less capable, or with less capable personnel, need to spend more time on the dredge. Some spend all their time there— actually living on the dredge. This is not to say, however, that even the best of superintendents do not occasionally have to live on the dredge on some particularly difficult jobs.

C. CHIEF ENGINEER.   Probably the next in line of responsibility would be the *chief engineer*. Often the question of where the chief and the superintendent stand in line of responsibility is vehemently debated by both. But, be that as it may, the chief engineer's duties are quite well defined. He is also on duty 24 hours a day. He is responsible for all of the equipment and machinery of the plant in the same manner as the superintendent is for the overall operation of the plant.

The chief engineer not only has to be well informed mechanically, but he must be particularly adapted to operating under conditions not always conducive to ease of maintenance and repair. With responsibility for all equipment used in the plant he has to have an exceedingly wide knowledge and experience in practically all phases of physical engineering, from electricity to hydraulics. He cannot be a purely practical man, but neither can he be a purely theoretical one either. He should be a combination of both. If he must be more one than the other, he probably should be on the practical side.

Under the chief engineer may be ten to fifteen other men whom he must direct and supervise to keep the dredge running, or in condition to run. These are the assistant engineers, oilers, greasers, welders and other engine-room employees.

D. DECK CAPTAIN.   On some dredges an additional supervisory category is added—the deck captain. He is directly responsible for

Fig. 143 — Shift Schedule for Seven-day Week Operation

Employee	First Week							Second Week							Third Week							Fourth Week							Fifth Week						
	M	T	W	T	F	S	S	M	T	W	T	F	S	S	M	T	W	T	F	S	S	M	T	W	T	F	S	S	M	T	W	T	F	S	S
No. 1	1	1	1	1	1̲	1̲	—	—	2	2	2	2	2	2	2	—	3	3	3	3	3	3	3	—	—	—	—	—	—	1̲	1̲	1̲	—	—	—
No. 2	—	2	2	2	2	2	2	2	—	3	3	3	3	3	3	3	—	—	—	—	—	—	—	—	1̲	1̲	1̲	1̲	—	2	2	2	2	2	2
No. 3	2	—	3	3	3	3	3	3	3	—	—	—	—	1̲	—	—	1̲	1̲	1̲	1̲	1̲	—	2	2	2	2	2	2	2	—	3	3	3	3	3
No. 4	3	3	—	—	—	—	1̲	1̲	1̲	1̲	1̲	1̲	1̲	—	—	2	2	2	2	2	2	2	3	3	3	3	3	3	3	3	—	—	—	—	—

NOTE: 1 = 8 TO 4 SHIFT; 2 = 4 TO 12 SHIFT; 3 = 12 TO 8 SHIFT

UNDERLINED SHIFTS (2̲) = LEVERMAN WORKS OUTSIDE

DASHED DAYS (—) = DAY OFF

Fig. 143. Shift Schedule for Seven-day Week Operation.

the outside activities of the dredge—as contrasted to inside activities, such as the engine room or lever room. He directs the operations of the mates in conjunction with the needs of the leverman. On jobs where there is a deck captain, the leverman would have little or no responsibility for the outside operations. The deck captain is generally classified along with the superintendent and chief engineer as a company man, as distinguished from hourly employees, and as a result he is on call 24 hours a day.

E. LEVERMAN.   Next in line on the dredge personnel pyramid is the *leverman*. He is the actual physical operator of the dredge. As explained earlier, he no longer has to pull levers, but he does control the motions of the dredge and in reality is probably more closely associated with the actual production than any other person. A poor leverman can make a dredge lose money; a good one can contribute tremendously to its earning ability. A dredging company with poor levermen will probably eventually go broke, regardless of the abilities of all the other personnel. A company that can hire and keep good levermen has the best chance of making a profit.

The leverman's responsibilities somewhat resemble those of the superintendent in that while he is on duty, he is directly responsible for the general dredge operation. He is not concerned with the future, however, such as the need for spare parts, supplies and employee payrolls, as is the superintendent. His interests are to cause the dredge to produce the maximum amount of output possible during the time he is on duty.

Unlike the superintendent, chief engineer, and the deck captain, he usually works only a certain number of hours a week, and when not on duty he has no responsibilities. He is, however, at the top of the echelon of hourly-paid, or hourly-limited, personnel. Usually he works a 48-hour week. In the United States where laws require it, the sixth day is paid for at time-and-a-half. Where the operation is on a seven-day, 24-hour basis, the time is distributed so that he may work seven or more eight-hour days straight, and then get from one to two days off, depending upon the shift schedule set up. All other hourly employees usually work a similar schedule. Such scheduling requires that four persons be available for each hourly-paid activity, the fourth providing the leverage so that all can obtain time off. For instance, a shift schedule could be as shown in Fig. 143.

F. MATE.   Next in line of responsibility following the leverman is the *mate*. He is in some respects the leverman's assistant outside the lever room. He takes directions from the leverman, but is generally responsible for the supervision of the deckhands in setting anchors, adding or removing the floating line sections, replacing cutters, and working on the pump. Mates must be practical men and have an intimate knowledge of the dredge and its operation. Although not as important productionwise as the leverman, the mate can be responsible for increasing production time of the dredge by his ability to complete his various tasks quickly.

G. DECKHAND. Deckhands help the mates get their work done. They work throughout the plant, not just on the dredge itself. They must be relatively able and many a superintendent has risen from their ranks.

H. MISCELLANEOUS. On large jobs where a considerable amount of shore work is required, particularly where numerous pipelines must be laid, another classification called the *dump foreman* is added. The dump foreman has as his responsibility all shore-based activities. Among them are the supervision of the pipe-laying crews, levee maintenance, the adding of discharge pipe at the spoil-disposal areas, and the supervision of clearing crews. His work is usually on an eight-hour basis but he is required to plan his work so that when he is off, operations will continue until he returns. Often he is required to work considerable amounts of overtime, so in many companies he is paid on a monthly basis to avoid overtime pay.

There are also *boat operators* for the dredge tenders. They work in shifts as do other hourly-paid employees. A tender operator must have dredge experience, not just tug or towboat experience, and it takes considerable time to obtain it. Most tender operators graduated from deckhand positions on the tenders.

There are a number of other employees connected with the dredge's successful operation. Where meals are served, there are usually one or more cooks, and depending upon the size of the crew, one or more assistant cooks and dishwashers. Where sleeping accommodations are provided on the dredge, a *crumb boss* takes care of the janitorial work under the supervision of the chief cook or steward.

On some dredges there are men who do nothing but weld, carpenters who do nothing but wood repair and construction, and there is sometimes a blacksmith. There is usually a time keeper and/or office clerk who is responsible for the paper work of the dredge. However, often much of the paper work—and sometimes all of it—is done by the *civil engineer*.

I. CIVIL ENGINEER. As a considerable amount of detail is given throughout the book involving the work of the civil engineer, it will only be said here that he is in the unique position of having plenty to do.

Chapter 7

Instruments—Production Measurement—Reports

122. Introduction. In hydraulic terminology, feet of water, inches of mercury, and pounds per square inch are all used to describe the relative pressure or vacuum shown on the various gauges. At sea level the atmospheric pressure is considered as 34 feet of water, 30 inches of mercury, or 14.7 pounds per square inch. As one goes above sea level this pressure is reduced—at 1,000 feet elevation it is 14.2 pounds per square inch, and at 6,000 feet it is 11.8 pounds per square inch.

A cubic foot of fresh water at sea level weighs 62.4 pounds. A square-inch column of water one foot high would weigh $62.4/144 = 0.433$ pounds. A pressure of 14.7 pounds per square inch, therefore, equals approximately the weight of a 34-foot column of water one square inch in area or, inasmuch as mercury weighs about 13.6 times as much as water, a pressure of 14.7 pounds per square inch would equal approximately the same pressure as would a column of mercury 30 inches high.

Pressure in dredging is always referred to in pounds per square inch, or in feet of fresh water above atmospheric pressure. Vacuum, which is the amount of pressure below atmospheric, is measured by the number of inches of mercury. That is, 10.2 pounds per square inch in a closed system would be equivalent to 4.5 pounds per square inch of vacuum, or approximately 9.2 inches of mercury at sea level. A total vacuum—14.7 pounds per square inch below atmospheric— would equal 30 inches of mercury. For example, when a vacuum is said to be eight inches, it is meant that the pressure is 3.9 pounds per square inch below atmospheric pressure. These comparisons are determined by the following equalities,

$$\text{ft}_w = (2.31)\ (\text{psi}) = (1.133)\ (\text{in}_{hg}) \tag{41}$$

$$\text{psi} = (0.4331)\ (\text{ft}_w) = (0.4905)\ (\text{in}_{hg}) \tag{42}$$

$$\text{in}_{hg} = (0.8826)\ (\text{ft}_w) = (2.0388)\ (\text{psi}) \tag{43}$$

123. Vacuum and Pressure Gauges. Probably the most important of all instruments available to the leverman are the vacuum and pressure gauges. Located directly in front of him in the lever room (Fig. 64) they indicate the instantaneous vacuum and pressure of the pump.

The line to the vacuum gauge is connected to the pump's suction pipe as near the eye as practicable. The line to the pressure gauge is connected to the pump's discharge line on the pump side of the flap valve. In addition to connecting to the instantaneous gauges, these lines are often attached to recording instruments for vacuum and pressure. These recording instruments (Fig. 144) record the instantaneous

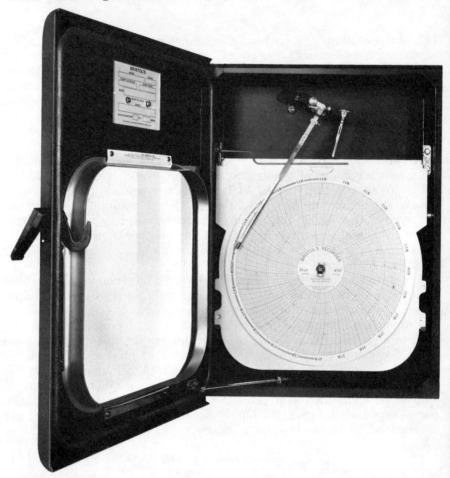

Fig. 144. Pressure Recorder. (Bristol Division of Acco)

values progressively over a 24-hour period. Although the leverman relies on the instantaneous gauges for his information, management uses the recording instrument data to review overall daily operation—and the activities of the leverman.

Bourdon-type gauges are usually used on dredges for vacuum and pressure measurements because of their ruggedness, reliability, and inherent accuracy. As previously noted, the gauges are connected to the pump by long, small-bore pipes or tubes which often clog. Large-diameter piping is used occasionally to overcome the clogging, but it reduces accuracy as some of the indication will then be kinetic head. One solution to clogging is to eliminate the long pipe and install the movement of the Bourdon tube near the pump where it can actuate a potentiometer which will transmit the information electrically to the point of use.

Purging systems, however, are usually more common. Figure 145 shows the schematic of such a system. A check valve installed near the point of contact with the pipeline prevents regular flow of material up the line to the gauge, but opens at the slight pressure of flow from the gauge toward the pipe when purging. It is usually installed at an angle to decrease the differential pressure required to open it.

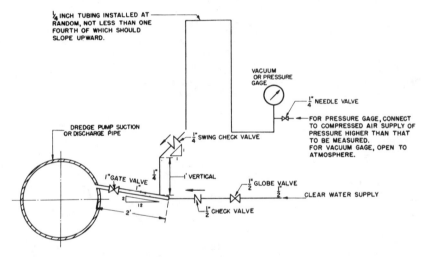

Fig. 145. Gauge Purging System. (Corps of Engineers)

A connection to a clear water supply through another check valve effects a continuous cleaning of the gauge line. Often a small amount of air is introduced continuously near the gauge. This forces out any dredged mixture that may have entered the line during rapid changes in pressure. The water and air pressures are regulated by a globe and needle valve and do not appreciably affect the gauge reading (15).

Vacuum and pressure applied to the recording instruments are recorded on circular charts which are marked by a pen scratching a fine line on the smoked surface of the chart, or tracing a fine line of ink on a *white chart* (Fig. 146). The *smoked charts* are far more practical, one reason being that the ink of the other type is messy, dries slowly, and tends to smear. After being dipped into a special solution, the smoked chart is permanentized and does not fade. Furthermore, any notes or comments written on the chart before dipping will also be permanentized.

Some of the important information obtainable from charts, but lost in the instantaneous readings of the gauges are: time and duration of dredge shutdown (no vacuum or pressure), time and duration of dredge operation (vacuum and pressure indication), relative effectiveness of the operation and operator (high and continuous, or low and jerky, vacuum and pressure), and trouble in the suction (erratic vacuum or pressure).

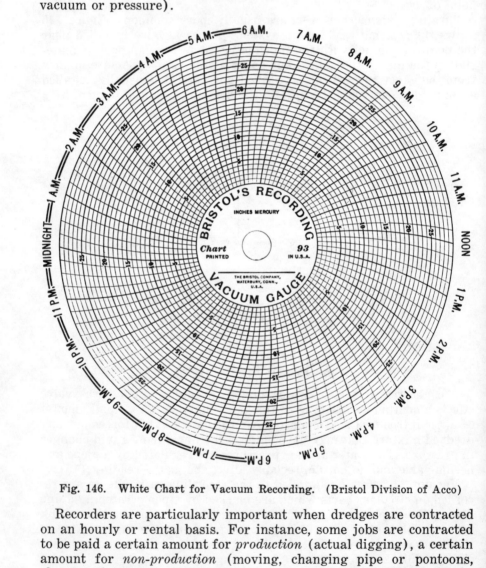

Fig. 146. White Chart for Vacuum Recording. (Bristol Division of Acco)

Recorders are particularly important when dredges are contracted on an hourly or rental basis. For instance, some jobs are contracted to be paid a certain amount for *production* (actual digging), a certain amount for *non-production* (moving, changing pipe or pontoons, cleaning the pump), and a certain amount, or nothing, for *shutdown* (repairs, breakdowns). The charts which are marked in five-minute intervals provide an accurate record of shutdowns and are generally irrefutable if a difference of opinion arises. They are a necessity, not a luxury.

These instruments indicate and record information about conditions at the point of contact with the pipeline. As they are mounted in the lever room, they are usually at a considerable height above the point of measurement. Consequently, they must be adjusted for elevation. Should the pressure gauge be located 20 feet above the top of the discharge line, the gauge must be set to read approximately 8.6 pounds per square inch when the pump is not operating, as the column of water must be lifted 20 feet before the gauge will start indicating.

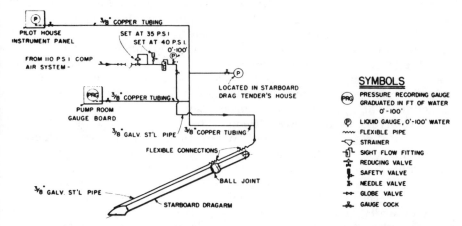

Fig. 147. Dredging Depth Indicating System. (Corps of Engineers)

124. Other Instruments. Other instruments used by the leverman are the cutter- and swing-motor ammeters (Fig. 64). When the dredge is operating and the cutter is digging into the bank, the current drawn by the cutter motor is an indication of the torque required. By watching the ammeter the leverman gets an indication of how hard the material is and how much torque he can apply before the motor reaches its design rating, or the 150-per cent load point. The same indications are obtained from the swing-motor ammeter. A cutter-speed indicator is often included as a supplement to the ammeter.

The simplest method of indicating dredging depth is a calibrated board attached to the A- or H-frame facing the lever room. A wire attached to the ladder pulls a pointer up and down on the board indicating the depth of cutter. This is quite a simple arrangement but it is accurate and relatively trouble-free.

A more modern dredging-depth indicator is based upon the change in pressure as water depth increases (Fig. 147). In this system a $\frac{1}{2}$- to $\frac{3}{8}$-inch diameter pipe is fastened to the ladder, the lower end near the cutter. It is connected to a hose at the trunnions for flexibility. At the other end, the hose is connected to another length of pipe which goes to a gauge in the lever room, engine room, or wherever a depth indication is needed. At the upper end of the pipe, low pressure air is introduced and so regulated that the water pressure is just balanced with a small amount of air seeping from the lower end. On each job the gauge is calibrated for the actual depth (15).

A pump-speed indicator, and often a speed recorder is sometimes installed in the lever room. The indicator gives instantaneous pump speed data. A recorder makes a record of what has occurred throughout a period.

Often a fathometer is used to show the depth of water behind the cutter, at the center of the dredge, or at the stern. More refined and expensive electronic equipment is available—as an example, see the profiler of Honeywell Company described in Art. 79.

Other instruments sometimes used to supplement the basic ones are the density and velocity meters (Art. 128), and the so-called echo boxes which transmit sounds of rocks and gravel bumping along the pipeline. Some dredgemen believe these latter ones can tell them the amount, or at least the type, of production.

125. Controls in the Lever Room. The main controls in the lever room are those for the winches. Where there is a five-drum winch—one drum for the ladder, and one for each spud and swing wire—a separate control is provided for applying the clutch and brake of each drum (Fig. 64). Air is almost universally used now to power these controls rather than the long-handled levers of earlier times.

Also available to the leverman are controls to vary the speed of the cutter and swing motors. These controls are usually rheostats which change the voltage across the motor field of adjustable-voltage systems. Should the cutter motor use step-control, the actuator might be a contactor for throwing resistances into the field.

126. The Hofer Valve. On the market for a number of years is a patented device called the Hofer Automatic Relief Valve, named for its inventor, A. L. Hofer (80). It was developed to eliminate suction-slugging caused by caving banks, sudden changes of material, or pockets of gas.

Its basic part is a suction-relief valve located on top of the suction line below the water surface (Fig. 148). The valve opens automatically whenever there is a drop of the pump discharge pressure below a predetermined value. When triggered by an abnormal pumping condition, the valve will remain open, admitting water in an amount required to maintain velocity. When the abnormal condition no longer exists, the valve closes slowly at a rate depending upon the recovery characteristics of the pump.

The valve is said to have a regulating effect on the pump engine by maintaining a more constant load on the pump. On diesel engines the exhaust temperatures are reported to remain more constant due to the better load regulation.

127. Gas Ejectors. Dredges operating in areas where decayed vege-
tation or other substances of gaseous nature have been buried for
years, or where natural gas is trapped, often have pumping difficulty
when the gases are released by the cutter and rise into the suction.

A combination of gas and material produces about the same effect
as does choking the suction with too much material—a reduction in

United States Patent No. 2,572,263 Claim: No. 14

In the combination, on a dredge, of a pump, a suction pipe leading from below
water to the intake of the pump, and a discharge pipe extending from the outlet of the
pump; a relief valve system comprising a relief valve connected in communication
with the suction pipe, said relief valve being arranged, when open, to deliver water
into the suction pipe above its lower end, selfacting mechanical means connected to
and tending to open the relief valve, and releasable power means resisting said
mechanical means and normally holding the relief valve closed; said power means
automatically releasable in response to abnormal pumping pressure in at least one
of the pipes.

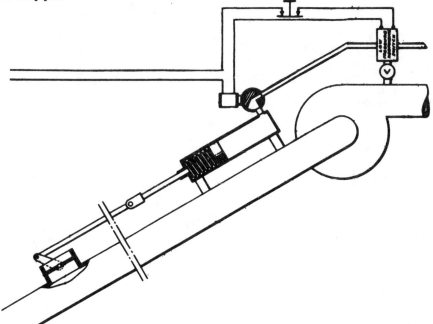

Fig. 148.   The Hofer Valve System.   (Mrs. D. L. Hofer)

volume occurs and there is a resulting drop in vacuum. When gas is
drawn into the suction it expands and takes up space normally occu-
pied by the mixture. If allowed to continue on into the pump it will
collect at the top and eventually will force out enough water to cause
the pump to lose its prime.

For a long time most dredgemen did not realize that gas was causing the reduction of output. However, once the problem was recognized it was obvious to most that the bubbles breaking the surface

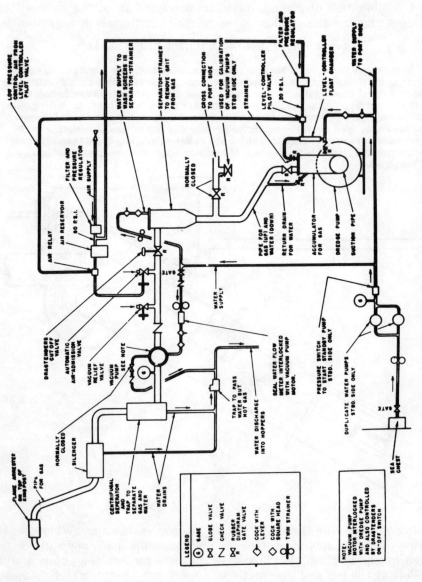

Fig. 149. Gas Ejection System. (Corps of Engineers)

214

(in extremely heavy-gas areas) were not just trapped air. In fact, the smell was often so bad it is a wonder why anyone could not help but suspect gas.

It is reported that the Corps of Engineers were the first to develop practical gas-ejecting equipment. Now there are many forms of gas ejectors. They differ generally in configuration and as to how they utilize the equipment and power available on the dredge. They are, of course, all automatic, and have instrumentation to give an indication of their performance while operating.

Some of the systems are operated by vacuum pumps, others by steam or water ejectors (15). Vacuum pump systems have high initial cost because of the vacuum pump. Operating costs are low, however, being around $0.10 to $0.20 an hour. Steam ejectors can be used where adequate boiler capacity and feedwater storage supply is available. Costs for their operation are about four times those of the vacuum-pump systems. Water-ejector systems are justifiable only when sufficient water pumping capacity is available. Costs are about the same as those of steam ejectors. From 650 to 700 gallons per minute of water at around 120 pounds per square inch per 100 square inches of suction pipe area are required. The water requirement for the vacuum-pump systems is about 50 gallons per minute for each 100 square inches of suction pipe area. Steam ejectors require a minimum of 250 pounds per square inch for 250 pounds of steam per hour for each 100 square inches of suction pipe area. A 50 per cent reduction in pressure (125 psi) would require about 20 per cent more steam (15).

The fundamental premise in the design of all ejection systems is that gases flow near the top of the suction pipe. Consequently, an accumulator is connected to the highest point in the suction line, this usually being near the pump suction (Fig. 149). The accumulator is usually a cylindrical iron tank $\frac{2}{3}$ to $\frac{3}{4}$ the diameter of the suction pipe and from four to six feet high. From it a gas-escape pipe extends upward to what is generally called a separator-strainer. From the separator-strainer the escape pipe continues to a vacuum pump or to a steam ejector.

The output of the vacuum pump is connected to another separator which discharges the gas into an overboard exhaust. Usually a flame arrestor is attached to the end of the exhaust pipe.

As the entrained gas flows along the top of the suction pipe it enters the accumulator which is at a higher vacuum (lower pressure) than the suction. Spoil and water also flow in, but there is a float level controller interconnected with the accumulator which allows only a certain amount of the mixture to enter. The gas rises through the mixture in the accumulator and flows into the separator-strainer where a constant supply of clear water flushes out any sand or other material that may have gotten that far. The gas continues through the vacuum pump and into the centrifugal-separator where any water is filtered out. The gas is then discharged through the exhaust. Some systems have a silencer installed between the centrifugal-separator and the exhaust to eliminate some of the noise.

A more simplified gas ejection system is sometimes still used on older dredges. It has an economical first cost, but it is subject to wear and has a high steam consumption. It is merely a pipe connected from the top of the suction line to a simple steam ejector (Fig. 150). The

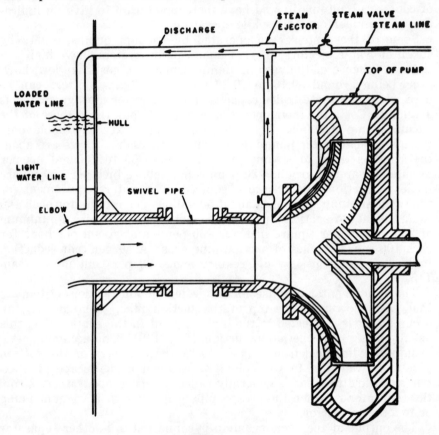

Fig. 150.   Simplified Gas Ejection System.   (Corps of Engineers)

gas is discharged through a pipe several feet below the water-line (15).

Gas removal has not only a balancing effect on the pump suction and discharge, but it has made dredging possible where it was previously impossible to get any reasonable production. Depending upon the amount of gas encountered, gas removal systems often increase production 100 per cent or more.

128. Production.   A dredge's relative instantaneous production can only be approximated from readings of the vacuum and pressure gauges. The highest rate of excavation will be obtained when vacuum and pressure are simultaneously held at their highest steady values. This is due to the fact that maximum steady pressure and vacuum indicate that maximum resistance is being created by the flow of excavated material (60).

Changes or variations in either of these two values (from a steady reading) indicate variance from maximum production. For instance, if the cutter is swung into the bank too rapidly, far more material may be taken into the suction than can be absorbed by the pump. Such a condition will first be indicated by a rapid rise in vacuum— indicating an increased material flow. However, as the material flow increases, the excess material will begin to block the suction and this will begin to limit the normal flow of water. This limits the flow of the mixture to the pump, which, in this example, is assumed to be discharging at its maximum. Consequently, with reduced flow the discharge pressure will begin to fall, indicating that the suction is becoming blocked.

If such a condition is allowed to continue, the suction will become completely choked. This can be prevented, however, by slowing down or stopping the swing and allowing the suction to clear itself, or by raising the ladder, thereby pulling the cutter out of the material and allowing more water to enter the suction. (*See* Art. 126 for another solution.)

A. SUCTION CONSIDERATIONS. The higher the vacuum gauge reading when pumping water, the less vacuum will be available for pumping material. When dredging material, vacuum may vary between 17 and 24 inches. As five to eight inches of vacuum is generally needed to pump water, the additional 12 to 16 inches is available to overcome the weight of the dredged material. The greater the difference between vacuum readings when pumping water and pumping material, the better production can be. If a vacuum of more than 12 inches is required to pump water at normal dredging depths, entrance or pipe losses may be excessive. However, a too-low water vacuum may indicate wear in the pump or leakage in the suction.

B. DISCHARGE CONSIDERATIONS. Changes in the pump's discharge pressure may also indicate abnormal conditions. For instance, a rise in pressure can indicate the discharge is clogging. If the discharge velocity is allowed to fall below that required to keep the dredged material in suspension, the spoil will start to slow down and fall to the bottom of the discharge pipe. If the velocity is allowed to remain low, the material will eventually fill and choke the line. Choking will cause a rise in the discharge pressure, and it will usually be accompanied by a fall in vacuum, inasmuch as not all the mixture in the pump is being discharged. As no more material can be sucked in, the suction pressure drops.

The falling vacuum will be followed by a lower than normal discharge pressure, again indicating that the flow is being further reduced. In such instances action must be taken quickly, for a pipeline can fill from end to end almost instantly. The best action is to stop the swing, raise the ladder, and pump water until the line is cleared (60).

C. OUTPUT MEASUREMENT. As was pointed out earlier, no practical method exists to date for accurately determining instantaneous or continuous output of a dredge. The main difficulty is in producing a measuring device that can effectively measure instantaneous output.

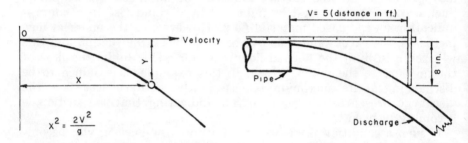

Fig. 151. Trajectory Measurement of Velocity.

This difficulty is attributable to the mixtures being handled. The percentage-mixture of spoil and water flowing in a pipeline changes from second to second as does its weight. Even the consistency of each cross section in the line at any one instant is different, being generally greater at the bottom of the pipe.

Today, to determine daily or continuous output, dredge contractors usually rely upon before-and-after hydrographic surveys. Unfortunately, data obtained in this manner are usually days, and sometimes weeks, behind. Where single dredging operations continue for months and years, the need for instantaneous information may not be so critical, but for the short job where quick results are needed, a more rapid method is desirable.

D. VELOCITY MEASUREMENT. Some of the tests used today to measure velocity are, (1) injecting salt solutions, (2) measuring the flow trajectory at the discharge, (3) coloring the water, and (4) using floating balls. Two of these tests which are more or less standard are, (1) the salt solution test, and (2) the trajectory test.

1. *Salt Solution Test.* In making a salt solution test, a concentrated brine solution is injected into the suction or discharge line and the time of its travel between a pair of electrodes located a short distance apart in the discharge line is measured. If an indicating ammeter is used and measurements are made between the beginning of each deflection, the velocity determined will be higher than the true velocity, because of the dispersion of the brine in the line. More accurate data can be obtained by using recording ammeters with which the time of passage of the center of the mass of the brine can

be more easily determined. When dredging in salt water this method is obviously impractical.

2. *Trajectory Test.* The trajectory method of measuring velocity is based upon the premise that a jet of water flowing from a horizontal pipe will fall with the acceleration of gravity, its trajectory forming part of a parabola. Figure 151 shows this fundamental law plotted as a curve and as the discharge from a pipe.

The test is made as follows. A straight stick with a downturned leg is laid along the upper edge of the discharge pipe. The length of the downturned leg is eight inches below the bottom of the straight stick. When the end of the downturned leg just touches the top of the discharge trajectory the horizontal distance between the point of the leg's contact with the water and the end of the discharge pipe is one-fifth of the velocity of the top of the stream, in feet per second. The average velocity of the stream is less, depending upon the percentage consistency of the solids. It is probably somewhere between 80 and 90 per cent of the measured velocity.

3. *Newer Methods of Measurement.* Studies and experiments are constantly being made to determine new techniques for measuring velocity, quantity, and other parameters, through the use of pneumatic, electronic, and radio-active systems. This work has been carried on in the United States almost exclusively by the Corps of Engineers.

One scheme is the *percent-solids meter.* The percentage of solids is measured by gauging the differential pressure between two identical lengths of pipeline with different gradients. Because the average friction loss of the two sections is equal, the difference between the pressure drops will be a function of the fluid density. This system has promise but to date not much work has been done on it (45).

Differential-pressure instruments for measurement of velocity and density have been tried on government dredges (45). A liquid-filled ring in the instrument responds to a differential pressure sensed at two separated points in the discharge line. This information is transmitted mechanically to a recording pen that marks a linear record of velocity. Another ring responds to a differential pressure created by density at two points a known distance apart in elevation on a rising section of pipe. This installation appears to have possibilities of being fairly successful and it has succeeded in demonstrating the feasibility of differential pressure metering. However, the meters respond to the rolling and pitching motions of the dredge and the display of the information is not available to the leverman who needs the information.

Electric systems are now under study and experimentation. Velocity is being measured by a magnetic flowmeter. The system operates on the principle that a fluid is a conductor, and if it moves through a magnetic field it will induce a voltage proportional to its velocity.

Density measurement experiments are being made with radioactive

DAILY REPORT

Dredge   *At*_____

*For 24 Hours Ending Noon*_____*19*

CREW EMPLOYED

___	Supt.	___	Asst. Engr.	___	Tug Oper.	___	Welder
___	Asst. Supt.	___	Levermen	___	Tug D'kh'ds	___	Carpenters
___	Civil Engr.	___	Mates	___	Deckhands	___	Helpers
___	Clerk	___	Oilers	___	Foremen	___	Tract'r Oper.
___	Captain	___	Firemen	___	Shoremen	___	
___	Chief Engr.	___	Commissary	___	Blacksmiths	___	

MATERIAL_____

Length of Pipe Line_____ { No. Land Pipes_____
                             { No. Pont. Pipes_____ { Floating_____
                                                       { Submarine_____

Height of Discharge_____ Aver. R. P. M. Pump_____

Average Boiler Pressure_____ Runner Diameter_____

Average Pump Pressure_____ Average Pump Suction_____

Turbine Ring Pressure_____.____ Number of Nozzles_____

Fuel Consumption (Bbls.)_____ Condenser Vacuum_____

Style of Cutter_____ Style of Blades_____

STATIONS_____

Number Feet Moved Forward_____

Average Width of Cut_____

Average Depth of Cut_____

Elevation Bottom of Cut_____

Number Yards Excavated_____

Total Yards for Month_____

Total Yards for Contract_____

Engine Hours for Day_____ Total Hours for Month_____

Yds. Per Eng. Hr. for Day_____ Yds. Per Eng. Hr. for Mo._____

Time and Cause of Each Delay: Hrs.   Min.

_____ | | |

_____ | | |

_____ | | |

LOST TIME

MACHINERY		SHORE LINE		SWING WIRE ANCHORS		FLOAT LINE		MIS-CELLANEOUS		TOTAL	
HRS.	MIN.	HRS.	MIN.	HRS.	MIN.	HRS.	MIN.	HRS.	MIN.	HRS.	MIN.

Fig. 152. Typical Daily Report.

220

sources (43, 44, 45). It is known that some of the energy of a gamma ray passed through a mixture will be absorbed, the quantity being a function of the mixture's density. Consequently, as concentration of the flow increases, less energy reaches the detector. The proportion lost will be an indication of the density. However, the electrical circuitry of these systems is extremely complex and far beyond the repair, or even maintenance abilities of dredge personnel. The response of the system to density changes is slow, space requirements are large, and providing safety from the radio-active source is a problem.

129. Daily Reports. Records of the daily dredging progress on every job are probably as important as are any of the other records prepared on the job. Not only do they give a daily picture of the progress, but they provide data for future estimating purposes. Figure 152 shows a representative daily report. This report, in conjunction with the engine-room log, the vacuum and pressure charts, and periodic reports of the dredge superintendent will give management a clear picture of the daily progress. Note that in Fig. 152 only a small amount of space was provided for indicating the actual causes of delays. This was because of space limitations. In the actual report, sufficient space should be available to list all reasons for delay.

Chapter 8

Pump Mechanics

130. Introduction. The pump is the heart of the dredge. Other components are highly important, individually as well as collectively, but all must work in close conjunction with the operation of the pump.

Dredge pumps are centrifugal. The word centrifugal is used to describe a force which causes a body traveling in a circular direction around a center to fly away from that center. However, the word is actually loosely used, for the force operating on the body is a tangential force. For instance, take a small weight and tie a string around it. Now swing it in a circle. The string is in tension and acts on the weight, tending to pull it in. This tension force is often referred to as a *centripetal force*. It is supposed that the weight reacts with an equal and opposite force, called *centrifugal* force—an outward force. However, if the string were suddenly cut, the weight would not go outward, but tangentially in the direction it was going when the string was cut. Nevertheless, the word centrifugal is generally used.

The nomenclature used to classify the various types of centrifugal pumps is preponderant. The dredge centrifugal pump has a classification as follows: it is a *volute, single stage, single suction, has a closed, single-curvature, non-clogging, overhung, radial, curved-vane runner, and a horizontal, split or solid casing.*

A *volute*, or spiral, pump is named after the shape of its casing which is a logarithmic spiral ($R = R_1 \epsilon^{\theta \tan \alpha}$), derived by the French scientist, Blaise Pascal. This spiral has a constant angle α between the radius and the tangent to the spiral. The equiangular shape provides for an equal velocity flow around the circumference, but at the same time the velocity is converted into pressure and is gradually reduced as it flows to the discharge.

A *closed runner*, in contrast to an open one, has *shrouds* or sides that totally enclose the vanes. This creates closed channels from the eye of the pump to the periphery of the runner.

A *straight*, or *single-curvature*, runner has its vanes curved backwards, opposite to the direction of rotation. This is in contrast to the double-curvature types which have their vanes curved in two directions much like a ship's propeller.

Non-clogging runners have few vanes so that there will be larger areas for material passage. Five vanes are about the maximum number used in dredge pumps, and this many are only used for very fine and soft materials.

A runner is *overhung* when it is supported by a shaft on one side only.

131. Pump Liners. If the pump casing were not protected it would soon wear out from abrasion by the materials going through it. To obtain this protection, replaceable *wearing rings* and *liners* are placed inside the pump casing to take the wear. These are set to close tolerances or running joints with the shrouds of the runner. In addition to protecting the pump casing, they create a seal between the low-pressure suction and the high-pressure discharge.

Some pumps have the back liner omitted. In such pumps, axial thrust generated by the runner and shaft is greater, because more open surface is exposed. The back liner should consequently seldom be excluded. *Throat liners* are also placed at the eye of the pump to protect the entrance. These have no effect on thrust, however.

132. Parts of the Pump. Figures 153 and 154 show various parts of a dredge pump. Inspecting the pump for wear, dismantling it for replacement of the runner or liners, or reassembling it requires a certain sequence which is generally as follows.

The suction-pipe section between the stone box and the pump mouthpiece is first loosened by removing the bolts from both flanges. The *suction mouthpiece* is next removed. This exposes the suction *throat piece* which is located between the runner eye and the suction. The throat piece seals the discharge from the suction. For maximum efficiency it should be kept in good condition, and should always be replaced or built up by welding when worn. (*See* Art. 136.)

At this point a check can be made to determine the effectiveness of the seal of the throat piece. The clearance should be as small as possible, usually about 0.130 inches or less on a new liner piece. This seal can often be checked without removing the mouth piece, by reaching through the stone box cover. On large dredges a man can crawl into the pump itself to check the clearances.

The pump front head (the suction side) is next removed. It is fastened to the casing by bolts spaced around its periphery, and has to be removed to change the runner. The runner can be taken out after the removal of the front head by supporting it with a chain hoist and unscrewing it. This is done by first blocking it and then turning its shaft over very slowly with the main engine, or jacking it around manually. Most runners are now threaded—such as an ACME 29° thread with single or double lead. The *back liner* will be exposed when the runner is removed and it too can be taken out.

A soft metal washer is usually installed between the hub of the runner and the protruding sleeve of the shaft to allow for horizontal positioning. This insures proper clearance between the side heads. In older pumps the front and back liners were usually bolted to the head with countersunk bolts. This has been discontinued because wear

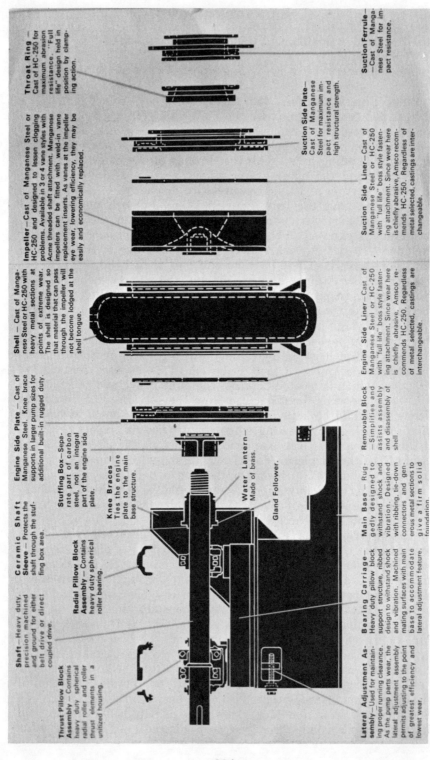

Throat Ring — Cast of HC-250 for maximum abrasion resistance. "Full life" design held in position by clamping action.

Impeller — Cast of Manganese Steel or HC-250 and designed to lessen clogging problems. Available in 3 or 4 vane styles with Acme threaded shaft attachment. Manganese impellers can be fitted with weld-in vane replacement inserts. As vanes at the impeller eye wear, lowering efficiency, they may be easily and economically replaced.

Shell — Cast of Manganese Steel or HC-250 with heavy metal sections at points of extreme wear. The shell is designed so that material that can pass through the impeller will not become lodged at the shell tongue.

Engine Side Plate — Cast of Manganese Steel. Knee brace supports in larger pump sizes for additional built-in rugged duty.

Ceramic Shaft Sleeve — Protects the shaft through the stuffing box area.

Stuffing Box — Separate part of carbon steel, not an integral part of the engine side plate.

Knee Braces — Ties the engine plate to the main base structure.

Water Lantern — Made of brass.

Gland Follower.

Removable Block — Simplifies and assists assembly and disassembly of shell.

Main Base — Ruggedly designed to withstand shock and vibration. Designed with ribbing, tie-down connectors and generous metal sections to give a firm solid foundation.

Bearing Carriage — Heavy duty pillow block support structure, ribbed design to withstand shock and vibration. Machined mating surfaces with main base to accommodate lateral adjustment feature.

Lateral Adjustment Assembly — Used for maintaining proper running clearance. As the pump parts wear, the lateral adjustment assembly permits adjusting to the point of greatest efficiency and lowest wear.

Shaft — Heavy duty precision machined and ground for either belt drive or direct coupled drive.

Thrust Pillow Block Assembly — Contains heavy duty spherical radial roller and roller thrust elements in a unitized housing.

Radial Pillow Block Assembly — Contains heavy duty spherical roller bearing.

Suction Side Plate — Cast of Manganese Steel for maximum impact resistance and high structural strength.

Suction Side Liner — Cast of Manganese Steel or HC-250 with "full life" boss style fastening attachment. Since wear here is chiefly abrasive, Amsco recommends HC-250. Regardless of metal selected, castings are interchangeable.

Engine Side Liner — Cast of Manganese Steel or HC-250 with "full life" boss style fastening attachment. Since wear here is chiefly abrasive, Amsco recommends HC-250. Regardless of metal selected, castings are interchangeable.

Suction Ferrule — Cast of Manganese Steel for impact resistance.

Fig. 153. Exploded View of Dredge Pump. (Abex Corp.—AMSCO Division)

from eddies around these bolts loosened them. Practically all liners are now made with inserts on their backs into which bolts from the outside can be screwed.

Pump liners are made from hard irons or steels with a hardness rating as much as Brinell 600. Soft materials such as mud or silt do not require hard irons or steels, but abrasion resistance is required

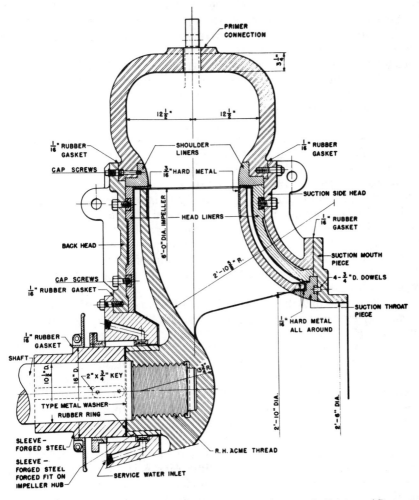

Fig. 154. Sectional View of Dredge Pump Casing and Parts. (Corps of Engineers)

when abrasive materials are being dredged. Not only the liners but the casing and all parts of the pump which are subject to abrasion are usually made of such materials as International Nickel's *Ni-Hard,* or manganese steel. Parts not subjected to wear or shock are made of ordinary cast ingot or grey iron.

Manganese steel is used principally for high shock-resistant parts. The alloy was discovered by Sir Robert Hadfield in England. It is non-magnetic, very ductile, highly resistant to shock, and becomes harder when cold worked. It is easily welded.

Most manganese is composed of 0.8 to 1.2 per cent carbon with 12 per cent manganese. If the amount of manganese in the steel is low, say around 1.5 per cent, the steel will be very brittle. As the percentage of manganese is increased up to about five per cent, so does the brittleness, and it can be pulverised by a common hammer. Increasing the manganese content further however, causes the steel to become ductile and very hard, being hardest at 12 per cent manganese. The annealed manganese steel has a tensile strength of around 90,000 pounds per square inch and an elastic limit of about 60,000 pounds per square inch.

Ni-Hard, a trade-name of International Nickel Company, is a nickel-chromium white cast iron with a Brinell hardness of from 550 to 750, and a Rockwell C of around 55. It can be obtained in four progressive compositions, each of which possesses an increasingly greater strength and impact resistance. *Ni-Hard* No. 4 has a total of 2.8 to 3.6 per cent carbon, 0.40 to 0.70 manganese, and 5.5 to 6.5 nickel. As the carbon is increased toward 3.6 per cent, the amount of carbide increases, resulting in a higher abrasion resistance, but at the same time giving a decrease in tensile strength. The tensile strength of *Ni-Hard* is between 75,000 and 85,000 pounds per square inch when sand cast, and 80,000 to 110,000 pounds per square inch when chill cast (46).

Ni-Hard has proven to be extremely wear-resistant and generally speaking, more so than manganese steel. Inasmuch as it is cheaper than manganese, it can prove an economic advantage for pumps when the shock is light or moderate. It is of course superior to unalloyed white cast irons in hardness, strength, and resistance to impact.

Some of the other names that are used for *Ni-Hard* are *ABK Metal* (American Brake Shoe Co.), *Flintmetal* (Morris Machine Works), and Gasite (Georgia Iron Works). It is, unfortunately, virtually unmachinable, and grinding is about the only method that can be used for finishing. Welding is not recommended either.

Hardness of irons and steels is not necessarily an indication of abrasion resistance. The controlling factor is microstructure (46). To attempt to determine some criterion for comparable wear resistance, the American Brake Shoe Company tested a number of irons and steels and compared their loss of weight to that of an arbitrary standard (SAE 1020, Brinell 105-110). The loss factors were published in the *American Society for Metals Handbook* for 1948. The loss in weight of the standard was assigned a factor of 1.00. The other irons and steels had the following factors: Ingot Iron, 1.4—it lost 1.4 times as much as the specimen under the same conditions. Grey cast iron had a factor of 1.00 to 1.5; white cast iron a factor of

0.9 to 1.00; austenite manganese steel a factor of 0.75 to 0.85; and *Ni-Hard* a factor of 0.25 to 0.60. In these tests it was indicated that *Ni-Hard* was superior to manganese in abrasion resistance.

133. Stuffing Box. The stuffing box provides a seal around the runner shaft where it enters the pump casing. It has a *lantern ring* which prevents outside air pressure from getting in when the pump is acting on a suction lift. Service water to the lantern ring is applied at a pressure greater than the head created by the pump, forming the seal. This pressure also prevents abrasive material from reaching the packing gland.

134. Thrust. The axial thrust of a single-suction runner is the result of two opposing forces (47). The smaller is due to the change in momentum of the mixture entering the runner. When it approaches the eye of the pump it has a velocity (V_o) parallel to the shaft and toward the back of the pump. The change in momentum is V_o (w/g). This tends to force the runner backward. The opposing force is caused by the discharge from the runner, as the pump's discharge is at a much higher pressure than it was when entering the suction. Therefore a force is created which tends to move the runner toward (V_o), or forward. Calculation of thrust is extremely difficult and should be left to the pump manfacturers. However, a good illustration of the magnitude of the thrust that can be experienced is given in Reference 47.

Runner thrust can be eliminated with radial ribs on the back shroud of the runner. These ribs reduce the pressure in the space between the runner and the casing. They do not increase the pump losses, for no more power is required to overcome the effects of the ribs than that lost through leakage under non-rib conditions. By reducing the clearance between the back shroud and the casing and increasing the clearance between the front shroud and the casing, the thrust can be reduced, or sometimes even reversed. On some dredge pumps the back shroud is made smaller in diameter than the front in an attempt to reduce thrust. The once-popular practice of drilling holes through the runner back shroud to reduce thrust is not as popular now as is the provision of a special channel arranged to connect the back chamber with the suction. Balance was lacking when holes were drilled and up to 25 per cent of the thrust remained, anyway.

135. Thrust Bearings. The load that can be carried by a thrust bearing varies with the velocity of the rubbing surfaces. A basic thrust bearing has projections or shoulders on its shaft which bear against the collars. Each collar takes a proportionate share of the thrust. Safe loads on these frictional type bearings vary from 60 pounds per square inch to 100 pounds per square inch.

A hydraulically-supported thrust bearing however, has low frictional resistance and is adapted to heavy pressures. These bearings are so designed that oil is forced between the collars and shoulders by a high pressure oil system, thereby supporting the load on a thin film of oil.

Professor Osborne Reynolds found that by rotating the journal, oil could be pulled between the collars and the shoulders. The oil kept them separated without high pressure. This adaption of the hydraulic bearing is known as the pivoted shoe bearing (20). At the low speeds of dredge pumps these bearings may be loaded to 100 pounds per square inch and more when heavy oil is used.

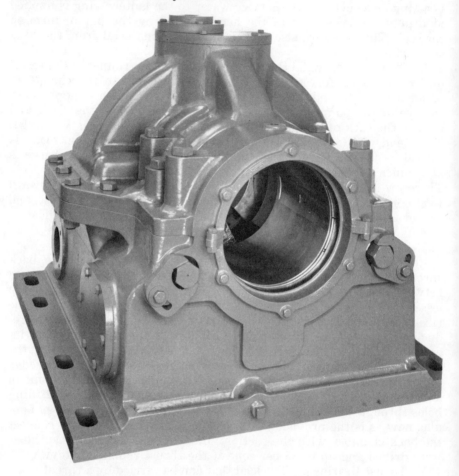

Fig. 155.   Thrust Bearing.   (The Union Diesel Engine Co.)

136. Welding and Hardfacing. Practically all dredge equipment wears, particularly the wetted parts of the pump system, such as the pump shell, pipeline, fittings, runners, and cutters.

When a pump is first delivered, many dredgemen make a contour template of the pump shell *plunge-distance.* Later on, when the pump has worn, these templates are used as patterns for rebuilding the shell (Fig. 156).

Expansion is a problem encountered when welding pump shells, due to the heat of welding. As the metal heats, it expands and then when it cools, it contracts. If not controlled it can cause serious pump-shell distortion. Jacks set around the inside circumference of the pump shell and crosswise between the side plates will help eliminate distortion. As welding progresses, continuous checks of the shell bore should be made to determine whether to loosen or tighten the jacks.

All build-up welding should run parallel to the flow. Where heavy pump wear has occurred, filler bars can be tacked on and then welded in. Bar spacing should be from 1.5 inches to two inches. The spaces

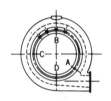
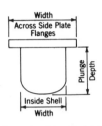

| Contour templates for the shell's plunge distance should be cut to the original dimensions of the shell. Contour templates will help determine the diameter of filler bar best suited to the size of the cavity to be filled. | The plunge depth measure of a pump shell progressively increases, starting at the area of point "A" around the shell to the discharge end in the area of point "D". Four contour templates are usually required. | Contour templates are generally homemade and cut from sheet metal. Time, and the expense of obtaining original dimensions, can be saved if these gauges are made before a new pump shell is put into service. |

Fig. 156.   Plunge Distance Template Detail.   (Abex Corp.—AMSCO Division)

between the bars should be built up just high enough to cover them with a smooth surface. *AMSCO Nicro Mang* is one good welding material for both these operations. Steels with a carbon content of much more than 0.3 may require special rods.

137. Building Up Runners.   Most of the wear on runners is on the leading edge of the vanes. If the leading edge of the vane is worn no more than $\frac{3}{16}$ of an inch the edge can be built up with *AMSCO X-53* electrodes, which will give a good hardface layer about $\frac{3}{16}$ of an inch with one pass. If the wear is greater, the edge can be built up to $\frac{3}{16}$ of an inch with *Nicro Mang* and then a layer of X-53 added.

Inasmuch as wear is generally uniform around the shaft, rebuilding when properly done should not affect the balance of the runner. Welding on the shrouds however, can easily unbalance the runner.

The inside of new elbows and many other fittings should be built up before being used. Cutter blades can be renewed with such rods as AMSCO manganese steel repointer bars followed by hard facing of the edges with X-53.

138. Cutting Down Runners and Vanes.   To increase the capacity of a pump at a given head, the trailing edges of the runner vanes are often cut down (Fig. 157). This increases the outlet angle and the tangential component of the velocity (48). Occasionally the efficiency is even increased.

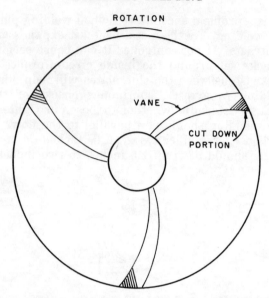

Fig. 157.   Cutting Down Runner Vanes.

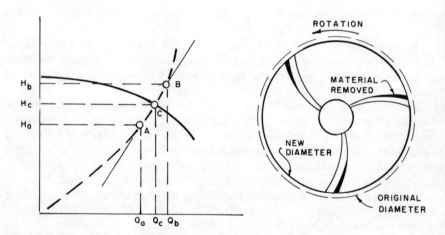

Fig. 158.   Reduction of Runner to Decrease Head.   (John Wiley & Sons, Inc.)

The diameter of the runner can also be reduced to decrease the head—sometimes up to 20 per cent. Characteristic curves can be helpful in determining how much to cut the runner. Reference 53 gives a method of determining the runner diameter required for a given head-capacity point. In Fig. 158 (l.) the point to be obtained is at (A). A point (B) is chosen which gives an output higher than at (A). The head at (B) is then calculated from $H_b = H_a (Q_b/Q_a)$.

Points (A) and (B) are connected by a straight line which intersects the characteristic curve (*see* Chapter 11 for discussion of characteristic curves) at (C_1). The required runner diameter ratio is then Q_a/Q_c. This ratio should be increased somewhat to compensate for the inaccuracies of the method. Trial and error will provide the best results.

It is usually desirable to also file down, or taper, the leading edges to reduce the disturbances caused by the newly blunted vane tips which were originally tapered. (*See* Fig. 158(r.) Before reducing the diameter, a pattern of the vane taper should be made so that the new taper can be made to conform as closely as possible to the original.

Chapter 9

Hydraulics

139. Introduction. A body floating in a liquid will displace its own weight of that liquid. If a dredge displaces a volume equal to, say, 10,000 tons of water, it will weigh that amount.

A liquid when contained exerts a force against its container. This force, stated in force per unit area, such as a square inch of surface, is called *pressure*. The usual measurement of this pressure is pounds per square inch (psi) in the British system, and grams per square centimeter (gcm²) in the metric system. Pressure can be expressed as $P = F/A$, or a force on a unit area.

If a column of water is contained in a vertical pipe it will exert a force at the bottom equal to the weight of the water. On a square inch of the bottom it will exert a pressure equal to the weight of a square-inch column of the water. For instance, in a 100-foot high pipe of fresh water the pressure on the bottom will be (100) (62.4/144) = 43.3 psi. In a body of salt water, such as a tide-water river, bay, or ocean, where the specific gravity (SG) of the water is greater than that of fresh water, at a depth of 100 feet the pressure will be (SG) (100) (62.4/144). Considering that the SG of the salt water is 1.032, the pressure will be (100) (64.4/144) = 44.7 psi.

When pumping salt water or a mixture of solids and salt water, the specific gravity and the density of the mixture are involved. The *density* of a mixture is its *mass per unit volume* ($D = M/V$), where mass is commonly referred to as its *weight*. It is usually expressed in pounds per cubic foot in the British system, and grams per cubic centimeter in the metric system. The *specific gravity* of a mixture is the ratio of the density of the mixture to the density of fresh water ($SG = D_m/D_w$). Thus, the specific gravity of a mixture weighing, say, 75 pounds per cubic foot (its density), would be $SG = 75/62.4 = 1.2$.

When a mixture is composed of water and some percentage of material, as the output of a dredge usually is, the *average specific gravity* of the mixture can be determined from

$$SG_a = (SG_m - SG_w)\, \frac{P}{100} + SG_w \qquad (44)$$

where SG_a = average specific gravity of the mixture, in terms of fresh water; SG_m = specific gravity of the *in situ* material, in terms of fresh water; SG_w = specific gravity of the water in the mixture, in

232

terms of fresh water, and P = percentage concentration of the solids, by volume.

As an example, assume a 10 per cent concentration of material weighing 120 pounds per cubic foot, and sea water with a specific gravity of 1.03. The specific gravity of the material would be 120/62.4 = 1.923. Then the average specific gravity of the mixture would be,

$$SG_a = (1.923 - 1.03)\frac{10}{100} + 1.03$$

$$= (0.893)(0.1) + 1.03$$

$$= 1.1193$$

Pressure in dredging is also referred to as *head*. When dredgemen use pressure they imply pounds per square inch above atmospheric pressure, but when they say *head* they are usually referring to the weight of so many feet of fresh water. Often it is not clear whether they mean fresh water, salt water, or a mixture of material and one or the other of the two waters! As will be brought out throughout this book, the distinction is quite important. In the preceding example, where the pressure was 43.3 psi, the equivalent head would be 100 feet—a column of fresh water 100 feet high. In the second example, where the pressure was 44.7 psi, the equivalent head would be 103.3 feet of fresh water, because of the increased weight of salt water. The following equation shows the comparison,

$$\text{Head, in feet} = H = h = \frac{(\text{psi})(2.31)}{SG} \tag{45}$$

where SG = specific gravity of the mixture, and 2.31 = equivalent feet of head per foot of fresh water. For instance, since a head of 100 feet of fresh water corresponds to a pressure of approximately 43.3 pounds per square inch, this head, if applied to the cross section of a 20-inch, I.D. pipe, would exert a force on the cross-sectional area of the pipe of approximately 13,600 pounds. If a mixture of water and material with a specific gravity of 1.3 was used instead, the pressure would be 56.3 psi, and the force would be 17,700 pounds.

140. **Flow in Pipelines.** In the dredge pump-pipe system, the fluid flow, whether it be fresh water or a mixture of water and material, will be *turbulent flow*. This is one of the two distinct types of flow that can occur in any piping system. The other, *laminar flow*, does not occur in dredge systems because of the high velocities. Turbulent flow is an irregular motion while laminar flow has a characteristic of viscous liquids. Where laminar flow has only one velocity—parallel to the flow—turbulent flow has three, one parallel to the main stream and two others which vary in their direction (49).

In laminar flow the pressure drop along the line is proportional to the velocity. That is, the drop in pressure with velocity is a straight line. As the velocity is increased there is a region where the pressure drop becomes unproportional. Then at some higher velocity the pressure drop again becomes proportional, but at a higher rate. This is the turbulent flow region, and the slope usually ranges between 1.7 and 2.0—that is, pressure increases at a rate of 1.7 to 2.0 times the rate of increase in velocity.

141. Pump Hydraulics. In a centrifugal pumping system, the pump does not lift anything. It acts as a device to assist the atmospheric pressure in pushing up the water, or the mixture of material and water. The pump assists the outside atmospheric pressure by removing some of the pressure within the suction. This then creates a lower pressure in the suction than on the outside. The outside pressure being greater, therefore tends to force the water or mixture into the suction to equalize the pressure.

Inasmuch as the actual atmospheric pressure is applied to the surface of the water, it might appear that the energy acting to force the mixture into the suction would be the atmospheric pressure plus the weight of the water above. This is not the case, inasmuch as the pump is at or near the surface, and the mixture therefore has to travel upwards the same distance as the depth of the water.

Consequently, in a normal dredging hydraulic system the only force acting to move the material in the suction is the effective force of the atmosphere.

All this force is not available, however. The capability of the pump to lower the pressure in the suction line will determine the amount of force that will be available. To create a complete vacuum in the suction the pump would have to lower the pressure 14.72 pounds per square inch at sea level. As one-half pound of pressure corresponds to approximately one inch of vacuum, this would be the equivalent of 30 inches of vacuum. It is practically impossible to obtain this vacuum anywhere, let alone in a dredge system. In dredging systems, 24 to 25 inches of vacuum are about the maximum that can be obtained. This allows only about ⅚ of the force of the atmosphere, or at sea level, 12.3 pounds per square inch of usable force.

As discussed in Article 139, one foot of head of fresh water is the equivalent of 2.3 psi. So, 12.3 psi would be the equivalent of approximately 28.3 feet of fresh water or head.

However, not all this head will be available for lifting the mixture. There are actually five jobs it has to do, (1) lift the material in the mixture, (2) overcome friction in the system, (3) give velocity to the mixture, (4) get the mixture started into the suction, and where necessary, (5) lift the mixture from the elevation of the surface of the water to the center of the pump. Where the center of the pump is at or below the water surface, this fifth job is eliminated.

In each of the above five job requirements, with the exception of the first, the effort expended is described as head. The energy expended in overcoming friction is called *friction head,* the energy expended in imparting velocity to the mixture is called *velocity head,* the energy expended in getting the mixture into the suction is called *entrance head,* and the energy expended in lifting the mixture above the surface of the water is called *static head.*

The sum of these four heads subtracted from the usable head is the head left available to lift the material (the water itself is pushed up by the equal amount of water above).

A head nomenclature often referred to by dredgemen is *suction head.* This is the friction head referred to above when only water is being pumped. It usually is in the region of five to eight inches of mercury.

142. Head Loss and Friction. In turbulent flow, friction is little affected by the viscosity, but the loss in head caused by friction will decrease as the percentage of material increases. A familiar equation for head loss in pipelines carrying fresh water is the Darcy-Weisbach equation,

$$H = (f) \frac{(L) \ (V^2)}{(d) \ (2g)} \qquad (46)$$

where H = head loss, in feet of fresh water; L = length of pipe, in feet; d = inside diameter of the pipe, in feet; V = average velocity of the water, in feet per second; g = acceleration of gravity, in feet per second per second, and f = a *friction factor* generally considered by some to vary with the velocity.

If the velocity is low enough to allow the materials to drop out and roll along the bottom of the pipe, the equation will not apply.

It is generally believed that the friction factor (f) will be independent of the mixture in dredging systems. That is, it will remain the same with a water-material flow as with a clear-water flow.

Another equation commonly associated with clear-water friction is that of William and Hazen,

$$H = (0.2083) \left[\frac{(100)}{C}\right]^{1.85} \left[\frac{Q^{1.85}}{d^{4.8655}}\right] \qquad (47)$$

where H = friction head, in feet of fresh, clear water per 100 feet of pipe; d = inside diameter of the pipe, in inches; Q = flow, in gallons per minute, and C = a constant accounting for pipe roughness (50).

Equation 46 is probably more practical than Equation 47. However, there has for some time been considerable thought given to the exponent of the velocity in Equation 46. Many engineers and researchers, including the author, believe the exponent of 2 is too high. A value of 1.75 has been proposed (51). Where 1.75 has been used it has been found that the friction factor becomes constant at a value of 0.0280 when applied to dredge mixtures. Thus Equation 46 becomes,

$$H = (0.0280) \frac{(L) \ (V^{1.75})}{(d) \ (2g)} \qquad (48)$$

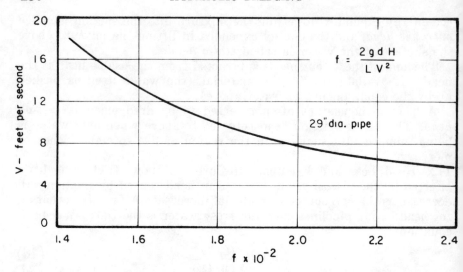

Fig. 159. Friction Factor As a Function of Velocity. (American Society of Mechanical Engineers)

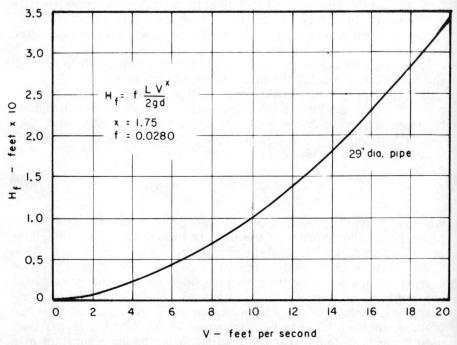

Fig. 160. Head Loss As a Function of Velocity. (American Society of Mechanical Engineers)

Figure 159 shows values of (f) obtained from test results applied to Equation 46 in which the friction factor is a variable, depending upon the velocity (51). Figure 160 shows the head loss relationship to velocity when Equation 48 is used (51). Figure 161 shows actual head losses occurring in different diameter dredge pipe as a function of velocity (49).

There are other exponential values that have been suggested for substitution in Equation 46. One is that the velocity exponent be 1.830 and the exponent of the pipe diameter be 1.170 (51).

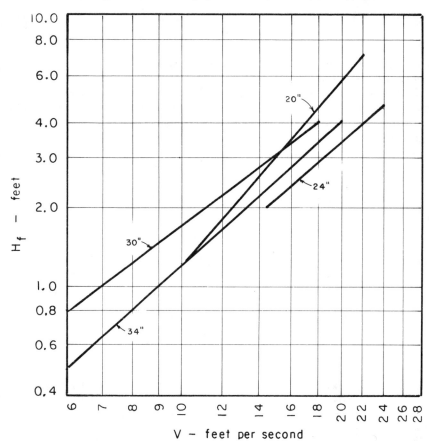

Fig. 161. Actual Head Losses in Dredge Pipes. (University of California Press)

In adapting these equations to dredging systems, not enough work has been done in studying the effects of introducing material into the regular clear water equations to adequately determine or predict the changes affected. To date the equations used to predict the losses in dredge systems are for the greater part hypothetical, although they have been somewhat substantiated by investigation. Much more work is needed in this phase of dredge hydraulics.

It is generally believed that the increase in head in a dredge pipe-line is dependent upon the friction loss plus the relative percentage of material in the mixture. By modifying the Darcy-Weisbach equation (Equation 48) to take this into account, a closer approximation of the losses can be obtained.

As the percentage material in the line directly affects the specific gravity of the mixture, multiplying the modified Darcy-Weisbach equation (Equation 48) by the specific gravity of the mixture gives,

$$H = (SG) \ (f) \ \frac{(L) \ (v^{1.75})}{(d) \ (2g)} \tag{49}$$

where SG = specific gravity of the mixture; f = 0.0280, and the others as previously defined.

To the author's best knowledge and experience, the closest approximation to the friction effects of water-spoil mixtures in dredge pipelines can be obtained from this adaptation of the Darcy-Weisbach equation.

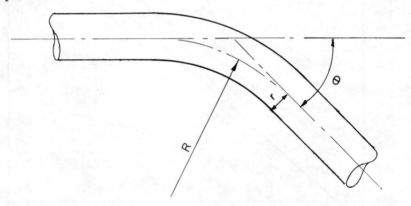

Fig. 162.   Parameters of a Pipe Bend.

143. Fitting Losses.   The head-loss equations above apply to straight sections of pipe. Where there are bends, elbows, fittings, or other irregularities in the line, an additional loss will occur in addition to that due to the actual length of the bend or fitting.

There are two variables to consider when attempting to find the loss due to a bend (58)—the radius and the degree of bend. A good approximation of the loss in a bend can be obtained from the familiar velocity-head equation, $H = kV^2/2g$ (*See* Art. 144). To determine k, the following can be used,

$$k = \left[(0.131) + (1.847) \left(\frac{r}{R} \right)^{3.5} \right] \frac{\phi}{180°}$$

where R = radius of the bend, in feet; r = radius of the pipe, in feet, and ϕ = degree of bend, in decimal degrees. (*See* Fig. 162.)

If it is desirable to obtain the loss in terms of feet of pipe directly, let L_1 = the additional pipe length to add to the actual length L, and f another constant. Then,

$$L_1 = \frac{(D)\ (K)}{(4)\ (f)} \tag{50}$$

where the value for the constant (f) for pipe six inches to 10 inches in diameter should be 0.006, for pipe 12 inches to 18 inches in diameter, 0.005, and for pipe 20 inches and up, 0.004, and D = diameter of the pipe in feet (58).

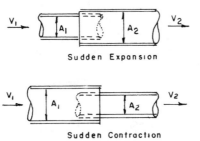

Sudden Expansion

Sudden Contraction

Fig. 163. Sudden Expansion and Contraction in Dredge Pipes.

Losses for flap valves increase proportionately as the size of the pipe. A good approximation can be obtained by multiplying the diameter of the pipe in feet, by 6.5 to obtain the equivalent length of pipe.

Losses in ball joints are usually determined by

$$H_b = C\ \frac{V^2}{(2g)} \tag{51}$$

where (C) can be considered as 0.10.

Losses of energy accompanying a velocity decrease are always greater than those accompanying an increase in velocity. Therefore, head losses will be greater whenever there is a sudden expansion of the hydraulic system.

One of the most familiar and common changes in system size in a dredge pipe system are the tapered-end, ram-type joints for shoreline connections. Here there is a sudden contraction, or expansion, depending upon how the pipe are laid. If the tapered end is downstream, there is an enlargement at each joint; if upstream, a contraction at each joint.

The head loss for a sudden expansion can be as much as ten times that of a sudden contraction. Where the taper is upstream (sudden contraction) (Fig. 163), the loss of head will be,

$$H_x = \frac{(V_2 - V_1)^2}{(2g)}\ (C_1) \tag{52}$$

where V_1 = input velocity, in feet per second; V_2 = output velocity, in feet per second; g = acceleration of gravity, in feet per second per second, and C = 0.4 to 0.5.

Where the taper end is downstream, the loss of head at each joint will be obtainable from Equation 52 by the substitution of the constant C_2 for C_1, C_2 being 1.0.

As an example of how the loss is increased by having the tapered end downstream rather than upstream, consider a 16-inch shoreline. Say that the I.D. of the banded end is 16 inches exactly and the I.D. of the tapered end 15 inches exactly. These dimensions will give an effective increase in area from the taper to the banded end of, $8^2/7.5^2 = 1.138$, and consequently, a decrease in velocity of 0.121. Assuming that the velocity in the taper is 20 feet per second, the velocity in the expanded banded pipe would therefore be (20) (0.879) = 17.58 feet per second. Thus the loss with the taper downstream would be

$$H_x = \frac{(20 - 17.58)^2}{64.4} = \frac{(2.42)^2}{64.4} = \frac{5.86}{64.4} = 0.09 \text{ feet}$$

With 500 sections of pipe this would be the equivalent of 45 feet of head.

On the other hand, with the taper upstream, the loss would be,

$$H_x = (0.09)(0.4) = 0.036 \text{ feet}$$

or with 500 sections, 18 feet of head. It would therefore appear that shorelines would be best laid with the tapered end upstream—from a hydraulic standpoint at least, if not from any other.

There is also another general misapprehension. Some think that when pieces of pipe of different sizes are connected together, the upstream section of the connection should be the smallest. Actually this makes the flow conditions worse.

144. Total Dynamic Head. The total dynamic head on a pump is the algebraic sum of all the individual heads in the pumping system and is usually expressed in feet of fresh water. These heads, starting with the suction and continuing through the discharge, are as follows:

A. SUCTION TOTAL HEAD. Suction total head is the head needed to overcome the suction entrance head, the suction static head, the suction velocity head, and the suction friction head. It is the algebraic sum of these four heads. Only the suction static head may be negative, the other three are always positive.

1. *Suction Entrance Head.* Suction entrance losses are generally small. However, where the suction is usually compressed to fit into the lower portion of the cutter ring, as contrasted to the full round suction mouth of a rotating suction, losses may be four to five times as much as the latter. On the other hand, compared to other

losses in the system, this loss can generally be disregarded. Head loss at the suction entrance can be obtained from

$$H_e = K_e \frac{V^2}{2g} \qquad (53)$$

where H_e = suction entrance head loss, in feet; V = suction velocity, in feet per second; g = acceleration of gravity, in feet per second per second, and K_e = coefficient of the mouthpiece. A *bell mouth*, which is the most desirable entrance, has a K_e of 0.04; a slightly rounded entrance has a K_e of 0.23, and a sharp-cornered entrance, such as a straight piece of pipe, has a K_e of 0.50. It can be seen from these coefficients that the suction entrance should be as near a bell mouth as possible for minimum loss.

2. *Suction Static Head.* Suction static head (H_{ss}) is the vertical distance in feet between the water surface and the centerline of the pump. It may be either positive or negative, depending upon the location of the pump centerline with respect to the water surface.

To determine the suction static head, the following formula can be used,

$$H_{ss} = SG_1 B - SG_2 C \qquad (54)$$

where H_{ss} = suction static head, in feet of fresh water; C = distance between the suction entrance and the water surface, in feet; B = distance between the pump centerline and the suction entrance, in feet; SG_2 = specific gravity of the water in which the dredge is operating, and SG_1 = specific gravity of the mixture being pumped.

If H_{ss} results in a negative value, as it may if the center of the pump is below the water surface, it must be subtracted from the sum of all other heads in the suction system to obtain the true total suction head. When the H_{ss} is negative it is not a head, but a vacuum and this will contribute to the reduction of total head. However, the density and quantity of material being pumped may cause it to be positive, particularly when the pump centerline is only slightly below the water line. Where it is positive, it should be added to the other heads, as will presently be shown.

3. *Suction Velocity Head.* The suction velocity head (H_{sv}) is the equivalent head through which the water would have to fall to acquire the velocity it has in the suction. It is therefore the head that must be developed to create the velocity in the suction.

In a pipe through which a quantity of fluid is flowing, the velocity is $V = Q/A$, where V = velocity of flow, in feet per second; Q = quantity of flow, in cubic feet per second, and A = pipe cross-sectional area, in square feet. Also, a falling body will obtain a velocity $V = (2gS)^{0.5}$ according to the law of gravity, where V = velocity, in feet per second; g = acceleration of gravity, in feet per second, and

S = distance of fall, in feet. Suction velocity head will consequently be,

$$H_{sv} = \frac{V^2}{2g} \tag{55}$$

Usually this head is low, due to the low velocity in the suction. When the flow is other than fresh water the density of the mixture must be considered, or

$$H_{sv} = \frac{(SG)\ (V^2)}{(2g)} \tag{56}$$

where SG = specific gravity of the mixture being pumped. This head is always positive.

4. Suction Friction Head. The head required to overcome friction in the pipe is called the friction head (H_{sf}). Suction friction head can be obtained from the modified Darcy-Weisbach Equation 49,

$$H_{sf} = (SG)\ (f)\ \frac{(L)\ (V^{1.75})}{(d)\ (2g)} \tag{57}$$

where H_{sf} = friction head, in feet of fresh water; L = equivalent length of suction line, in feet; d = inside diameter of the suction pipe, in feet; V = velocity of the mixture being pumped, in feet per second; g = acceleration of gravity, in feet per second per second; SG = specific gravity of the mixture, and f = a friction constant equal to 0.028 (*See* Art. 142 for discussion of this constant.)

B. TOTAL DISCHARGE HEAD. The total discharge head is the sum of the static, velocity, and friction heads in the discharge system.

1. Discharge Static Head. The discharge static head (H_{ds}) is obtained by using a method similar to the one used to determine the suction static head. It is the vertical distance, in feet of fresh water, between the centerline of the pump and the point of discharge. The density of the material being pumped must be taken into consideration to obtain the correct value of this head, whatever the vertical distance. The specific gravity multiplied by the height in feet will give the discharge static head.

2. Discharge Velocity Head. Discharge velocity head (H_{dv}) is defined exactly as suction velocity head. In simplest terms it is the head created by the pump—being the output head less the input head—and is proportional to the ratio of the diameters of the suction and discharge pump openings. If the suction and discharge openings are of equal diameter, the discharge velocity head will be zero. It can be found from,

$$H_{dv} = SG\ \frac{V_d^2 - V_s^2}{2g} \tag{58}$$

where H_{dv} = discharge velocity head, in feet of fresh water; V_d = velocity of the mixture in the discharge, in feet per second; V_s =

velocity of the mixture in the suction, in feet per second; g = acceleration of gravity, in feet per second per second, and SG = specific gravity of the mixture being pumped.

3. *Discharge Friction Head.* The discharge friction head (H_{df}) is the head required to overcome friction losses in the discharge line. It can be computed from Equation 49, or determined from Table 9. In determining the equivalent length of discharge pipe, the length of floating line is sometimes multiplied by a constant of 1.3 to 1.5 to

Table 9. Head Loss As a Function of Velocity in Various Sizes of Dredge Pipe

V	6"	8"	10"	12"	14"	16"	18"	20"	24"	27"	30"
ft/sec	Nom	Nom	Nom	Nom	OD	OD	OD	OD	OD	OD	OD
10	4.89	3.67	2.93	2.44	2.17	1.89	1.68	1.50	1.25	1.08	1.00
11	5.78	4.33	3.47	2.89	2.57	2.24	1.98	1.78	1.48	1.28	1.18
12	6.73	5.05	4.04	3.36	2.99	2.60	2.31	2.07	1.72	1.49	1.37
13	7.74	5.80	4.64	3.87	3.44	3.00	2.65	2.38	1.98	1.72	1.58
14	8.81	6.61	5.29	4.41	3.92	3.41	3.02	2.71	2.25	1.96	1.80
15	9.94	7.45	5.97	4.97	4.42	3.85	3.41	3.06	2.54	2.21	2.03
16	11.13	8.34	6.68	5.57	4.95	4.31	3.82	3.42	2.84	2.47	2.27
17	12.38	9.28	7.43	6.19	5.50	4.79	4.24	3.81	3.16	2.75	2.52
18	13.68	10.25	8.21	6.84	6.08	5.29	4.69	4.21	3.49	3.04	2.79
19	15.04	11.27	9.02	7.52	6.68	5.82	5.16	4.62	3.84	3.34	3.07
20	16.45	12.33	9.87	8.22	7.31	6.37	5.64	5.06	4.20	3.65	3.36
21	17.91	13.43	10.75	8.96	7.96	6.93	6.14	5.51	4.58	3.98	3.65
22	19.43	14.57	11.66	9.72	8.64	7.52	6.67	5.98	4.97	4.31	3.96
23	21.01	15.74	12.60	10.50	9.34	8.13	7.21	6.46	5.37	4.66	4.29
24	22.63	16.96	13.58	11.32	10.06	8.76	7.76	6.96	5.78	5.02	4.62
25	24.31	18.22	14.58	12.15	10.80	9.41	8.34	7.47	6.21	5.40	4.96

Note: Pipe from 6 through 12 inches is nominal (inside diameter) size pipe. Pipe 14 through 30 inches is OD pipe with 0.250 wall thickness. All head losses are for 100 feet of pipe, obtained by using Equation 49 with a specific gravity of 1.00 and a friction factor of 0.0280.

correct for the additional friction caused by the ball joints and elbows in the floating line, when these are not determined individually. (*See* Art. 143.) Shoreline pipe length is sometimes multiplied by a constant of 1.1 to correct for the friction created by the ram-joint connections. Fittings and bends are equated in terms of equivalent lengths of pipe as shown in Art. 143.

145. **Example of Head Calculation.** Imagine a dredge with a hydraulic layout as shown in Fig. 164. Suction velocity is 15 feet per second, and spoil concentration is 15 per cent, the dry spoil weighing 120 pounds per cubic foot. The various heads are computed as follows:

A. SUCTION STATIC HEAD. Here the pump centerline is two feet below the loaded water line. Therefore it would seem that the suction

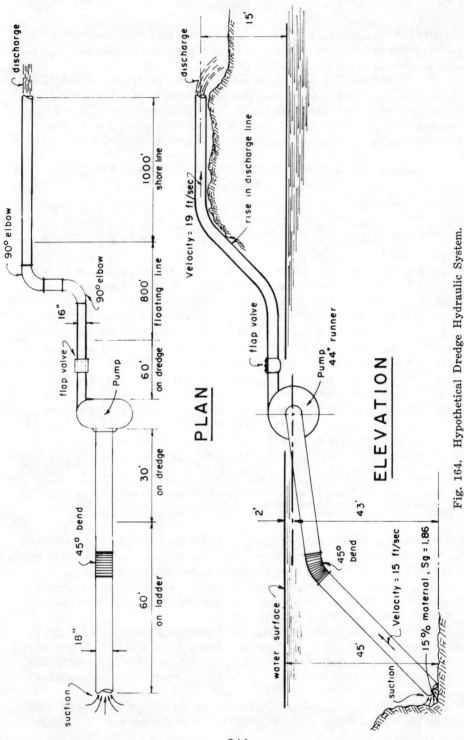

Fig. 164. Hypothetical Dredge Hydraulic System.

244

static head might be negative. However, when the mixture's specific gravity is considered,

$$SG = \frac{(120) (0.15) + (64.4) (0.85)}{62.4} = 1.16$$

and the true static head is positive. This can be seen as follows—as the vertical distance from the cutter to the centerline of the pump is 43 feet, the true suction static head is, from Equation 54,

$$H_{ss} = SG_1 B - SG_2 C$$

$$= (1.16) (43) - (1.025) (45)$$

$$= 3.76 \text{ feet}$$

This is a positive head and must be added to the following two heads to obtain the total suction head.

B. SUCTION VELOCITY HEAD. Using Equation 56, the suction velocity head is,

$$H_{sv} = SG \frac{V^2}{2g}$$

$$= \frac{(1.16) (15^2)}{64.4}$$

$$= 4.05 \text{ feet}$$

C. SUCTION FRICTION HEAD. As Fig. 164 shows, the length of straight suction pipe is 90 feet and has a diameter of 18 inches. There is one 45° bend at the trunnions, for which the equivalent length of 30 feet is added. Using Equation 57, the suction friction head is,

$$H_{sf} = (SG) (f) \frac{(L) (V^{1.75})}{(d) (2g)}$$

$$= (1.16) (0.028) \frac{(120) (15^{1.75})}{(1.5) (64.4)}$$

$$= 4.62 \text{ feet}$$

D. SUCTION ENTRANCE HEAD. To the above heads the suction entrance head should be added. This is,

$$H_e = (SG) (0.25) \frac{V^2}{2g}$$

$$= 1.16 \frac{(0.25) (15^2)}{64.4}$$

$$= 1.01 \text{ feet}$$

E. SUCTION TOTAL HEAD. The suction total head is the algebraic sum of all the suction heads. Therefore,

$$H_{st} = 3.76 + 4.05 + 4.62 + 1.01$$
$$= 13.44 \text{ feet of fresh water}$$
$$= 11.86 \text{ inches of vacuum}$$

If the ladder was raised and only water pumped, the head required would be called the *water vacuum*, and would be only that required for the water, or

$$H_{wv} = -2.05 + 3.49 + 3.98 + 0.87$$
$$= 6.29 \text{ feet of fresh water}$$
$$= 5.55 \text{ inches of vacuum}$$

F. DISCHARGE STATIC HEAD. The discharge is 15 feet above the centerline of the pump. The discharge static head is, therefore

$$H_{ds} = (15)(1.16) = 17.40 \text{ feet}$$

G. DISCHARGE VELOCITY HEAD. The amount of mixture entering the suction must equal the amount leaving the discharge. Therefore, the velocity in the 16-inch discharge is increased inversely as the square of the diameters of the suction and discharge pipes, or

$$V_d = (15)\frac{D_s^2}{D_d^2} = (15)\frac{18^2}{16^2} = 18.98 \text{ ft. per. sec.}$$

and then

$$H_{dv} = 1.16\left(\frac{V_d^2 - V_s^2}{2g}\right) = 1.16\left(\frac{360.24 - 225}{64.4}\right)$$
$$= 2.45 \text{ feet}$$

H. DISCHARGE FRICTION HEAD. The discharge friction head is computed from Equation 49, or from Table 9. There are 60 feet of pipe on the dredge, 800 feet of floating line, and 1,000 feet of shoreline. There is one flap valve and two 90° elbows. The equivalent line length will be

Pipe on dredge	60 feet
Floating line	1,200 feet
Shoreline	1,100 feet
Two 90° els	120 feet
Flap valve	10 feet
Total equivalent line length	2,490 feet

therefore the discharge friction head will be,

$$H_{df} = (1.16)(0.028)\frac{(2,490)(19^{1.75})}{(1.3)(64.4)}$$
$$= 167 \text{ feet}$$
$$= 72.33 \text{ pounds per square inch}$$

I. DISCHARGE TOTAL HEAD. The discharge total head is the sum of all the discharge heads, and therefore $H_{dt} = 17.40 + 2.45 + 167 = 186.9$ feet. This is to say that it would take a head of 186.9 feet of fresh water to push the material through the 1,950 feet (2,490 feet equivalent) of 18-inch diameter suction and 16-inch diameter discharge pipe with a discharge elevation of 15 feet and at a velocity of 19 feet per second. As read on the pressure gauge at the discharge of the pump, this would be $(210)\ (0.434) = 81.11$ pounds per square inch.

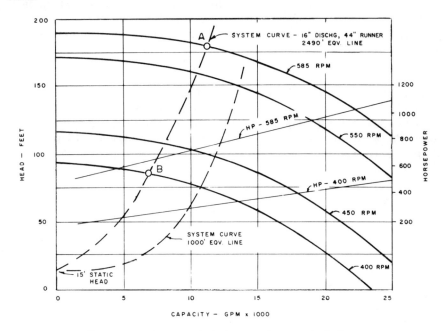

Fig. 165. Characteristic Curves for a 16-inch Pump.

An equality that can often be used to approximate the head developed by a specific runner is,

$$H_r = \left[\frac{(D)\ (n)}{(1840)\ (K_u)}\right]^2 \qquad (59)$$

where H_r = head developed at maximum efficiency by the runner, in feet of fresh water, D = runner diameter, in inches, n = speed of runner, in revolutions per minute, and K_u can be assumed to be 1.03. Equation 59 then becomes (70),

$$H_r = \left[\frac{(D)\ (n)}{1900}\right]^2 \qquad (60)$$

Applying Equation 60 to the above example, and assuming a 44-inch runner at 585 rpm, the total head developed would be,

$$H_{dt} = 183.5 \text{ feet}$$

which compares favorably with the calculations. From Fig. 165, the characteristic curve of this pump (actual pump manufacturer's data) a head of 180 feet also compares favorably, although it is probable that the curve was obtained with clear water.

The peripheral velocity of the runner required for a certain head can be obtained from Equation 60. Inasmuch as the periphery of the runner, in feet, is $\pi D/12$, the peripheral velocity, in feet per minute, is

$$\text{P. V.} = 497 \, (\text{H})^{0.5} \tag{61}$$

In connection with this discussion of runner diameters, it is an old rule-of-thumb in dredging that the diameter of the runner should never be less than 2.3 times the diameter of the pump discharge. For example, a 20-inch pump should have a runner at least 46 inches in diameter (83).

Chapter 10

Output—Horsepower—Efficiency—Testing

146. Introduction. Dredge output is a function of many variables—velocity, size of discharge, length of line, lift, horsepower, efficiency, type and quantity of material, and depth of dredging. These are all intertwined to affect output. In this chapter an attempt is made to isolate these variables and to show their effect on dredge output, separately and collectively.

147. Output. Dredge output is usually measured in cubic yards of *in situ* material per hour. The number of yards per hour is a function of the discharge-pipe diameter, the velocity of flow, and the concentration of the material in the mixture.

The total flow of the pump in gallons per minute as it is usually expressed does not involve the concentration of the mixture. The output in gallons per minute (Q) can be found from,

$$Q = (352.51)\ (d^2)\ (V) \tag{62}$$

where Q = flow, in gallons per minute, d = inside diameter of the discharge pipe, in feet, and V = velocity of flow, in feet per second. The quantity (Q) above can be reduced to cubic yards per hour by multiplying by 0.2971, or

$$Q = 104.72\ (d^2)\ (V) \tag{63}$$

If the concentration of spoil is known, its quantity can be calculated by taking the results of Equation 63 and multiplying by the concentration percentage. (*See* Tables 10 and 11.)

148. Horsepower. The power actually expended in forcing the material and water out the discharge is called *water horsepower,* and

$$HP_w = \frac{SG\ (Q)\ (H_t)}{3960} \tag{64}$$

where HP_w = water horsepower; Q = discharge, in gallons per minute; H_t = total dynamic head on the pump, in feet, and SG = specific gravity of the mixture being pumped.

The power expended in forcing the material out the discharge, plus the power required to turn the pump and supply all losses, is called *brake horsepower,* or

$$HP_b = \frac{HP_w}{E} \tag{65}$$

250 HYDRAULIC DREDGING

where HP_b = brake horsepower, HP_w = water horsepower, and E = efficiency of the pump in per cent as a decimal.

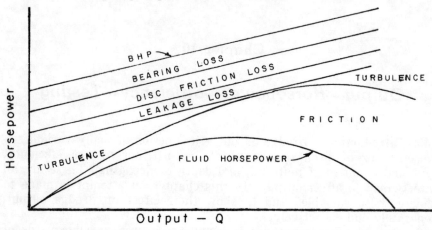

Fig. 166. Losses in a Dredge Pump.

Table 10. Output As a Function of Velocity for Various
Sizes of Dredge Pipe

Discharge Velocity ft/sec	Discharge Output gal/min										
	6 Nom	8 Nom	10 Nom	12 Nom	14 OD	16 OD	18 OD	20 OD	24 OD	27 OD	30 OD
10	900	1620	2570	3670	4460	5880	7500	9310	13520	17190	21120
11	990	1780	2830	4040	4910	6470	8250	10240	14870	18910	23240
12	1080	1940	3090	4410	5350	7060	9000	11170	16220	20620	25350
13	1170	2100	3340	4770	5800	7640	9740	12100	17570	22340	27460
14	1260	2260	3600	5140	6250	8230	10500	13030	18930	24070	29580
15	1360	2420	3860	5510	6690	8820	11240	13960	20280	25790	31690
16	1450	2580	4110	5880	7140	9410	11990	14890	21630	27500	33800
17	1540	2750	4370	6240	7580	10000	12740	15820	22980	29220	35910
18	1630	2910	4630	6610	8030	10590	13490	16760	24330	30940	38020
19	1720	3070	4890	6980	8480	11170	14240	17680	25690	32670	40140
20	1810	3230	5140	7350	8920	11760	14990	18620	27040	34380	42250
21	1900	3390	5400	7710	9370	12350	15740	19550	28390	36100	44360
22	1990	3550	5660	8080	9810	12940	16490	20480	29740	37820	46470
23	2080	3720	5910	8450	10260	13530	17240	21410	31090	39530	48590
24	2170	3880	6170	8820	10710	14110	17990	22340	32440	41250	50700
25	2260	4040	6430	9180	11150	14700	18740	23270	33800	42980	52810

Note: Pipe from 6 through 12 inches is nominal size pipe. Pipe 14 through 30 inches is OD pipe with 0. 250-inch wall thickness.

Pump brake horsepower varies as the cube of the speed of the runner and directly as about the second power of the pipe diameter. The actual horsepower requirements of the dredge pump are determined by the head against which it works.

149. Efficiency. Pump efficiency is not synonymous with dredge efficiency. Pump efficiency is moving a unit of material at the lowest prime mover power cost. Dredge efficiency however, is moving a unit of material at the lowest over-all cost. Moving material at the least power plant cost is not necessarily good dredge operation (60).

Table 11. Output As a Function of Velocity for Various
Sizes of Dredge Pipe

Discharge Velocity ft/sec	Discharge Output cu yds/ hr										
	6 Nom	8 Nom	10 Nom	12 Nom	14 OD	16 OD	18 OD	20 OD	24 OD	27 OD	30 OD
10	270	480	760	1090	1320	1750	2230	2770	4020	5110	6280
11	290	530	840	1200	1460	1920	2450	3040	4420	5620	6900
12	320	580	920	1310	1590	2100	2670	3320	4820	6130	7530
13	350	620	990	1420	1720	2270	2900	3590	5220	6640	8160
14	380	670	1070	1530	1860	2450	3120	3870	5620	7150	8790
15	400	720	1150	1640	1990	2620	3340	4150	6020	7660	9410
16	430	770	1220	1750	2120	2800	3560	4420	6430	8180	10040
17	460	820	1300	1860	2250	2970	3790	4700	6830	8680	10670
18	480	860	1380	1960	2390	3140	4010	4980	7230	9190	11300
19	510	910	1450	2070	2520	3320	4230	5250	7630	9700	11920
20	540	960	1530	2180	2650	3490	4450	5530	8030	10210	12550
21	560	1010	1600	2290	2780	3670	4680	5810	8430	10720	13180
22	590	1060	1680	2400	2920	3840	4900	6080	8840	11240	13800
23	620	1100	1760	2510	3050	4020	5120	6360	9240	11750	14430
24	640	1150	1830	2620	3180	4190	5350	6640	9640	12260	15060
25	670	1200	1910	2730	3310	4370	5570	6910	10040	12770	15690

Note: To obtain cubic yards per hour output of material, multiply above values by the percentage concentration.
   Pipe from 6 through 12 inches is nominal size pipe. Pipe 14 through 30 inches is OD pipe with 0.250-inch wall thickness.

The efficiency of the pump is called its hydraulic efficiency. It is affected by hydraulic losses, leakage losses, and mechanical losses (Fig. 166). Hydraulic losses are those due to eddies, turbulence, shock, and friction of the fluid mixture. They can be reduced, but not eliminated, by having large radius curves in the pump, avoiding sudden changes in section or abrupt changes in direction.

Leakage losses are caused by leakage from high-pressure areas to low-pressure areas, and are sometimes called flow-back losses. These losses are greatest in the circuit from the discharge to the suction when liners are not making good running joints. Mechanical losses include those in the bearings and stuffing boxes and disc friction of the runner in the fluid.

150. Velocity Effects Upon Efficiency. Since pipeline losses vary almost as the square of the velocity, a high pipeline velocity would seem to be detrimental to dredge efficiency (not pump efficiency). This is not necessarily true. High velocity, because of its greater material-carrying capacity can, within certain limits, increase dredge efficiency. At low velocities (10 to 12 feet per second) pipe friction is relatively low in the larger-diameter pipes (*See* Table 9), but so is material-carrying capacity. In contrast, at high velocities (20 to 22 feet per second), pipe friction in the larger-diameter pipes is not high enough to offset any advantage of increased carrying capacity, particularly in the largest sizes. However, much higher velocities are usually detrimental, even on the largest dredges (60).

For example, a velocity of nine to ten feet per second in an eight-inch pipe will cause a friction loss of about 3.5 feet per 100 feet of pipe, while a 30-inch diameter pipe will, at the same velocity, have only about one foot friction loss per 100 feet of pipe (Table 9). If the velocity is increased to, say 20 feet per second, the eight-inch pipe will have a friction loss of about 12 feet, while the 30-inch pipe will have only about three feet. It would seem therefore, that the size of the discharge would determine the maximum, economical velocity.

The optimum velocity is that which transports the maximum amount of material at the lowest velocity. The lower the discharge velocity, the lower the suction velocity, and therefore the lower the head loss in the suction, leaving more head for lifting the material.

Consider a situation where the discharge velocity is 20 feet per second. Say there was a six-inch water vacuum and a safe vacuum of 24 inches. This would allow 18 inches of vacuum for lifting the material. Now if the discharge velocity were lowered to 18 feet per second, the water vacuum would be $18^2/20^2$ (6) = 4.8 inches. With the lower velocity, a higher total vacuum could be used, say 26 inches, so there would be 21.2 inches available for lifting the material. Consequently, it can be seen that where more lifting vacuum is needed, it can often be obtained by reducing the discharge velocity. The velocity of the discharge must be high enough to move the material, however. Usually 10 feet per second is about the lowest for light materials, heavier materials requiring proportionally higher velocities.

151. Specific Speed. Although not directly connected with horsepower and efficiency, the *specific speed* of a pump is a factor which can be used to compare all pumps. It definitely establishes a pump's operating capabilities. The specific speed of a pump is the speed at which an exact model of the pump would run if it were designed to give one gallon per minute against a head of one foot. It is a function of the runner speed, the output, and the total head (47). Thus,

$$N_s = n \frac{(Q)^{0.5}}{H^{0.75}} \qquad (66)$$

where N_s = specific speed, in rpm; Q = output, in gallons per minute; n = speed of runner, in rpm, and H = head on pump, in feet.

For a given head and capacity a pump with a low specific speed will operate at a greater suction lift than will one with a higher specific speed. If the suction lift is over 15 feet, it is often necessary to use a lower speed or a larger pump. On the other hand, if the suction lift is low, or there is a positive head at the suction, the speed may be increased and a smaller pump used. Increasing speeds higher than design values without proper suction conditions often causes vibration, noise and wear.

For a pump with an output (Q) of 10,000 gallons per minute; n = 350 rpm; H = 100 feet, and a suction diameter of 20 inches, the specific speed at its operating point would be,

$$N_s = (350) \frac{(10,000)^{0.5}}{(100)^{0.75}} = 1,109 \text{ rpm}$$

Specific speed and its determining equation may be more easily understood by taking speed and head separately (47). As the specific speed is that of an exact model which would produce a foot of head at one gallon per minute, the speed can be reduced to that necessary by the equation $n' = n (1/H)^{0.5} = 350 (1/H)^{0.5} = 35$ rpm. The capacity (Q) for this speed will then be $Q' = Q (n'/n) = (10,000) (35/350) = 1,000$ gallons per minute. The runner diameter is reduced to give one gallon per minute discharge. In doing this the speed will have to be increased to maintain the one foot of head, so by multiplying by $(Q)^{0.5}$, or $(1,000)^{0.5}$, the speed becomes $(31.6) (35) = 1,106$—approximately the value obtained by the specific speed equation above.

Dredge pumps, because of their need for high dynamic suction lifts, are all low specific speed pumps. The term low is usually considered as being below 1,000 rpm. The maximum speed of small dredge pumps is usually not more than 800 rpm, and speeds of large ones usually not more than 400 rpm.

152. Testing. Pump performance can be understood most easily by studying the pump's characteristic curves (Chapt. 11). A whole family of curves can be obtained by plotting output versus head (Q-H) data at different speeds and from maximum output to shutoff. Usually the manufacturer supplies Q-H curves for a particular pump at its recommended speed, and at several other speeds near that recommended. These, however, are usually for clear water. In dredging where high-density fluids are involved, additional information should be procured by plotting Q-H curves from data obtained while the

dredge is actually operating. The collecting of these data can be easy or difficult, depending upon the degree of instrumentation involved.

A more representative picture of the pump's capacity can be obtained if it can be set up in an area where there is an adequate supply of soft, fine, material, such as silt, sand, or mud. Clay, rocks, or gravel are usually not suitable.

By testing the pump in the soft materials, a mixture can be obtained that will resemble most closely the mixtures found in normal dredging. However, water is usually used because of the difficulty in obtaining smooth mixtures. The head developed by the pump at a

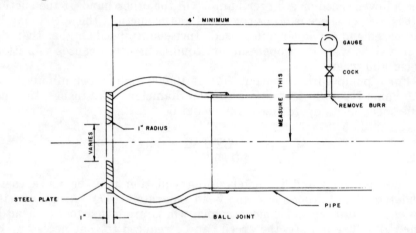

Fig. 167.   Orifice Installation for Dredge Test.

given discharge will be different for different mixtures, and in general will become lower as the concentration of material and density increase. This is in direct contrast to the flow in pipelines where head loss remains the same regardless of the mixture, and pressure drops in proportion to specific gravity of the mixture.

Without becoming involved in the intricate details of a complicated testing activity, the following is one method for obtaining data in the field that can be used to plot a pump's characteristic curves.

Of primary importance is providing an orifice. This is a device widely used in pump testing to measure the quantity of flow of water (Fig. 167). It can be used on all sizes of dredges and is by far the most practical device for dredge testing.

Theoretically, water discharging from an orifice under a head will have a velocity of $V_o = (2g\ H_o)^{0.5}$. Actually however, the stream through an orifice will flow with a slightly less velocity, $V_o = C\ (2g\ H_o)^{0.5}$, where C = a coefficient of discharge applicable to the particular orifice being used. The coefficient's value, always less than one, depends upon the shape of the orifice, its position, the type of edge, and the corresponding head. For the orifice of Fig. 167 the coefficient is 0.98. Using this orifice, the flow will be

$$Q = (19.636) (C) (d^2) (H_o^{0.5})$$ (67)

where Q = flow, in gallons per minute; d = inside diameter of the discharge pipe, in inches; H_o = head on the orifice, in feet, and C = the coefficient. This equation is only applicable where d_1/d is less than 0.30, d_1 being equal to the diameter of the orifice, in inches.

With the dredge pumping material or water as constantly as possible, record the pressure on the gauge at the orifice for pump speeds 20 per cent above rated speed, at rated speed, and 20 per cent below rated speed, in steps of approximately 20 rpm. When these data are obtained, the section of pipe holding the orifice and gauge should be removed, and additional pipeline (either floating or shore) added. This length should equal about one-half the length normally used, or, depending upon the size of the pipeline and the velocities obtained in the initial test, the amount of line added should increase the pressure approximately 20 per cent. This length can be determined by the explanation given in Art. 145 on pipe friction.

The pipe holding the orifice and gauge is reconnected at the end of the lengthened line. The pump is brought up to speed, the cock on the gauge opened, and pressure readings taken at the same speeds as before.

For the best spread of curves, the procedure should be repeated for at least five different lengths of line, the final length being one that will reduce the output to a value of at least 50 per cent of the maximum rated output of the pump at rated speed.

For more comprehensive data, the pump should be tested with different runners. For complete data, tests should be made with the smallest runner available, the test repeated with an intermediate-size runner, and then again with a maximum-size runner, each being tested from maximum capacity down to at least 50 per cent capacity. The tests of any one runner can be modified to predict the results obtainable for any other diameter runner as long as it is designed and built to the same specifications and runs at the same rpm. By making these tests with the different-size runners, this fact can be verified, and the testing procedure checked by the following equalities, where (D) is the diameter of the runner, in inches. (*See* Art. 157.)

$$Q \text{ varies as } D$$
$$H \text{ varies as } D^2$$
$$HP_b \text{ varies as } D^3$$

During the tests, readings should be taken of the dredge's vacuum and pressure gauges, engine rpm, and, if the pump is powered by an electric motor, current voltage, temperature and kilowatts. If the pump is powered by a diesel engine, record the cooling water temperature in and out, lubricating oil temperature in and out, and the exhaust temperature. All temperatures should be allowed to become stable before recording them. *See* Table 19 in the Appendix for test data of a 16-inch dredge.

153. Weirs and Spillways. A spillway is nothing more than a rectangular orifice or weir with its upper edge at zero pressure. Weirs are widely used for measuring the flow of water. By application of Equation 68, the quantity of flow over a spillway can be fairly well approximated. The flow over a standard spillway (Fig. 106) is from the Francis formula, approximately

$$Q = (5.349)\ (C_d)\ (L)\ (H^{1.5}) \tag{68}$$

where Q = flow, in cubic feet per second (if gallons per minute are desired, multiply the above equation by 448.8); L = width of spillway opening, in feet (it should be at least $6H$); H = head on spillway, in feet, and $C_d = 0.623$.

The size of the spillway will of course be determined by the flow of water into the area. A 16-inch dredge discharge will not require as large a spillway as will a 30-inch dredge. However, this is not necessarily the only criterion. Occasionally it is necessary to release all of the water in an area rapidly—say where a levee is failing. This can be accomplished by building a spillway to handle a normal flow with a three- to five-inch head, but installing sufficient flash boards to be able to accommodate a head of two or three feet if necessary.

As an example of spillway flow determination, consider a dredge pumping 10,000 gallons per minute with a 10 per cent spoil concentration. With a steady six-inch head on the spillway, the width would have to be

$$L = \frac{(10,000)\ (0.9)}{(5.349)\ (0.623)\ (0.5^{1.5})\ (448.8)}$$

$$= 16.9 \text{ feet}$$

Drop inlets can be designed in a similar manner, the space openings on all four sides—or as many as desired—adding up to the required length of crest.

Chapter 11

Characteristic Curves

154. Introduction. Pump characteristic curves are usually plotted in terms of Output vs Head (Q-H), with output increasing to the right on the abscissa, and head increasing upward on the ordinate. System and horsepower curves, which will presently be described, are usually plotted on the same graph sheet. The interrelation of these curves gives an over-all picture of the dredge hydraulic-system operation.

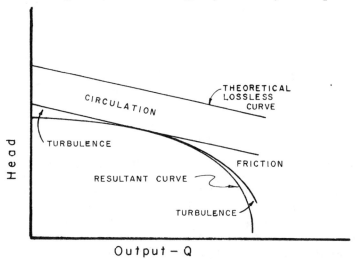

Fig. 168. Internal Losses in a Dredge Pump.

The fundamental curve of output (Q) versus head (H) for a theoretical, frictionless, and lossless pump is a straight line. In an actual pump, though, there are several losses (Fig. 168). There is a circulatory or leakage loss from the discharge back to the suction which drops the head of the curve. There is also a friction loss in the passages. This is zero at zero discharge, but increases approximately as the square of the capacity. Finally, there are turbulence losses that occur when the pump is operated at speeds above or below design capacity, the fluid entering the runner vanes at an angle different from that designed.

155. Head. Figure 165 shows four characteristic curves for the 16-inch pump of Art. 145 using a 44-inch diameter runner turning at 400, 450, 550 and 585 revolutions per minute. Note that as speed is decreased and head remains the same, the output decreases. A decrease in runner diameter will do the same thing, as this is effectively reducing the speed, and as capacity varies directly with speed, head varies as the runner diameter squared.

The characteristic of a dredge pump should be a steeply rising one—as the output decreases, the head should rise rapidly. When the velocity drops in a loaded line, the pressure will rise more rapidly, giving added impetus to the mixture. A steam turbine operating below governor speed, or a constant horsepower motor, will help provide the pump with this sort of operation.

Although the characteristic curves of the pump determine its operating range, it can operate at only one point on its characteristic curve at any one instant. This point is determined by the intersection of the *system curve* with the characteristic curve.

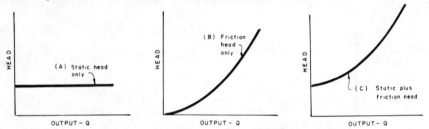

Fig. 169.   System Curves.

156. System Curves.   A system curve indicates graphically the head against which a pump has to work for any particular pipeline. When this curve is plotted on the same graph as the Q-H curve, its intersection with the Q-H curve indicates the point of operation.

The system curve is determined by the discharge static head and the discharge friction head. A pump operating against a static head only (no friction) would have a horizontal system curve displaced vertically from zero by the amount of the static head, as shown in Fig. 169 (1).

A pump operating with a pipeline at constant elevation—no lift— would expend all its head in overcoming friction. As the friction in a pipeline increases approximately as the square of the output, the system curve would be a parabola with its origin at zero head. (*See* Fig. 169 (center).

Where there was a combination of these two conditions, friction plus lift, the system curve would be a parabola originating at a point on the ordinate, or head-axis, a distance above zero equal to the total static lift, as shown in Fig. 169 (r.) This is the usual situation.

As an example of how a system curve is developed, consider the 16-inch dredge of Figs. 164 and 165. Discharge velocity was 19 feet per second, static lift 15 feet; there were 800 feet of floating line, 1,000 feet of shoreline, two elbows and a flap valve.

A 16-inch pipe with a flow velocity of 19 feet per second would produce (from Equation 62 or Table 10), 11,170 gallons per minute. Note that the 16-inch pipe's inside diameter is actually 15.50 inches—0.25-inch wall thickness assumed.

The equivalent length of line, as determined previously in Art. 145, is 2,490 feet. Using the 11,170 gallons per minute discharge, the 2,490 equivalent feet of line, and a velocity of 19 feet per second, the head loss can be determined from Equation 49 or Table 9 as 5.82 feet per 100 feet of line. The total loss for the entire line will then be (24.9) (5.82) = 144.92 feet. This must be multiplied by the specific gravity, which in this case is 1.16. So, (1.16) (144.92) = 168.10 feet. Adding to this the static head multiplied by the specific gravity, (15) (1.16) = 17.40 feet, will give a total head of 185.5 feet. The velocity head will be so small that it is disregarded in this example. This value, 185.5 feet, is one point of the system curve—and actually the operating point, as will be shown.

To obtain additional points for the system curve, assume different outputs. From Table 10 or Equation 62 determine the velocity, and then from Table 9 or Equation 49, determine the head loss for each output. For instance, the head loss per 100 feet of line for outputs of 5,880, 6,470, 8,230, 9,410, 10,590, and 11,760 gallons per minute would be, using Tables 9 and 10, 1.89, 2.24, 3.00, 3.41, 4.31, 5.29 and 6.37 feet, respectively. Multiply each by 24.9 to obtain the loss for the entire line, then by 1.16 to account for the specific gravity. Then add the 17.40-foot effective static head to each. This will give, respectively, 71.98, 82.09, 104.04, 115.88, 141.87, 170.18 and 201.37 feet.

With these data points available, begin the system curve on the ordinate (H-axis) at the static elevation—in this instance 17.40 feet. Connect all the points by a smooth curve. If this curve is plotted on the same graph sheet as the pump's characteristic curves, the intersection of the two will indicate the operating point of the hydraulic system, point (A) on the 585-rpm characteristic of Fig. 165.

Should the speed of the pump be changed to, say 400 rpm, a new Q-H curve would be generated and the operating output and head would be changed to point (B) in Fig. 165. Should a different-diameter runner be used, rather than changing the speed of the pump, another Q-H curve would be generated, and its intersection with the system curve would provide a new operating point.

A change in the system curve would likewise change the operating point. For example, should some of the floating line be removed, the friction head would be reduced, and a new system curve, lower than the former, would be obtained. Its intersection with the characteristic curve would provide a new operating point.

When some of the line was removed, a new system curve would be determined similarly as was the original curve. Points for it would be calculated similarly, but the new length would be used to determine the frictional head-loss for different assumed outputs. Any number of system curves could be determined, each curve representing a different length of line. Each one would be obtained by assuming different quantities of flow and calculating head loss for each flow for each length of line.

157. Interpretation of Curves. Characteristic, system, and horsepower curves are extremely useful in predicting operating conditions. A few examples will be discussed using Fig. 165. First though, it is desirable to point out the mathematical relationships (known as affinity laws) between quantity, speed, horsepower, head and runner diameter. These relationships are,

With the same runner,

$$\frac{Q_1}{Q_2} = \frac{rpm_1}{rpm_2} \qquad \frac{H_1}{H_2} = \frac{(rpm_1)^2}{(rpm_2)^2} \qquad \frac{HP_1}{HP_2} = \frac{(rpm_1)^3}{(rpm_2)^3}$$

With different runners, but the same speed,

$$\frac{Q_1}{Q_2} = \frac{D_1}{D_2} \qquad \frac{H_1}{H_2} = \frac{D_1^2}{D_2^2} \qquad \frac{HP_1}{HP_2} = \frac{D_1^3}{D_2^3}$$

where Q_1 = capacity in gallons per minute at H_1 and rpm_1, or with runner diameter D_1; and Q_2 = capacity, in gallons per minute at H_2 and rpm_2 or with runner diameter D_2.

As can be seen in the system plotted in Fig. 165, a decrease in speed or runner diameter decreases the output, requiring less horsepower. Increasing the speed or runner diameter will do the opposite. A change in pipeline length, or an increase in elevation of the discharge, will change the system curve, it becoming steeper with the addition of pipe and therefore producing a reduction of output.

The advantageous use of different-sized runners is shown by these curves. On short lines lower head is required, and as head is directly proportional to the peripheral velocity of the runner, a lower peripheral velocity will be required. This can be obtained by slowing down the pump, or reducing the size of the runner. As a reduction in pump speed will reduce the horsepower capacity of the pump engine, a smaller diameter runner is the best solution.

On long lines, or lifts, higher head is required. Here again, head is directly proportional to the speed of the runner. A higher peripheral velocity will therefore be required. This can be obtained by speeding up the pump, or increasing the size of the runner. As pump drivers have a maximum speed at which they can be run to obtain maximum power and also as the speeds of pumps are relatively slow, the solution here is to use a larger diameter runner and keep the pump speed at the optimum value for maximum power. Using a runner that gives the lowest velocity for maximum output is the proper choice in every instance (60, 83). *See* Art. 145-I.

Change in line length is reflected in the curves. Consider the curves of an assumed pump in Fig. 170. Assume that more than 3,000 feet of line were required. If 5,000 feet were used it can be seen that a higher discharge head would result, shown by the increase in slope of the system curve and its change of intersection with the characteristic curve, and a lower quantity would be produced.

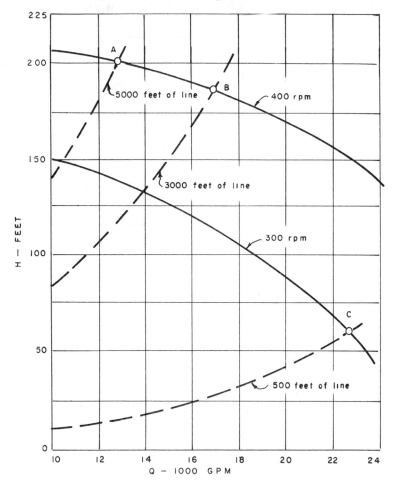

Fig. 170. Characteristic and System Curves of a Hypothetical Pump.

Now suppose that even more line were added. With no increase in pump speed, the output would decrease further—higher head would be required—and the velocity would drop. It could become so low that it could not carry the material in suspension, and the line would plug.

On the other hand, suppose that the pipeline was reduced to 1,000 feet. If no other changes were made, a reduced head would be the result. There would be a lower slope of the system curve and an increased output, and consequently, an increased velocity. The velocity, if it were excessive, could be reduced by slowing down the pump. However, should this speed reduction require an engine speed that was lower than that at which the engine developed full power, it would be better to replace the runner with one of a smaller diameter.

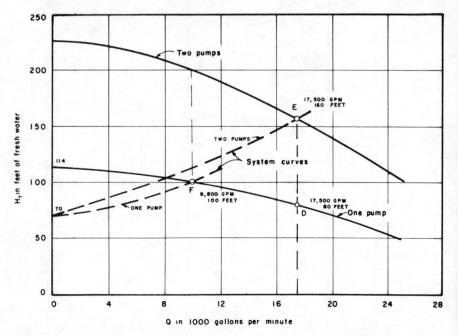

Fig. 171. Characteristic and System Curves of Booster and Dredge Pump in Series.

Finally, assume that while working on a 3,000-foot line, the pipeline suddenly broke at the 500-foot point. The output and pipeline velocity would instantly jump to a very high value and as a result there would be a very high horsepower demand. The pump engine would probably stall (60).

158. Pumps in Series. Where long lines and high lifts are required, or where speed or runner diameter cannot be increased sufficiently to overcome the increased head, pumps are often placed in series, the additional ones being called *boosters*. A booster pump can be placed anywhere in the discharge line, the only criterion being that it have sufficient suction pressure—that is, the flow to its suction from the preceding pump be at a positive pressure. Only a small amount is needed, in the region of four to five pounds per square inch above atmospheric, or just enough to keep air out of the system.

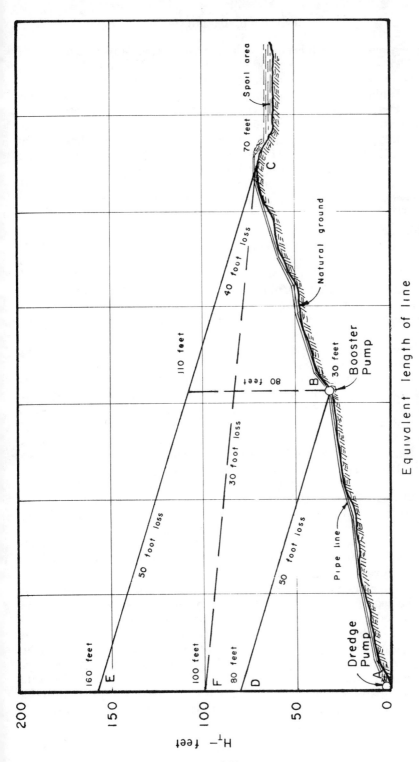

Fig. 172. Hydraulic Gradient of Dredge Pump and Booster in Series.

263

When a booster is placed in a line, new system and characteristic curves are created. The new system curve will be somewhat steeper than the one-pump curve, inasmuch as the output is increased, resulting in a higher velocity and therefore a higher friction loss. The new characteristic for both pumps in series will be the arithmetical sum of the head of each pump at identical outputs. In Fig. 171 it is assumed that both pumps have identical characteristics. Their combination in series is therefore just double the individual characteristic of one of them. For instance, at point (D) on the one-pump characteristic, the head at 17,500 gallons per minute is 80 feet. When both are in series, the total head at 17,500 gallons per minute is 160 feet (point E). Pumps with different characteristics could have been used as well.

Without the booster the dredge pump will produce 9,800 gallons per minute at a head of 100 feet (point P). However, when the booster is added, the output increases to 17,500 gallons per minute at 160 feet (point E). With both pumps in the line, the total flow of 17,500 gallons per minute goes through both. Consequently, the head on the dredge pump will be 80 feet (point D). As the total head is 160 feet, the head on the booster is also 80 feet.

Another way of studying the effect of a booster pump is by plotting the hydraulic gradient of the system—the pressure variation along the line (54). Figure 172 shows the hydraulic gradient of the example above. As before, the total head required to deposit the spoil in the disposal area is 160 feet (point E), this head being comprised of 70 feet of static lift and 90 feet of loss in the system.

The dredge pump (point A) produces, as before, a differential head of 80 feet—a static lift of 30 feet and a friction loss of 50 feet. Assuming that the suction head on the dredge pump is 15 inches of mercury (17 feet), the discharge head of the pump will be 30 + 50 − 17 = 63 feet. With a friction loss of 50 feet in the line to the booster pump at point (B), a suction head of 13 feet will be applied to the booster.

Pump B, as before, must produce a differential head of 80 feet—40 feet static and 40 feet friction. With the positive 13 feet of head, its discharge pressure will be 40 + 40 + 13 = 93 feet.

By placing the booster pump nearer the spoil area, the dredge pump would be required to produce additional head, because of the increased line loss and increase in static lift. Respectively, the booster would be required to produce less, and therefore the duties of each pump would be more equalized. With all other conditions equal, it is usually preferable to distribute the load as evenly as possible between each pump, one reason being the reduction of the total pressure in the line. When pumps of different characteristics are used, it is best practice to distribute the load proportionally with their characteristics (54, 83).

Chapter 12

Prime Movers

159. Introduction. Dredge pumps turn at relatively slow speeds—generally between 100 and 800 rpm. Usually the higher the speed, the smaller the pump. Prior to the invention of the steam turbine, practically all pumps were slow speed and heads were consequently limited. However, the high speed of the turbine allowed higher speed pumps and heads of up to and beyond 400 feet became common.

This increase in speed presented difficulties not previously experienced. Cavitation became a problem and wear increased almost in proportion to the increase in speed. Also, as the speed went up the available vacuum in the suction decreased. This created lifting problems (52).

Generally speaking however, slow speeds still predominate in dredge pumps. The reasons are several. One reason is that the speed of the pump—actually the speed of the periphery of the runner—determines the head the pump will produce. As the heads required are not great, high speeds are really not necessary. In addition, the materials the pump must handle are usually large and bulky. Consequently large openings are required for them to pass through the pump. Large openings require large runners, and with large runners high speeds are not necessary to develop the heads required.

160. Constant Power. At the same time as requiring slow speeds, dredge pumps require constant-power drivers. Unlike other types of pumps, they handle flows in which the material concentration varies from instant to instant. At one moment it may be 10 per cent; at another it may be 30 per cent. Density of the mixture is directly proportional to the concentration (Art. 139), so density fluctuates. Friction head is in turn directly proportional to the density of the mixture (Art. 142), so as the density changes, velocity will change proportionately.

In view of these factors, consider a situation where the concentration of the material in the flow is increasing. The velocity decreases, the head on the system increases and there is a lower power demand on the pump. Some of the material starts to drop out. Now if the prime mover is a constant-power source, the same power being supplied to the pump will result in an increase in speed. The velocity will then increase and the situation will be relieved.

On the other hand, should the prime mover have not been a constant-power source, the speed would have remained at its lower value, the head at its higher value, and the line would have probably plugged, had not some manual relief been instigated by the leverman.

With speed control of the prime mover, full power can always be used—if proper sized runners are used. However, with a constant-speed driver the power demand drops as the speed drops and the full power capabilities of the system cannot be utilized.

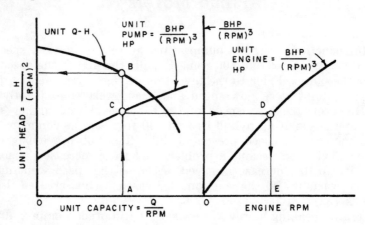

Fig. 173. Performance of Engine-driven Pump at Given Power Rating. (John Wiley & Sons, Inc.)

In Reference 54 a method is given for determining the performance of an engine-driven pump for a given engine power rating. It is as follows:

Suppose the engine is directly coupled to the pump. Engine horsepower can be equated to unit speed by dividing it by speed squared. Brake horsepower can be equated to per unit speed similarly. If head and capacity are also then reduced to per unit quantities by dividing them by the speed squared and to the first power, respectively, the performance of the pump can be plotted in terms of unit capacity, unit head, and unit brake horsepower (Fig. 173).

The operating point of the pump can then be determined by observing that for any unit capacity (A) the unit head will be (B), and the unit horsepower on the pump will be (C) and equal to the brake horsepower of the engine (D). Speed will therefore be (E).

To find the capacity in gallons per minute, multiply the unit capacity by speed; to find the head in feet, multiply the per unit head by the speed squared. If a reduction gear is used it should be considered as a part of the prime mover and the output speed of the gear used in the computations.

161. Types of Drives. There are three main types of pump drives generally available for dredges: (1) internal combustion (reciprocating type) engines, (2) constant or variable-speed electrical motors, and (3) rotating turbines.

Of the three, the internal-combustion diesel engine is probably the most predominant, particularly on small and medium-sized dredges. Gasoline or automotive-type engines are seldom used, and only on the most antiquated of dredges can you find a reciprocating steam engine today.

Up to about 5,000 horsepower, direct diesel drive is probably used more than turbine drive (52). Diesels are economical in fuel con-

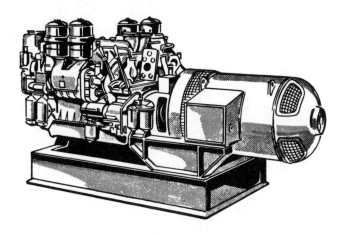

Fig. 174. General Motors' 6-71 Diesel Engine. (General Motors Corp.—Detroit Diesel Division)

sumption and require fewer and less-skilled personnel. However, the turbine weighs considerably less per horsepower than reciprocating engines, has no internal lubrication problems, and provides a more even torque. It does require a large condensing plant which precludes its use on small dredges.

Probably the most desirable drive of all is the d-c electrical motor. This is principally because of its ease of speed control and its practically unlimited capacity. However, the first cost of d-c power-drives or the means to convert to them is relatively high, and consequently d-c drives for pumps are not general. A-c wound rotor motors are used extensively (Art. 18). For low power factor electrical systems, the synchronous motor would be an ideal drive, because it can be operated at a leading power factor and thereby improve the power factor of the entire system. However, its speed control is extremely involved and therefore not generally used.

162. Diesel Drives. Unlike other internal combustion engines, the diesel has no spark plugs or electrical ignition system. The fuel oil is sprayed into a combustion chamber where the air has been compressed and heated, and combustion occurs without electrical spark.

These engines are generally rated at the load they will carry continuously at rated speed. Some, however, are rated for the load they can carry on test at full throttle.

Low-power diesels (125 to 600 horsepower) operate at speeds in the vicinity of 1,000 to 1,300 rpm. As the engine horsepower increases, the speed usually decreases. Engines in the 1,000-plus horse-

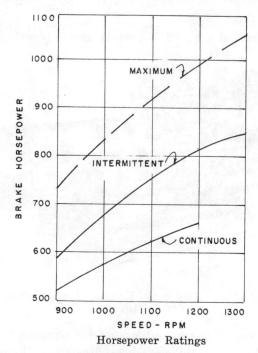

Horsepower Ratings

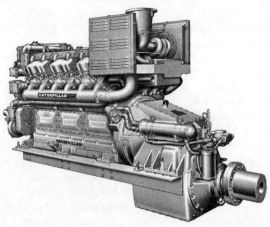

Fig. 175.   Caterpillar D-398.   (Caterpillar)

power range have, on an average, speeds in the region of 600 to 900 rpm. Larger horsepower engines have speeds as low as 120 rpm and up to 500 rpm. The weight of a diesel per horsepower increases with capacity. Average values for the medium and large horsepower engines would probably be around 20 to 40 pounds per brake horsepower, with the smaller horsepower engines running about half as much.

A diesel engine used on many small dredges, and particularly as a drive for main or auxiliary electrical plants, is the *General Motors'*

Fig. 176. Enterprise-De Laval DSRV-16-3. (De Laval Turbine Inc.)

6-71 (Fig. 174). It is sometimes used on small dredges for pump drive, and two or more are often combined to increase the driving horsepower.

Basically it has six cylinders in line with a $4\frac{1}{4}$-inch bore and a five-inch stroke, the total displacement being around 425 cubic inches. The displacement is calculated from the equation

$$\text{Cubic Inches} = (0.7854) \ (D^2) \ (S) \ (N) \qquad (69)$$

where D = diameter of the cylinder, in inches; S = length of the stroke, in inches, and N = number of cylinders. The basic engine has a brake horsepower rating of around 70 at 1,200 rpm and 96 at 1,800 rpm. It has a compression ratio of 16 to 1. Fuel oil consumption at continuous rating and 1,200 rpm is about seven or eight gallons of 0.83 specific gravity fuel per hour. No. 2 diesel fuel has a specific gravity of 0.9690 and Bunker C, No. 6 has a specific gravity of around 0.99. The basic engine has an average weight of around 3,800 pounds. Table 12 shows specifications for this unit.

Table 12. Specifications for GM 6-71 of Fig. 174
(General Motors Corp. —Detroit Diesel Div.)

	2 cylinder	3 cylinder	4 cylinder	6 cylinder
Cylinder Arrangement	Vertical In Line	Vertical In Line	Vertical In Line	Vertical In Line
Number of Cylinders	2	3	4	6
Bore and Stroke	4½ x 5 in.	4¼ x 5 in.	4¼ x 5 in.	4¼ x 5 in.
Total Displacement	141.9 cu. in.	212.8 cu. in.	283.7 cu. in.	425.6 cu. in.
Compression Ratio	16 to 1	16 to 1	16 to 1	16 to 1
Firing Order (Right-hand Engine)	1-2	1-3-2	1-3-4-2	1-5-3-6-2-4
Combustion Chamber	Open Type	Open Type	Open Type	Open Type
Lubrication	Forced Feed	Forced Feed	Forced Feed	Forced Feed
Air Scavenging System	Uniflow	Uniflow	Uniflow	Uniflow
Fuel System	G.M. Unit Injectors	G.M. Unit Injectors	G.M. Unit Injectors	G.M. Unit Injectors
Starting System	12 volt Electric	12 volt Electric	12 volt Electric	12 volt Electric

		2 cylinder	3 cylinder	4 cylinder
*Rated BHP-Basic engine equipped with 60 injectors	1200 RPM	40	62	82
	1500 RPM	48	75	100
	1600 RPM	50	78	104
	1800 RPM	53	83	111
*Continuous BHP-basic engine equipped with 60 injectors	1200 RPM	34	52	69
	1500 RPM	43	64	85
	1600 RPM	45	67	89
	1800 RPM	48	72	96
*Torque-maximum developed 1200 RPM with 60 injectors		175 lbs. ft.	270 lbs. ft.	360 lbs. ft.
Piston Speed	1200 RPM	1000 ft./min.	1000 ft./min.	1000 ft./min.
	1600 RPM	1333 ft./min.	1333 ft./min.	1333 ft./min.

For electrical power generation sets, one GM 6-71 is usually adequate for a 60- or 75-kw generator. Two of them in parallel will handle up to 200 kw, but 175 kw is a more reasonable load for continuous full-load operation.

The *Caterpillar* diesels are used considerably as pump prime movers. They are generally available in horsepower ratings from 125 to 1,200. The *Caterpillar D-398* marine engine (Fig. 175) will produce 650 horsepower continuously and around 850 intermittently (for

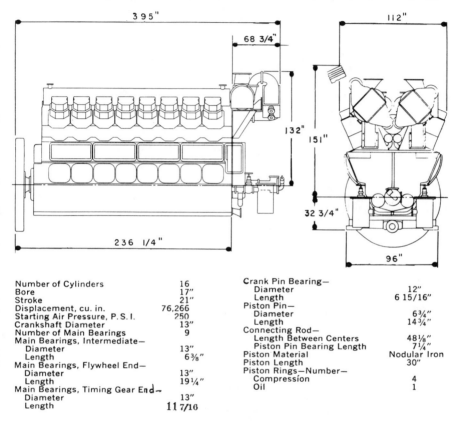

Number of Cylinders	16	Crank Pin Bearing—	
Bore	17"	Diameter	12"
Stroke	21"	Length	6 15/16"
Displacement, cu. in.	76,266	Piston Pin—	
Starting Air Pressure, P.S.I.	250	Diameter	6¾"
Crankshaft Diameter	13"	Length	14¾"
Number of Main Bearings	9	Connecting Rod—	
Main Bearings, Intermediate—		Length Between Centers	48⅛"
Diameter	13"	Piston Pin Bearing Length	7¼"
Length	6⅜"	Piston Material	Nodular Iron
Main Bearings, Flywheel End—		Piston Length	30"
Diameter	13"	Piston Rings—Number—	
Length	19¼"	Compression	4
Main Bearings, Timing Gear End→		Oil	1
Diameter	13"		
Length	11 7/16		

Fig. 177. Dimensions of the DSRV-16-3 of Fig. 176. (De Laval Turbine Inc.)

about one hour continuously). It is a V-12 cylinder type with a 6.25-inch bore and an eight-inch stroke. It has a total displacement of around 2,950 cubic inches and weighs, with the reduction gear attached, approximately 18,000 pounds. At the 1,000 rpm speed and 650 horsepower, it will burn in the neighborhood of 35 gallons of 0.83 specific gravity fuel per hour. The engine is quite often placed in tandem with others to provide more horsepower than is available from a single unit.

There are several manufacturer's models available for horsepower ratings above 1,000 in single-unit engines. *Enterprise-De Laval* diesels have horsepower ratings from around 1,200 up to and above

5,000, with speeds from 600 to 360 rpm, respectively. One of these units, the DSRV-16-3 (Fig. 176), has an average horsepower rating of 5,000 continuous at 360 rpm. It has a 17-inch bore and a 21-inch

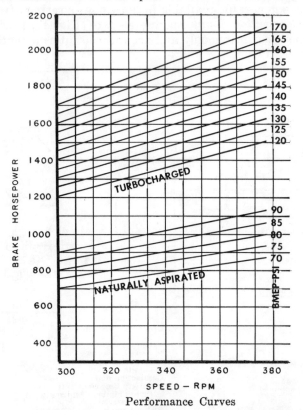

Performance Curves

Fig. 178. White Superior Model 80-S-8. (White Superior Division—White
Motor Corp.)

stroke and a total displacement of around 76,265 cubic inches. Its fuel consumption is around 260 gallons per hour and it weighs approximately 260,000 pounds. Figure 177 shows some of the dimensions for this unit.

White-Superior engines can be obtained in horsepower ratings up to 2,300 at 300 to 400 rpm. Their Model 80-S-8 (Fig. 178) has eight cylinders in line, a 14½-inch bore and a 20-inch stroke. The total displacement is around 26,500 cubic inches. The basic unit weighs approximately 94,000 pounds. Figure 179 shows the 40-SX-8 turning three generators in tandem.

Fig. 179. White Superior Model 40-SX/-8 Turning Three Generators in Tandem. (White Superior Division—White Motor Corp.)

Fairbanks-Morse diesels are available in horsepower ratings as high as 22,500 with speeds of 400 to 450 rpm. The 38D8 has 12 cylinders and a 2,000 brake horsepower rating at 100 per cent load and 750 rpm; at 900 rpm it has a 2,525 horsepower rating. It weighs approximately 42,000 pounds. Figure 180 shows some of the dimensions of the engine.

163. Steam Turbines. The steam turbine antedates from the early heat engines which were known as far back as 1,000 BC. In 130 BC, Hero of Alexandria, a mathematician, wrote a book in which he described an aeolipile which was turned by a jet of steam—a prototype of the reaction steam turbine (Fig. 181). The steam turbine was probably invented by the Italian architect Giovanni Baranca around 1630. However, little was done with the idea inasmuch as the single runner could develop only small power, and speed was excessive. The first steam turbine patent granted in the United States was not until 1831. All of these developments antedated De Laval's and Parson's

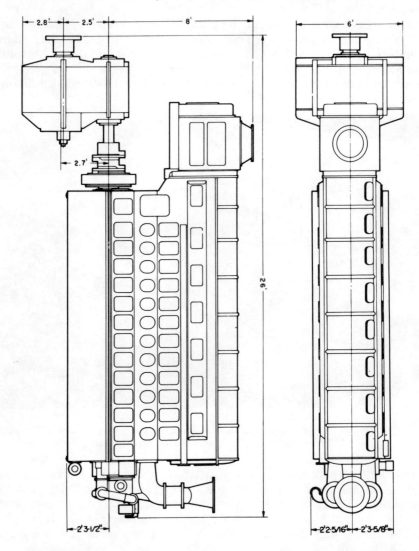

Fig. 180. Fairbanks-Morse 38D8 Dimensions. (Fairbanks-Morse—Colt Industries)

efforts in the 1880's. Parson's turbine, a reaction type, (see explanation of *reaction* below) developed about five horsepower at a speed of around 18,000 rpm. Parson later developed a condenser for his turbine which increased the efficiency and power. In 1910 he introduced the reduction gear.

The difference between a steam turbine and a steam engine is that the velocity of the steam in the engine, relative to the moving parts, is zero, while in a turbine it is relatively high—as much as 2,000 feet per second. Where the reciprocating steam engine uses the pressure energy of the steam to push a piston, the turbine uses the velocity energy of the steam to turn a rotor.

There are two fundamental types of steam turbines: (1) impulse and (2) reaction. The difference between the two is the manner in which the steam is applied to the rotor blades. The *impulse turbine* creates rotation by the impact—or impulse—of the steam on the rotor blades (Fig. 182), rotation being in the same direction as the steam jet. The *reaction turbine* creates rotation by the reactive—or reverse—force of the steam escaping from the rotor blades (Fig. 182)—

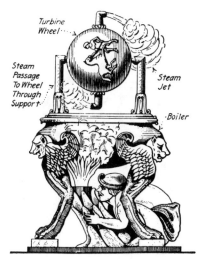

Fig. 181. Aeolipile from an Early Woodcut.

somewhat like the force that turns a lawn sprinkler. The steam velocity increases and pressure drops in the nozzles or stationary blades, and both velocity and pressure drop as the steam goes through the moving blades. In the *reaction turbine*, however, the steam velocity increases and pressure drops as it goes through the nozzles; velocity drops and pressure remains constant as the steam goes through the moving blades. The *reaction turbine* is much longer per horsepower than the *impulse turbine*, weighing more and taking up much more space.

164. Power of Steam Turbines. In either type of turbine, steam is applied to the rotor blades through the nozzles, the steam dropping from a high pressure area to one of low pressure. It loses heat in doing so, but at the same time acquires a higher velocity. In flowing through the nozzle the steam acquires a velocity of $V = 223.7 \ (H_1 - H_2)^{0.5}$, where H_1 and H_2 are the heat of the steam entering and leaving the nozzle, respectively, in British thermal units per pound (55).

If the turbine were 100 per cent efficient, the mechanical work done would be equal to the heat liberated, or $W = 778 \, (P) \, (H_1 - H_2)$, where W = work done, in foot pounds; P = weight of steam, in pounds, and H_1 and H_2 are as defined as above. Therefore the horsepower of the 100 per cent efficient turbine would be,

$$HP = \frac{(778) \, (P) \, (H_1 - H_2)}{(60) \quad (33,000)} = \frac{(P) \, (H_1 - H_2)}{2,545} \tag{70}$$

where P = rate of steam in pounds per hour per horsepower, and H_1 and H_2 are as defined above.

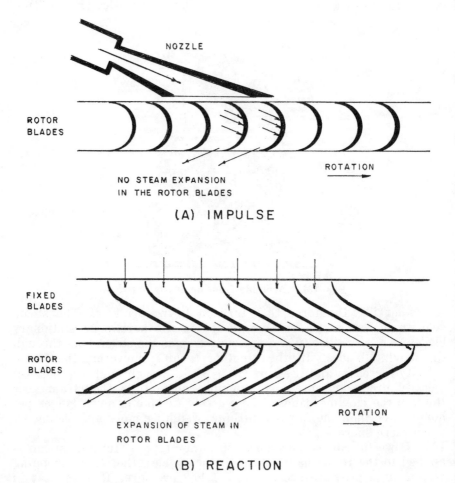

Fig. 182.   Steam Flow in the Impulse and Reaction Turbine.

In another sense, the horsepower would be,

$$HP = \frac{W\ (V_1{}^2 - V_2{}^2)}{(2g)\ (t)\ (550)} \tag{71}$$

where W = weight of steam, in pounds; g = acceleration of gravity, in feet per second per second; t = time of application of the steam, in seconds, and V_1 and V_2 = velocity of the steam applied to the blades, and the velocity of the exhaust steam, respectively, in feet per second.

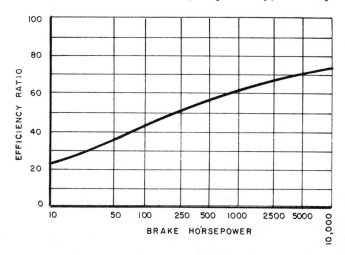

Fig. 183. Efficiency Ratios As a Function of Horsepower in a Turbine.
(McGraw-Hill Book Co., Inc.)

No turbine is 100 per cent efficient, however. Energy is lost in friction of the steam, eddy losses, windage, radiation, bearing friction, exhaust velocity, and leakage. Consequently, Equations 68 and 69 would have to be multiplied by the efficiency if they were to be used to determine the horsepower. Figure 183 shows efficiency ratios that are applicable in commercial turbines (55).

165. Power Measurement. The horsepower output of a turbine cannot be measured by taking an indicator diagram from the working cylinders as it can be done with a reciprocating steam engine. One method commonly used is to measure the torsional twist of the shaft, using the Hopkinson-Thring torsion meter (56).

166. Steam Turbine Characteristics. A pump cannot overload a steam turbine without the throttle being fixed. The turbine develops constant horsepower, so the speed always adjusts itself to a point where the power demand is met. As most steam turbines are constant-speed machines, governors are built to be speed responsive. Only small-capacity machines use direct-acting governors. Large-capacity machines use centrifugal governors which, in addition, operate a pilot valve through which oil under pressure is provided to move a piston that opens or closes the steam valves.

Since turbines operate at relatively high speeds (about one-half the speed of the steam applied to the rotor blades) and pumps must rotate at relatively slow speeds, a reduction gear must be interjected between them. Just as in cutter reduction gears, they are classified as single, double and triple reduction. The single reduction gear can be used if the speed of the turbine is not more than eight or so times the speed of the pump. Ordinarily this is not the case and double reduction gears are usually necessary.

167. Gas Turbines. Two Frenchmen, Armengaud and Lemale, were probably the first to introduce gas into a practical turbine. In 1894 they converted a 25-horsepower De Laval turbine into a gas turbine. It produced 500 horsepower at 5,000 rpm.

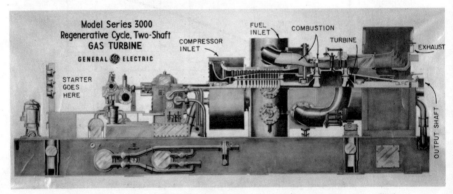

Fig. 184. Gas Turbine Arrangement. (General Electric Co.)

Although at present the gas turbine has not yet seen much application in the dredging field, the time will come, probably within the next ten to fifteen years, when these units will replace most of the high-power drivers of today. Just as the diesel replaced the gasoline engine, and the steam turbine the steam engine, the gas turbine will take its place in line.

The gas turbine operates by drawing air into a compression chamber where it is compressed adiabatically (without the transfer of heat) two to six times its original atmospheric value. Fuel oil is then interjected and the mixture of gas and air ignites. This increases its volume—at constant pressure—and the mixture is forced through the nozzles of the turbine into the blades. A small portion of the exploded mixture is used to turn the air compressor, the remainder being used to turn the turbine (Figs. 184 and 185).

Some of the present deterrents to the use of the gas turbine are its cost, high fuel consumption, heat problems, noise, and high speeds. Efficiency and lack of maintenance problems will eventually offset many of these disadvantages, however.

The weight of the gas turbine is an extreme advantage. Gas turbines, horsepower for horsepower, weigh about one-tenth that of diesels. In high horsepower units, the weight differential may be as much as 30 to 1.

The gas turbine, like the steam turbine, is a centrifugal machine. Because of this, and in contrast to the reciprocating, internal combustion engines, there is a minimum number of moving parts—and consequently less friction and vibration. Other advantages are its compactness and its ability to use almost any fuel that will flow and burn. It needs practically no cooling system.

Fig. 185.   Gas Turbine Arrangement.   (General Electric Co.)

Many gas turbines have two shafts. This allows the turbine to be started without the load being connected, so starting power requirements are less than for single-shaft units. Also, speed flexibility is provided without the loss of horsepower as in single-shaft units. Two-shaft units also have a torque converter characteristic which eliminates a number of gear speeds.

The exhaust gases from the turbine, which are used for propulsion in aircraft, could very well be used on dredges for steam generation. Steam generated thusly would probably cost only 10 to 20 per cent as much as it would if generated by conventional means. As much as 100,000 to 200,000 pounds of steam per hour could be generated with supplementary firing in the larger units.

Appendix

PER-UNIT CONTRACTS

<u>168. Invitation to Bidders Form.</u> The following is adapted from forms used by the Corps of Engineers for making an invitation to bid to prospective contractors. It has been written with descriptive and advisory information included so that it may be used on most projects.

INVITATION TO BIDDERS

(Place)_____

(Date) _____

Sealed bids, in duplicate, subject to the conditions contained herein, will be received until_____, 19___, and then publicly (or otherwise) opened for furnishing all labor and materials and performing all work for:

(Note: The above paragraph should state the hour and date of opening bids, and in concise form, the amount, nature, and location of the work to be done.)

A. Maps. Where copies of maps (drawings) are requested no deposit will be (a deposit of $_____ will be) required to insure their return. The deposit should be in the form of a United States money order or a certified check made payable to _____ The maps which will become part of this contract are designated in paragraph 1-03 of the specifications.

Other maps (drawings) showing the location and the latest soundings, probings and borings made on the various areas and other available data (the general features of the work) may be seen at this office and should be consulted by prospective bidders before submitting their bids.

B. Guarantee. A guarantee will be required with each bid as follows: Bid bond will be executed in a penal sum approximately equal to and not less than _____ per cent of the total amount bid. Individual sureties will justify in sums aggregating not less than double the penalty of the bid bond.

C. Performance and Payment Bonds. Performance and payment bonds will be required as follows:

(1) A performance bond with good and sufficient surety or sureties will be executed in a penal sum approximately equal to and not less than fifty (50) per cent of the full amount of the consideration of the contract.

(2) If the consideration of the contract exceeds $2,000.00 in amount, a payment bond with good and sufficient surety or sureties for the protection of persons furnishing material and labor for the work will be executed in a penal sum approximately equal to and not less than

_____ per cent of the full amount of the consideration of the contract; when the latter is not more than one million dollars, _____ per cent will be required.

D. Liquidated damages for delay will be prescribed. (See par. 1-05 of the specifications.)

E. Partial payments will (will not) be made. (See par. 1-07 of the specifications.)

F. Experience. Each bidder shall state in his bid whether he is now or ever has been engaged on any contract or other work similar to that proposed, giving the year in which it was done and the manner of its execution, and shall submit such other information as will tend to show his ability to prosecute vigorously the work required by these specifications.

G. Plant. Bids will state the character and amount of plant that the bidder proposes to employ on the work. After bids are opened, any bidder may be required to show that he owns, controls, or can procure the plant necessary for commencing, prosecuting, and completing the work as required by the specifications.

Each bidder will state in his bid whether or not his plant will have the facilities for furnishing meals in accordance with paragraph 3-02 of the specifications.

H. (1) Completion. Each bidder will state in his bid the period of time in which he will agree to complete the work, time being reckoned from the date on which he receives the notice to proceed. The time of completion proposed by bidders will be given due weight in canvassing the bids, at the rate of $_____ per calendar day.

(2) Completion. Each bidder will state in his bid the average monthly rate of progress he will guarantee. The time in calendar days required for completion will be determined by dividing the estimated yardage to be used in comparing bids by the proposed monthly yardage and multiplying the result by 30. In canvassing bids, time will be given due weight at the rate of $_____ per calendar day.

(Use par. (a) when par. 1-05(c) of the specifications is used; use par. (b) when par. 1-05(d) is used.)

I. (1) Bid and Contract. The bid form has an entry for each item on which estimates will be given or payments made, and no other allowances of any kind will be made unless specifically provided for in the specifications or the contract. The quantities of each item of a bid, as finally ascertained at the close of the contract, in the units given and the unit prices of the several items stated by the bidder in the accepted bid, will determine the total payments to accrue under the contract. The unit price bid for each item must allow for all collateral or indirect cost connected with it.

(2) Bid and Contract. The bid form has an entry for the item on which estimates will be given or payments made, and no other allowances of any kind will be made unless specifically provided for in the specifications or the contract. The quantity of material as finally ascertained at the close of the contract in the unit given and the unit price stated by the bidder in the accepted bid, will determine the total payments to accrue under the contract. The unit price bid must allow for all collateral or indirect cost connected with it.

(Par. (1) will be used when bids on a plurality of items are invited; par. (2) when bids are invited on one item only.)

J. Award of Contract. Subject to the rights hereinafter reserved, the work will be awarded

----

(state here whether it is contemplated to award the work as a whole to one bidder, or to divide it among two or more bidders).

A bid may be rejected if the bidder cannot show that he has the necessary capital and experience, and owns, controls, or can procure the necessary plant to commence the work at the time prescribed in the specifications, and thereafter to prosecute and complete the work at the rate or time specified; and that he is not already obligated for the performance of other work which would delay the commencement, prosecution or completion of the work contemplated in this advertisement.

Any unbalanced bid which, in the opinion of the owner, jeopardizes the interest of the owner will be subject to rejection for that reason.

The right is reserved to reject any and all bids, to waive any informality in bids received, and to accept or reject any items of any bid, unless such bid is qualified by specific limitation.

Envelopes containing bids must be sealed, marked and addressed as follows:

Bid for_____
To be opened_____

169. Bid Form. The following is adapted from forms used by the Corps of Engineers for receiving bids from prospective contractors. It has been written with descriptive and advisory information included so that it may be used on most projects.

(Place)_____

(Date) _____

To _____

_____

In compliance with your invitation for bids dated_____ and subject to all the conditions thereof, the undersigned

----

a corporation organized and existing under the laws of the State of_____

a partnership consisting of_____

----

or an individual trading as_____

----

of the city of _____

hereby proposes to furnish all plant, labor, and materials, and perform

all work required for --

----
in strict accordance with the specifications, schedules, and drawings, for the consideration of the following prices:

Quantities for canvassing bids	Unit	Description	Unit price	Amount

Note: All amounts and totals given above will be subject to verification. In case of variation between unit bid price and totals shown by bidder, the unit price will be considered to be his bid.

PLANT TO BE USED ON THE WORK

Name	Kind	Capacity	Condition

The plant $\begin{bmatrix} \text{will} \\ \text{will not} \end{bmatrix}$ have the facilities for furnishing the meals required by paragraph 3-02 of the specifications. (See Invitation for Bids.)
Experience. (See Invitation for Bids.) -------------------------
----

The undersigned agrees, upon receipt of written notice of the acceptance of this bid within 60 days after the date of opening of the bids, to execute the contract, in accordance with the bid as accepted, and give performance and payment bonds, with good and sufficient surety or sureties, for the faithful performance of the contract, and for the protection of all persons supplying labor and materials in the prosecution of the work, within 10 days after the prescribed forms are presented for signature.

(a) Performance will begin within---------- calendar days after the receipt of notice to proceed and will be completed as specified in paragraph 1-05 of the specifications.

(b) Performance will begin within------- calendar days after the receipt of notice to proceed and will be completed within-----------
calendar days after date of receipt of said notice to proceed.

(c) The undersigned agrees to begin the work within------------
calendar days after the receipt of notice to proceed, and complete it within ------- calendar days after date of receipt of said notice to proceed.

(d) The undersigned agrees to begin the work within------- calendar days after the receipt of notice to proceed, and guarantees to prosecute it at an average rate of not less than---------- cubic yards per month after the limiting date fixed for commencement as specified in paragraph 1-05 of the specifications.

Note: Use (a), (b), (c), or (d) when paragraph 1-05 (a), 1-05 (b), 1-05 (c), or 1-05 (d) of the specifications, respectively, is to be used.

By----------------------------

(Business address)

170. Specifications. The following is adapted from forms used by the Corps of Engineers for general and special specifications. It has been written with descriptive and advisory information included so that it may be used on most projects.

SPECIFICATIONS

SECTION I. GENERAL PROVISIONS

1-01. Location. (Describe the location of the work, giving the name of the waterway, harbor, or roadstead and a general description of the vicinity.)

1-02. Work to Be Done. The work to be done consists of (describe the work fully as suggested in Note below).

Note: Define concisely the work, the accomplishment of which is to be required under the contract, the completion of which will constitute the completion of the contract. Detailed descriptive matter or technical requirements should not be included. For channel excavation, give the definite limits of the excavation required, its length, width and depth referred specifically to a plane of reference. Depths in excess of project depth may be specified to lessen the cost of future maintenance. Where the width varies, the length of the channel for which each width is required should be stated. When only a part of an existing channel is to be dredged, that part should be clearly described to show that it is not intended to cover the entire area. When the work to be done is the removal of accumulated shoals and the shoal areas do not extend over the entire length and width of the channel covered by the specifications, and shoaling is at so slow a rate that the precontract soundings show reliably the areas to be dredged in the execution of the work, the precise areas to be worked over by the dredge should be shown on the drawings and indicated by suitable cross hatchings or otherwise, and overdepth dredging should be allowed throughout the areas so shown. In such cases the areas to be dredged should be laid out in suitable dredge cuts of proper width or multiples thereof for the type of dredge that will probably be used on the work, these ordinarily being from 30 to 40 feet for bucket and dipper dredges, and from 100 to 200 feet for pipe-line dredges, depending on the size of the dredge appropriate for the work. Isolated shoal areas of soft material having a depth within a half foot or so of the required depth should ordinarily be omitted from the areas to be dredged, since the cost of removal is out of proportion to the benefits; but if it is of importance to have full project depth throughout the channel, and funds are sufficient for the purpose, the required dredging depth should be made at least one foot in excess of the project depth, and isolated areas and part-width dredge cuts showing depths between the project and required depths should not be included in the areas to be dredged. In all cases the wording must describe exactly what work is to be performed under the contract.

For purposes of acceptance, the area to be excavated is divided into sections as follows: (define sections clearly).

Note: Unless the work is of such small magnitude that it can be promptly completed as a whole, the division of the work into sections should be such as will make possible final examination and acceptance of each section in accordance with paragraph 4-07 and generally not to exceed two months after the section has been dredged. In extensive contracts, the division into sections should, if practicable, be so made that the contractor can be required to prosecute the work to afford a continuous through channel for navigation without undue delay in acceptance of completed work.

1-03. Maps. The work shall conform to $\begin{bmatrix} \text{maps} \\ \text{drawings} \end{bmatrix}$ ---------------
----
which form a part of the specifications, and which are filed
at --

Note: All maps pertaining to the specifications should be so marked that if any question arises requiring their use they may be clearly identified as the ones mentioned in the specifications. Bulky maps or blue prints larger than 8 by 10 inches, or 10 by 16 inches (one fold) should not be attached to contracts. The map or maps which are intended to form a part of the specifications should not only show the limits of the proposed work so clearly that no question can arise whether any work will be or will not be a part of the contract to be entered into, but, in addition, should contain sufficient soundings that a bidder may judge intelligently the approximate location and amount of work covered by the specifications, and every map forming a part of the specifications should have a notation to that effect.

1-04. Quantity of Material. The total estimated $\begin{bmatrix} \text{quantity} \\ \text{quantities} \end{bmatrix}$ of material necessary to be removed from within the specified limits, exclusive of allowable overdepth, to complete the work described in paragraph

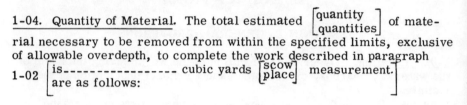

1-02 $\begin{bmatrix} \text{is} \text{-----------------} \text{ cubic yards } \begin{bmatrix} \text{scow} \\ \text{place} \end{bmatrix} \text{ measurement.} \\ \text{are as follows:} \end{bmatrix}$

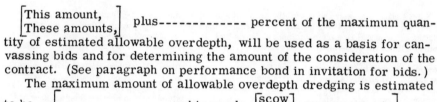

$\begin{bmatrix} \text{This amount,} \\ \text{These amounts,} \end{bmatrix}$ plus ------------ percent of the maximum quantity of estimated allowable overdepth, will be used as a basis for canvassing bids and for determining the amount of the consideration of the contract. (See paragraph on performance bond in invitation for bids.)

The maximum amount of allowable overdepth dredging is estimated to be— $\begin{bmatrix} \text{-----------------cubic yards } \begin{bmatrix} \text{scow} \\ \text{place} \end{bmatrix} \text{ measurement.} \\ \text{as follows:} \end{bmatrix}$

The contractor will be required to excavate the entire quantity of material necessary to complete the work specified in paragraph 1-02 hereof, be it more or less than the amounts above estimated.

1-05. (a) Commencement, Prosecution, and Completion. The contractor will be required to commence work under the contract within------ calendar days after the date of receipt by him of notice to proceed, to prosecute the said work at an average rate of not less than----------- cubic yards per month during the first $\begin{bmatrix} \text{month} \\ \text{------months} \end{bmatrix}$ after the limiting date fixed for commencement, and at an average rate of not less than ----------- cubic yards per month thereafter, and to complete it within the time determined by applying to the total quantity of material to be paid for actually removed under the contract the average monthly rates above stipulated, for the periods to which each rate applies; provided, that the contractor may be required so to conduct his work that at the end of each month during the life of the contract the total progress from the beginning of the contract to the end of that month shall be not less than that required by the above-stipulated rates of progress; provided further, that the quantity of material removed in any one month shall in no case be less than ------------- cubic yards; provided further, that no waiver by the contracting officer of any failure of the contractor to make in any month or series of months the rate of progress required by this paragraph shall be construed as relieving the contractor from his obligation to make up the deficiency in future months and to complete the entire work within the time allowed by the contract.

In case of failure on the part of the contractor to complete the work within the time thus determined and agreed upon for its completion, plus any extensions duly granted under articles 3, 4, 5, and 9 of the contract, the contractor shall pay to the owner as liquidated damages the sum of $-------- for each calendar day of delay until the work is completed or accepted.

1-05. (b) Commencement, Prosecution, and Completion. The contractor will be required to commence work under the contract within --------- calendar days after the date of receipt by him of notice to proceed, to prosecute the said work with faithfulness and energy, and to complete it within --------- calendar days after said date of receipt of notice to proceed; provided, that should the total quantity of material to be paid for actually removed under the contract exceed the quantity on which bids will be canvassed as stated in paragraph 1-04 of these specifications, additional time will be allowed at the rate of ------- calendar days for each ----------- cubic yards in excess of such estimated quantity.

In case of failure on the part of the contractor to complete the work within the time thus determined and agreed upon for its completion, plus any extensions duly granted under articles 3, 4, 5, and 9 of the contract, the contractor shall pay the owner as liquidated damages the sum of $------ for each calendar day of delay until the work is completed or accepted.

1-05. (c) Commencement, Prosecution, and Completion. The contractor will be required to commence the work under the contract within--- calendar days after date of receipt by him of notice to proceed, and to complete it within the time stated in his bid, time being reckoned from the date on which he receives notice to proceed; provided, that should the total quantity of material to be paid for actually removed under the contract exceed the estimated quantity (par. 1-04), additional time will be allowed for such excess yardage in the ratio that the total of pay-- ments for the estimated yardage stated in paragraph 1-04 of the specifications.

In case of failure on the part of the contractor to complete the work within the time thus determined and agreed upon for its completion, plus any extensions duly granted under articles 3, 4, 5, and 9 of the contract, the contractor shall pay to the owner as liquidated damages the sum of $------ for each calendar day of delay until the work is completed or accepted.

1-05. (d) Commencement, Prosecution, and Completion. The contractor will be required to commence the work under the contract within -------- calendar days after date of receipt by him of notice to proceed, and to complete it within the number of calendar days determined by dividing the estimated yardage stated in paragraph 1-04 of these specifications by the monthly yardage proposed by the contractor in his bid and multiplying the result by 30, time being reckoned from the limiting date fixed for commencement; provided, should the total quantity of material to be paid for actually removed under the contract exceed the estimated quantity (par. 1-04), additional time will be allowed for such excess yardage at the rate of one calendar day for the number of yards determined by dividing the monthly rate by 30.

In case of failure on the part of the contractor to complete the work within the time thus determined and agreed upon for its completion, plus any extensions duly granted under articles 3, 4, 5, and 9 of the contract, the contractor shall pay the owner as liquidated damages the sum of \$------ for each calendar day of delay until the work is completed or accepted.

Note 1. An average rate of progress (par. 1-05 (a) should always be used when the quantity of work to be done will be determined by the price bid. A fixed time of completion may be stated if preferred; in which case paragraph 1-05 (b), 1-05 (c), or 1-05 (d) should be used.

Note 2. In cases where it is desired to charge the contractor only with the direct increased contract supervision costs due to his delay in completing the work, the amount of liquidated damages to be inserted in the appropriate spaces above should be based only on the estimated cost of inspection and superintendence, including necessary traveling expenses connected therewith.

Note 3. When there are unusual reasons for making the time of completion a competitive feature, paragraph 1-05 (c) or 1-05 (d) should be used. If 1-05 (c) or 1-05 (d) is used the rate per day used in canvassing the bids and the amount per day of liquidated damages should be the same. A high rate adds to the risks of the contractor and often leads to unnecessarily high bids and to damage claims. Therefore the rate should not exceed the clearly evident injury.

Note 4. Time of commencement and completion should be based upon a careful consideration of the needs of the work and the conditions in the dredging business at the time the advertisement is issued. The time provisions then should be made as liberal as will permit, with a view to securing the lowest bids compatible therewith.

Note 5. In parts of the country where suspension of work by ice or inclement weather during all or a portion of the winter months is to be expected, the following provisions should be added to paragraph 1-05 (a), (b), (c), or (d), as selected:

No work will be required during the period between---------- and ---------, inclusive. If he so desires, the contractor may work during any part or all of this period upon giving written notice of his desire to the owner; but whether he works or not, no part of the period above named will be considered in computing the time allowed for completion or in computing liquidated damages.

If, however, the contractor elects to work during any part of the period above named, the monthly average work accomplished is any percentage less than $\left[\dfrac{\text{---------cubic yards,}}{\text{the average monthly work necessary to complete the contract within the time specified,}}\right]$ and the contracting officer maintains an inspection force during this time for the purpose of supervising the work, the contractor will be charged this same percentage of the cost of maintenance of such inspection force.

Note: The last sentence may be omitted where not applicable.

1-06. Sundays, Holidays, and Nights. No work shall be done on Sundays (omit this clause where not applicable) except in cases of emergency, and then only with the written consent of the owner, nor shall any work be done at night unless authorized in writing by the owner.

1-07. (a) Payments. Payments will be made in accordance with article 16 of the contract.

1-07. (b) Payments. Payments will be made monthly on estimates of such material as has been excavated and deposited in accordance with the specifications and not included in any prior estimate, except that 10 percent of the amount of each estimate will be retained until the——

(w) Full completion and acceptance of all work covered by the contract, when final payment will be made.

(x) Full completion and acceptance of all work covered by the contract: Provided, however, That the owner, at any time after 50 percent of the work has been completed, if he finds that satisfactory progress is being made, may make any of the remaining partial payments in full.

(y) Total amount so retained shall equal $---------, after which the amount retained will remain unchanged until the full completion and acceptance of all work covered by the contract.

(z) Contract work is---------- percent completed; and thereafter with each monthly payment there will be paid such portion of the amount so retained as is in excess of -------- percent of the estimated cost of completing the work remaining to be done, until the amount retained is reduced to $--------, after which it will remain unchanged until the full completion of all work covered by the contract.

The amount available for payment of contractor's estimates is about $--------.

Note: Clause (w) will be used in small contracts, and in contracts which require that the sum retained should increase until the work is completed. Clause (y) will be used in large contracts in which a maximum retained sum is sufficient protection. Clause (z) will be used in large contracts where the retained sum may be reduced toward the completion of the work. The last sentence (as to the amount of funds available) will be used when it is doubtful whether the funds available are sufficient to do the entire work or when it is believed that it will not be sufficient.
Notes: In all "continuing contracts" paragraph 1-07 (c) will be used in lieu of 1-07 (a) or 1-07 (b).

Payments will be made monthly on estimates of such material as has been excavated and deposited in accordance with the specifications and not included in any prior estimate, except that --------- percent of the amount of each estimate will be retained until the contract work is---- percent completed, and thereafter with each monthly payment there will be paid such portion of the amount so retained as is in excess of --------- percent of the estimated cost of completing the work remaining to be done, until the amount retained is reduced to $---------, after which the amount to be retained will remain unchanged until the completion of the contract.

1-08. Physical Data.

Note: These include general features affecting the work, such as range of tides, wave action, exposure to storms, unusual currents, duration of usual working season, presence of cables, pipes, or tunnels, bridges across the channel or across the route to the dumping ground, and a reference to the regulations concerning the same.

1-09. Datum and Bench Marks. The plane of reference of------------ as used in these specifications is that determined by the following bench mark:

(Here give location and description of bench mark or bench marks and relation to the stated plane of reference.)

Note: On the Great Lakes the plane of reference should be low-water datum, and its relation to mean sea level and the datum of the Lake Survey charts should be stated.

1-10. Condition of Channel.

Note: Describe the present conditions as to depth and width of channel. If any previous work has been done over the area proposed to be dredged, the result of which might affect the conditions to be found, that work should be described. If the work is divided into sections, the present condition of each section should be given. (See par. 1-02, Note 2.)

Note: Describe the usual character of traffic in the channel with reference to the effect it may have on contract operations.

1-11. Plant. The contractor agrees to place on the job sufficient plant of size suitable to meet the requirements of the work. Plant shall be kept at all times in condition for efficient work, and subject to the inspection of the owner. It is understood that award of this contract shall not be construed as a guaranty by the owner that plant listed in statement of contractor for use on this contract is adequate for the performance of the work.

(a) All scows must be kept in good condition, the coamings kept repaired, and the pockets provided with proper doors or appliances to prevent leakage of material.

(b) All pipe lines for hydraulic machines must be kept in good condition at all times, and any leaks or breaks along their length must be promptly and properly repaired.

No reduction in the capacity of the plant employed on the work shall be made except by written permission of the owner. The measure of the "capacity of the plant" shall be its actual performance on the work to which these specifications apply.

Note: Clause (a) will be used when it is possible that the material will be handled in scows. Clause (b) will be used when it is possible that hydraulic pipe-line machines will be used on the work.

1-12. Claims and Protests. If the contractor considers any work required of him to be outside the requirements of the contract, or considers any record or ruling of the inspectors or contracting officer as unfair, he shall ask for written instructions or decision immediately, and then file a written protest with the owner against the same within 10 days thereafter, or be considered as having accepted the record or ruling. (See arts. 3 and 15 of contract.)

1-13. Liability of the Contractor. The contractor will be responsible that his employees strictly observe the laws of the United States affecting operations under the contract. He shall comply with the laws of the United States and of the States as to the inspection of hulls, boilers, and other equipment, and the licensing of masters, engineers, and other members of the crews of his vessels. He shall conduct the work with due regard to safety against accidents to his employees and to the employees of others supervising the work, all in conformity with current safety engineering practice as set forth in the Manual of Accident

Prevention in Construction published by the Associated General Contractors of America and the publications of the National Safety Council, or as required by State or municipal law regulations or ordinance. He shall provide such machinery guards, safe walkways, ladders, bridges, gangplanks, and other safety devices as may be required by the owner as requisite to the prevention of accidents. He shall promptly report to the owner in form prescribed by him all accidents occurring to the contractors' employees. He shall conform to such sanitary requirements as may be prescribed by the owner. Nothing in this paragraph shall be construed as modifying the responsibility of the contractor as set forth in article 10 of the contract.

1-14. Patents. (a) The contractor shall hold and save the owner, his officers, agents, servants, and employees harmless from liability of any nature or kind, including costs and expenses, for or on account of any patented or unpatented invention, article, or appliance manufactured or used in the performance of this contract.

(b) The contractor shall hold and save the owner, his officers, agents, servants, and employees, harmless from liability of any nature or kind, including costs and expenses, for or on account of any patented or unpatented invention article, or appliance manufactured or used in the performance of this contract, and the contractor shall give a bond in an amount satisfactory to the owner, the terms of which shall fully protect the owner against loss should the contractor default in the obligation under this article.

Note 1. Subparagraph (a) above will ordinarily be used for dredging work.
Note 2. When competitive bids are invited for an item known to be patented or to contain patented features, or to require a patented process in its manufacture, and all manufacturers invited to bid are known to be financially responsible, subparagraph (a) above will be used. No special bond in addition to the regular performance bond will be required when this clause is used.
Note 3. When competitive bids are invited for items known to be patented and the financial responsibility of prospective bidders is unknown, subparagraph (b) above will be used in lieu of subparagraph (a). It is only when subparagraph (b) above is used that a special infringement bond will be required in addition to the regular performance bond.

1-15. Reports. The contractor will report monthly, and will cause all subcontractors to report in like manner, within 5 days after the close of each calendar month, on forms to be furnished by the owner, the number of persons on their respective pay rolls, the aggregate amount of such pay rolls, the man-hours worked, and the total expeditures for materials. He shall furnish the owner the names and addresses of all subcontractors on the work at the earliest date practicable, provided that the foregoing shall be applicable only to work at the site of the construction project.

SECTION II. CONDUCT OF WORK

2-01. Order of Work. The work is to be carried on at such localities and also in such order of precedence as may be found necessary by the owner. The location and limits of the work to be done will be plainly indicated by the owner or his agents by stakes and ranges or otherwise, and gages will be established to show the stage of water with reference to the datum plane for dredging. The contractor may be required to

suspend dredging at any time when for any reason the gages or ranges
cannot be seen or properly followed.

In order that the contractor may receive payment, the full depth required under the contract must be secured in the whole of the area
worked over as the work progresses, unless prevented by ledge rock,
nor will payment be made for excavation in any area not adjacent to and
in prolongation of areas where full depth has been secured except by
special decision of the owner. Should any such nonadjacent area be excavated to full depth during the operations carried on under the contract,
payment for all work therein may be deferred until the required depth
has been made in the area intervening.

Note. Gages should be established so as to be observable from any part of the work, in order
that the proper depth may at all times be determined. Where important parts of work might be left
by the contractor to the last because of his small profit thereon it may be proper to specify or require early completion of such parts. As a general rule, no special order of work should be prescribed unless essential. When it is necessary to prescribe the order of work it should be established in the specifications if practicable, or at least before the commencement of contract work.
The phrase "unless prevented by ledge rock" in line 9 should be omitted when rock work is included. Also see Note 3 of paragraph 1-02.

2-02. Misplaced Material. Any material that is deposited elsewhere
than in places designated or approved by the owner will not be paid for,
and the contractor may be required to redredge such material and
deposit it where directed.

Should the contractor, during the progress of the work, lose, dump,
throw overboard, sink, or misplace any material, plant, machinery, or
appliance, which in the opinion of the contracting officer may be dangerous to or obstruct navigation, he shall recover and remove the same
with the utmost dispatch. The contractor shall give immediate notice,
with description and location of such obstructions, to the owner or inspector, and when required shall mark or buoy such obstructions,
until the same are removed. Should he refuse, neglect, or delay compliance with the above requirement, such obstructions may be removed
by the owner, and the cost of such removal may be deducted from any
money due or to become due the contractor, or may be recovered under
his bond.

2-03. Lights. The contractor shall keep proper lights each night, between the hours of sunset and sunrise, upon all floating plant connected
with the work, upon all ranges and other stakes in connection with it,
when necessary in the opinion of the owner, and upon all buoys of such
size and in such locations as to endanger or obstruct navigation, and
shall be responsible for all damages resulting from any neglect or
failure in this respect. If work at night is permitted by the owner (see
par. 1-06), the contractor shall maintain, from sunset to sunrise, such
lights on or about his plant as the owner may deem necessary for the
proper observation of the dredging operations.

2-04. Obstructions. The owner will not undertake to keep the channel
free from vessels or other obstructions. The contractor will be required to conduct the work in such manner as to obstruct navigation as
little as possible, and in case the contractor's plant so obstructs the
channel as to make difficult or endanger the passage of vessels, said
plant shall be promptly moved on the approach of any vessel to such an
extent as may be necessary to afford a practicable passage. Upon the

completion of the work the contractor shall promptly remove his plant, including ranges, buoys, piles, and other marks placed by him under the contract in navigable waters or on shore.

SECTION III. SUPERVISION

3-01. Inspection. The work will be conducted under the general direction of the owner and will be inspected by inspectors appointed by him, who will enforce a strict compliance with the terms of the contract. The inspectors will keep a record of the work done, and see that the gages, ranges, and other marks are kept in proper order; but the presence of the inspector shall not relieve the contractor or his responsible agent of any responsibility for the proper execution of the work. The contractor will be required:

(a) To furnish on the request of the inspectors the use of such boats, boatmen, laborers, and material forming a part of the ordinary and usual equipment and crew of the dredging plant as may be reasonably necessary in inspecting and supervising the work. However, the contractor will not be required to furnish such facilities for the surveys prescribed in paragraphs 4-07.

(b) To furnish, establish, and maintain in good order all range marks, stakes, gages, and buoys required for the proper execution of the dredging.

(c) To provide, when required by the owner or his assistants, suitable transportation from all points on shore designated by the owner to and from the various pieces of plant, and to and from the dumping grounds.

The cost of meeting all of the foregoing requirements must be included in the price bid.

Should the contractor refuse, neglect, or delay compliance with these requirements the specific facilities may be furnished and maintained by the owner, and the cost thereof will be deducted from any amounts due or to become due the contractor.

The owner will furnish on the request of the contractor all survey lines, points and elevations reasonably necessary for the setting of ranges, stakes, gages, and buoys. Except as specified in this paragraph, in the last subparagraph of paragraph 1-05, in paragraph 4-07, and in paragraph 3-02, all expenses of inspection, surveys and superintendence will be borne by the owner.

It is understood that any instructions, or decisions given by official representatives of the owner are to be considered instructions or decisions of the owner, in all cases where under the terms of this contract decision rests with the owner.

Note 1. Cancel reference to last subparagraph of paragraph 1-05 when said subparagraph is not used.

Note 2. When conditions are such as to render requirements in addition to those specified as (a), (b), and (c), advisable additional specific requirements may be inserted.

3-02. Accommodations and Meals for Inspectors. The contractor shall furnish regularly to inspectors on board the dredge or other craft upon which they are employed a suitable separate room for office and sleeping purposes. The room shall be fully equipped and maintained to the satisfaction of the owner; it shall be properly heated, ventilated, and lighted, and shall have a desk which can be locked, a comfortable bed and chair for each inspector, and washing conveniences. The entire cost to the contractor for furnishing, equipping, and maintaining the foregoing accommodations shall be included in the price bid for dredging. If the contractor fails to meet these requirements, the facilities referred to above will be secured by the owner, and the cost thereof will be deducted from payments to the contractor.

If the contractor maintains on this work an establishment for the subsistence of his own employees, he shall, when required, furnish to inspectors employed on the work, and to all owner's agents who may visit the work on official business, meals of a quality satisfactory to the owner. The meals furnished will be paid for by the owner at the rate of _____ cents per person for each meal.

Note 1. The above paragraph is intended to apply to large dredges on extensive works, where rooms can be furnished, and the crews are ordinarily subsisted on the plant. When it is expected that smaller plants will be employed, and rooms will not be available, or the crews subsisted on the plant, the paragraph should be modified by eliminating so much of it as is not applicable.

Note 2. As the number of meals which the contractor will be required to furnish cannot be determined in advance, it is considered preferable to pay the contractor a fair price for each meal furnished rather than to require him to include the cost of the meals in his price bid for dredging.

SECTION IV. TECHNICAL PROVISIONS

4-01. (a) Character of Materials. Probings (and borings) (and tests pits) made by the owner to determine the character of materials to be removed are shown on sheets nos. _____ of the maps referred to in paragraph 1-03.

(Add all other pertinent data, especially as to boulders, stumps, sunken logs, and timber, etc.)

The owner does not guarantee that other materials will not be encountered nor that the proportions of the several materials will not vary from those indicated by the explorations. Bidders are expected to examine the site of the work, the logs of the probings (borings) (test pits) and the samples (and cores) which are available at_____ and,
(Give location)
after investigation, decide for themselves the character of the materials and make their bids accordingly. In the execution of the work prescribed in paragraph 1-02, all materials of the character developed by the explorations, in whatever proportions they may be encountered, or as otherwise above described, and all other materials which, in the opinion of the contracting officer, can be removed and disposed of with substantially equal facility by the plant stated in the acceptance bid, shall be removed and disposed of by the contractor at the contract price (s). (See paragraph 4-06.)

4-01. (b) Character of Materials. The material to be removed to restore the depths within the limits specified in paragraph 1-02 is that composing the shoaling that has occurred since the channel was last dredged. Bidders are expected to examine the site of the work and the

records of previous dredging which are available at_____
and after investigation decide for themselves the character of the materials and make their bids accordingly. In the execution of the work prescribed in paragraph 1-02, all materials of a character reasonably to
be anticipated as a result of shoaling and all other materials which, in
the opinion of the owner, can be removed or disposed of with substantially equal facility by the plant stated in the accepted bid shall be removed and disposed of by the contractor at the contract price. (See par.
4-06.)

4-01. (c) Character of Materials. The material to be removed to ac-
complish the work specified in paragraph 1-02 as determined by_____
_____ is_____,
  (Give basis for determination)   (Give specific description of material)
but bidders are expected to examine the site of the work, decide for
themselves the character of the material and make their bids accordingly. All material included within the work specified in paragraph 1-02,
which, in the opinion of the owner, can be removed and disposed of with
substantially the same facility as the material above described by means
of the plant stated in the accepted bid shall be removed and disposed of
by the contractor at the contract price. (See par. 4-06.)

4-01. (d) If materials, structures, or obstacles of a substantially
different character are encountered in the execution of the prescribed
work and the cost of their removal or satisfactory treatment obviously
would be, in the opinion of the owner, either in excess of, or less than
the contract price, the owner, in either alternative, will then proceed
in accordance with the provisions of article 4 of the contract.

  Note. Clause (a) will be used for new work that has been properly and adequately explored.
  Clause (b) will be used for maintenance dredging.
  Clause (c) may be used for minor work in shallow cuts when the character of the material is so
well established by prior dredging in the vicinity or by general knowledge that the time and cost of
its exploration is clearly unwarranted. If the definite character of the material is not known beyond
any reasonable doubt, adequate probings or borings must be made and clause 4-01 (a) used.
  Clause (d) will be used in all cases.

4-02. Disposal of Excavated Material. The material excavated must
be transported and deposited at (give specific location)_____
_____. The maximum distance to
which the material must be transported will not exceed_____
_____ and the average distance will not exceed_____
_____. The dumping ground must be plain-
ly marked by the contractor by conspicuous buoys or stakes, and no
dumping shall be done unless an inspector appointed by the owner is
present at the time.

  In case the material is deposited in confined areas, all embank-
ments or bulkheads needed for confining or grading the material, with
necessary waste weirs, must be provided and maintained by the contractor, and the cost thereof shall be included in the price bid.

  Provided that a bidder submits with his bid an adequate description
of a dumping ground other than that stipulated in these specifications,
such deviation as to the place of disposal will be considered in making
the award. If, after the award of the contract, a dumping ground other
than that stipulated in these specifications is proposed, its acceptance
will be subject to the approval of the owner. In either event the con-

tractor shall obtain the written consent of the owners of the substituted grounds and furnish evidence thereof to the owner before proceeding with the work. All expenses incurred in connection with providing and making available such dumping grounds shall be borne by the contractor and all materials deposited thereon, and all operations in connection therewith shall be at the contractor's risk.

The second provision is especially applicable in cases where it is probable that the contractor can make advantageous use of dredged material.

Note 1. When material is to be placed on adjacent land by hydraulic process, or deposited by rehandling from scows, or by other means, the specifications must further explain local conditions.
Note 2. Where the material can be deposited in waters immediately adjacent to the channel, and the construction of bulkheads is not deemed necessary, the minimum permissible distance from the channel to the place of deposit should be clearly stated.
Note 3. When the excavated material is to be dumped systematically to utilize a given area to the utmost, or so as to make a fill, as for the base of a breakwater, or is to be placed in a breakwater, or levee, or other embankment, the requirements should be clearly stated.

4-03. Overdepth and Side Slopes. To cover inaccuracies of the dredging process, material actually removed within the specific $\begin{bmatrix} \text{area} \\ \text{areas} \end{bmatrix}$ to be dredged to a depth of not more than _____ $\begin{bmatrix} \text{foot} \\ \text{feet} \end{bmatrix}$ below the required depth will be estimated and paid for at $\begin{bmatrix} \text{full} \\ \text{one-half} \end{bmatrix}$ contract price.

(a) The owner will prescribe the overcuts to be made to prevent the encroachment of material from the sides of the dredged cut, and material actually removed on his order from the prescribed overcuts, whether dredged in original position, or after having fallen into the cut, will be estimated and paid for. Material taken from beyond the limits as extended in this paragraph will be deducted from the total amount dredged as excessive overdepth dredging or excessive side-slope dredging and will not be paid for.

(b) Material actually removed, within limits approved by the owner, to provide for final side slopes not flatter than_____ on_____, but not in excess of the amount originally lying above this limiting side slope, will be estimated and paid for, whether dredged in original position or after having fallen into the cut. In computing the limiting amount of side-slope dredging $\begin{bmatrix} \text{net dimensions, without allowance for overdepth,} \\ \text{an overdepth of_____ft. measured vertically,} \end{bmatrix}$ will be used. Material taken from beyond the limits above described will be deducted from the total amount dredged as excessive overdepth dredging, or excessive side-slope dredging, and will not be paid for.

Note 1. Clause (a) will be used for scow-measurement contracts, and may be used for place-measurement contracts when the material actually removed from the overcuts can be closely estimated. It requires the issuance of definite instructions in writing to the contractor directing the location, width, and depth of the overcuts to be made. The overcuts may be an additional width of cut, or additional depth adjacent to the slopes, or both, as may be best suited to the character of the material dredged, and the dredge used. If the overcut to be made is certainly and definitely known when the specifications are prepared, and can be concisely stated, the clause should be amended to stipulate it. Clause (b) will be used when clause (a) is not applicable.
Note 2. Where the material is very soft, and shoaling is rapid, it may be advisable to allow for overdepth on the side slopes.
Note 3. The vertical allowance for overdepth within the limits of the project channel will depend upon the character of the material to be dredged and the probable rapidity of future shoaling.

4-04. (a) Method of Measurement. If the material is removed in scows, it will be measured by scow measurement; if removed other than in scows it will be measured by place measurement. Proposals will be

accepted in terms of $\begin{bmatrix} \text{scow} \\ \text{place} \end{bmatrix}$ measurement only. If the alternate method
of disposal is used in the execution of the work, the quantities will be
converted in the ratio fixed by paragraph 4-05.

Scow Measurement.
4-04. (b) Method of Measurement. The material to be paid for will be
measured by the cubic yard in scows at the dredge by inspectors appointed by the owner, but the contractor will be held responsible for its
satisfactory disposal, and proper deductions will be made for all material that is not deposited according to the specifications. (See par. 4-02.)
No scow will be used in the work until the measurements for determining
its capacity have been made under the direction of the owner; and, if
necessary, it must be hauled out or beached for this purpose. Scows
will be remeasured without hauling or beaching whenever in the opinion
of the owner it is expedient.

The contractor is invited to be present in person or to be represented
by an authorized agent during the measuring of scows. When the capacities of the scows are determined, or redetermined, a record of allowed capacities will be sent the contractor; if he protests within 5 days,
the scow will be remeasured at his expense, and he must be present in
person, or be represented by a capable accredited agent, so that correct
measurements can be agreed upon. Failure to protest within 5 days will
be equivalent to expressing satisfaction with the measurements. If any
alterations are made in any scow it must be inspected, and, if necessary,
remeasured, before again being used in the work. Each scow will be
plainly marked by a distinctive number, letter, or name, which shall
not be changed or given to any other scow during the period of contract.
To insure correct measurement, the pockets shall be filled evenly, as
far as practicable. The judgement of the inspector as to whether or not
a scow is properly loaded, or to what extent it is short or overloaded,
will be final, unless a protest is made by the contractor or his duly
accredited representative before the scow is moved away from the
dredge. In case a protest is made, the contents of the scow shall be
leveled off immediately by the contractor and properly measured to the
satisfaction of the inspector, and the measurements shall within------
------------ days thereafter, be submitted to the owner for decision.
The estimates of work to be paid for monthly will be totaled from the
above measurements.

Preliminary and approximate estimates of any excessive overdepth
dredging and excessive side slope dredging determined from soundings
taken behind the dredge as the work proceeds will be deducted from the
monthly partial payments. The final determination of the amounts of
excessive overdepth dredging and of excessive side slope dredging will
be based wholly on the surveys made for final examination and acceptance (see par. 4-07), and the total quantities to be paid for under the
contract shall be the total quantities as measured in scows and disposed
of in accordance with the provisions of the specifications, less the
amount of excessive overdepth dredging and excessive side slope
dredging as determined by the final examination.

Note: While it is very desirable that the pockets shall be filled evenly either to the bottom or to
the top of the coamings, and that this should be required whenever practicable, circumstances may
make such filling impracticable, and then the contractor should be allowed whatever each pocket

actually contains. In order that the inspector may have a ready means of determining the contents of each pocket when it is only partially full, each pocket of all scows should be measured and tables prepared for the inspector's use, showing the quantity contained in each pocket when it is full to the top of the coamings and the quantity it contains when filled to different levels, varying from each other by not more than half a foot, from the top of the coamings to the bottom of the pocket. The lower levels of these tables are useful when material is brought back from the dump in a pocket (as sometimes happens, due to freezing or other causes) in enabling the inspector to make proper deduction from the load credited at the time when the scow was towed away from the dredge. Copies of these tables should be furnished the contractor. (See foregoing paragraph.)

Place Measurement.
4-04. (c) Method of Measurement. The material to be paid for by the cubic yard under the contract will be measured in place by computing the volume between the bottom surface shown by the soundings of the last survey made before dredging and the bottom surface shown by a survey made as soon as practicable after the
entire work specified in paragraph 1-02 (b)
work specified in each section in paragraph 1-02 (d)
has been completed.

The maps already prepared (par. 1-03) are believed to represent accurately [average existing conditions / conditions existing date] but the depths shown thereon [will / may] be verified and corrected by soundings taken before dredging.

Determination of quantities removed and the deductions made therefrom to determine quantities by place measurement to be paid for in the area specified, after having once been made, will not be reopened, except on evidence of collusion, fraud, or obvious error.

Monthly partial payments will be based on approximate quantities determined by soundings or sweeping taken behind the dredge.

Excessive overdepth dredging and excessive side-slope dredging will in all cases be excluded as provided in paragraph 4-03.

Note 1. Paragraph 4-04 (a) will be used when the material may be disposed of at the option of the contractor either by scows or by the hydraulic process, and is to be measured in scows if scows are used, or in place if otherwise removed. Whenever paragraph 4-04 (a) is used it will be followed by paragraphs 4-04 (b) and 4-04 (c) and the lower alternative headings of these paragraphs will be canceled.
Note 2. Paragraph 4-04 (b) will be used when the material is to be removed and measured in scows only. When so used, the alternative heading "Scow measurement" will be canceled, as will paragraphs 4-04 (a) and 4-04 (c).
Note 3. Paragraph 4-04 (c) will be used when the material is to be measured in place, whatever may be the method of disposal. When so used, the alternative heading "Place measurement" will be canceled, as will paragraphs 4-04 (a) and 4-04 (b).
Note 4. During the progress of the work the owner will notify the contractor promptly of any excessive overdepth dredging, or too shallow dredging, in order to reduce to a minimum the necessary deductions for excessive overdepth and also to avoid as far as possible, in hydraulic work, redredging after anchors have been shifted.

4-05. (a) Equivalent Measurements. When necessary for any cause to convert "scow measurement" into "place measurement," or the reverse, ------------ yards of the former will be taken as the equivalent of ---------------- yards of the latter.

4-05. (b) Equivalent Measurements. When necessary for any cause to convert "scow measurement" into "place measurement," or the reverse ------------ yards of blasted rock measured in scows will be taken as the equivalent of---------- yards measured in place, and---------- yards of material other than blasted rock measured in scows will be taken as equivalent of----------- yards measured in place. A mixed

load, consisting of both blasted rock and material other than blasted
rock, will be considered as consisting of_____ percent of
the former and_____ percent of the latter, and will be converted
into place measurement by using the ratio above mentioned for each
class of material.

Note: No opportunity should be neglected to obtain reliable data for the best value of the coefficients in each locality where dredging is in progress.

4-06. (a) Work Covered by Contract Price. The contract price per
cubic yard for dredging shall cover the cost of removal and disposition
of all material as specified in paragraph 4-01.

Note: This paragraph will be used for maintenance dredging when it is known that no rock will
be encountered.

4-06. (b) Work Covered by Contract Price. The contract price per
cubic yard for dredging overlying material and for rock excavation,
respectively, shall cover the cost of removal and disposition of all materials as specified in paragraph 4-01. Material to be classified as
ledge rock must be of such composition as, in the opinion of the owner,
shall require blasting or the use of special plant for its removal, and
shall not include wrecks, snags, stumps, piles, and fragments of rock
or boulders capable of being removed by the dredge in one piece. All
other materials, including wrecks, snags, stumps, piles, fragments
of rock and boulders capable of being removed by the dredge in one
piece will be classified and paid for as overlying material.

Note: This paragraph will be used when it is known that rock will be encountered and it is the
intent of the contract to secure a completed channel.

4-06. (c) Work Covered by Contract Price. The contract price per cubic
yard for dredging shall cover the cost of removal and disposal of all
materials as specified in paragraph 4-01, except ledge rock, rock
fragments, boulders, wrecks, snags, stumps, and piles, which cannot
be removed or buried below project depth by a powerful_____
inch diameter discharge hydraulic dredge without blasting. If ledge
rock, rock fragments, wrecks, snags, stumps, piles, and boulders
are encountered which cannot be removed or buried below project
depth by the hydraulic dredge above specified without blasting, the
contractor shall remove therefrom all such overlying material as in the
judgment of the owner can be removed by the plant above specified.
Nothing in this paragraph shall be construed as prohibiting the removal
of excepted material by special means at prices agreed upon and appro-
ed in accordance with article 4 of the contract.

Note: This paragraph will be used for dredging by the hydraulic method when it is possible that
ledge rock, boulders, stumps, snags, or piles may be encountered. If stumps are known to be
present, and it is the intent of the contract to require their removal and to pay for it as the contract price per cubic yard, the paragraph will be amended to show clearly such intent.

4-06. (d) Work Covered by Contract Price. The contract price per
cubic yard for dredging shall cover the cost of removal and disposal of
all materials as specified in paragraph 4-01 except ledge rock and
large boulders or fragments of rock and wrecks which cannot be removed by the plant specified in the accepted bid, or the equivalent of
such plant, without blasting. The removal of ledge rock and other excepted material will not be required. Material to be classified as ledge
rock must be of such size and composition as in the opinion of the owner
shall require special plant for its removal, and shall not include fragments of rocks or boulders capable of being removed by the dredge in

one piece. Should ledge rock or other material which cannot be removed by the plant specified in the accepted bid, or its equivalent, without
blasting be encountered, the contractor shall remove therefrom all
overlying material which in the judgment of the owner can be removed
by the use of plant so specified or its equivalent. Nothing in this paragraph shall be construed as prohibiting the removal of excepted material by special means at prices agreed upon and approved in accordance
with article 4 of the contract.

Note: This paragraph will be used for dredging with dipper or bucket dredges when it is even
remotely possible that ledge rock or other material requiring special plant for its removal will be
encountered. If there is real likelihood that boulders will be found in quantity to appreciably delay
the dredging, the following clause may be appended: The contractor will be paid at the rate of
$--------- per cubic yard, for the removal of boulders and fragments of rock exceeding---------
cubic yards each in size.

4-07. Acceptance. As soon as practicable after the completion of
the entire work, it
[any section established in paragraph 1-02 as in the opinion of the
owner will not be subject to injury by further operations under the
contract, such section
will be examined thoroughly by sounding, or by sweeping, or by both,
as deemed advisable by the owner. Should any shoals, lumps, or other
lack of contract depth be disclosed by this examination, the contractor
will be required to remove them by dragging the bottom or by dredging,
at the contract rate for dredging, but if the bottom is soft and the shoal
areas are small and form no material obstruction to navigation, the
removal of such shoal may be waived, in the discretion of the owner.
The contractor or his authorized representative will be notified when
soundings and/or sweepings are to be made, and will be permitted to
accompany the survey party. When the area is found to be in a satisfactory condition, it will be accepted finally. Should more than two
sweeping operations by the owner over an area be necessary by reason
of work for the removal of shoals disclosed at a prior sweeping, the
cost of such third and any subsequent sweeping operations will be
charged against the contractor at the rate of $---------- per day for
each day in which the owner's sweeping plant is engaged in sweeping
and/or is en route to or from the site or held at or near the said site
for such operations.

Final acceptance of the whole or a part of the work and the deductions
or corrections of deductions made thereon will not be reopened, after
having once been made, except on evidence of collusion, fraud, or
obvious error, and the acceptance of a completed section shall not
change the time of payment of the retained percentages of the whole or
any part of the work stated in paragraph 1-07.
4-08. Shoaling. If, before the contract is completed, shoaling occurs
in any section previously accepted, including shoaling in the finished
channel, because of the natural lowering of the side slopes, redredging
at contract price, within the limit of available funds, may be done if
agreeable to both the contractor and the owner.

RENTAL CONTRACTS

171. Bid Form. The following is adapted from forms used by the Corps of Engineers for receiving bids from prospective contractors for the rental of dredge plants. It has been written with descriptive information included so that it may be used on most projects.

RENTAL OF DREDGE PLANT

(Place) _____

(Date) _____

In compliance with the invitation for bids, the undersigned hereby proposes to furnish, deliver and operate the following plant in strict accordance with the specifications: One cutterhead, hydraulic, pipeline dredge and attendant plant with the following characteristics:

Dredge Name or Number _____

Bunker Capacity (gallons, tons) _____

Hull:
    Material of construction _____
    Length _____feet; Breadth _____feet
    Depth_____feet
    Spud diameters_____inches
    Distance between spud centers_____ feet
    Draft, light_____ feet; Draft, loaded_____ feet
    Date built_____
    Date last dry docked_____
    Minimum width of channel in which
        dredge can operate   _____ feet
    Minimum depth of water in which
        dredge can operate   _____ feet
    Maximum current in which dredge
        can operate   _____ feet
Ladder:
    Material of construction_____
    Length_____ feet; Weight_____ tons
    Length can be extended_____ feet
    Cutter shaft diameter_____ inches
    Cutter motor
        Horsepower_____; Type_____
    Cutter types available_____
    Cutter speed: _____ rpm min; _____rpm max
    Other type cutter drive_____
Main Pump:
    Type_____; Make_____
    Diameter: _____ suction;_____ discharge
    Runners available:_____ in. _____ in. _____ in. _____ in.
    Maximum speed _____ rpm
    Brake horsepower applied to pump (max)_____

<u>Pump Drive:</u>
    Type _____; Make _____
    When new _____
    Brake horsepower:
    _____ at _____ rpm; _____ at _____rpm
    Reduction gear:
    Type_____; Make_____
    When new_____; Horsepower_____
<u>Power Plant:</u>
    Type_____; Make_____
    Size_____
    Pressure_____psi
    Last pressure test_____
    Last overhaul_____
    Fuel used_____
    Fuel consumption per day_____ gal.
    Total horsepower_____
<u>Auxiliary Plant:</u>
    Type_____; Make_____
    Horsepower_____; Last overhaul_____
<u>Attendant Plant:</u>
    Quarterboat accommodations_____ men
    Dredge accommodations_____ men
    Tender(s):
        Size_____ feet; Draft _____ feet
        Horsepower_____ Age_____ years
        (if more than one, attach additional sheet)
    Skiffs and launches:
        Length_____feet; Draft_____ feet
        Length_____feet; Draft_____ feet
        (attach additional sheets for others)
<u>Discharge Line:</u>
    Floating Line:
        Number pontoons_____; Length each_____ feet
        How connected_____; Age_____months
    Shore Line:
        Number pipe_____; Length each_____ feet
        Age oldest pipe_____ months
        Wye branches_____; Landings _____
    Auxiliaries:
        Elbows_____; Other_____
<u>Additional Plant:</u>
    Derricks_____; Tonnage_____ tons
    Age_____; How propelled_____
    Dimensions_____ ft; _____ ft;_____ ft.

Equipment, such as tractors, draglines, automobiles, sleds, baffle plates, barges, and all other equipment of plant, not already listed, is:

The rate bid for the above-listed plant complete with a full com-

plement of operating personnel, materials, supplies and all necessary items to a complete dredging operation will be:
A. For operation of the dredge
$_____(dollars) and _____ (cents) per hour.
B. For mobilization and demobilization:
$_____(dollars) and _____ (cents) lump sum.

The bidder agrees that upon written acceptance of this bid he will within_____ days execute the required form for hire of the above dredge plant as prescribed by the owner. If awarded the contract the bidder agrees to commence work within_____calendar days after notice to proceed and will complete the work in accordance with the specifications attached hereto.

172. Payment. Pay time will be computed on the basis of hours and factions thereof to 5-minute intervals for effective time and hours and fractions thereof to 5-minute intervals for noneffective time. The following will define effective and noneffective time.

A. Effective Time. Actual time of dredging when the dredge is under operation, with the cutterhead removing material, and such material being passed through the pipeline. Time lost in making such openings in floating discharge pipelines or in swinging to one side of the channel and slacking off the swing wires as may be necessary for the passage of vessels. Actual time in transit from point of delivery to the first position of work. Actual time of moving from one location to another at the direction of the owner. On such moves the contractor will maintain the average operating strength on each working shift and be prepared to commence dredging or preparing the dredge and plant for pumping immediately upon arriving at the new location.

B. Noneffective Time. Payment for noneffective time will be at 80 per cent (or other value) of the actual applicable contract price per hour. Noneffective time will be considered as actual time lost due to moving and changing swing anchors and wires, making necessary changes in shorelines or pontoon lines as are necessitated by the progress of the work, such as adding pontoons to the floating line or shore pipe to the shoreline, or making changes at the transition of the floating line to the shoreline.

Noneffective time will also be considered as time of moving around on one location at the direction of the owner. For the purpose of replacing runners four hours will be allowed. Four hours will be allowed for replacing cutters. In such instances, replacement must be for the purpose of improving the efficiency of the operation under changing conditions, such as changing material, length of line or trash, and not for the purpose of replacing worn runners or cutters.

Actual time lost due to removal of logs, driftwood and other trash from the pump, cutterhead or pipeline, or removal of drift from the pontoon line, and for washing out the pipeline, will also be considered noneffective time.

When operations are suspended by the owner under the provisions of these specifications, payment will be continued at 80 per cent (or other value) of the contract price per hour for a period not to exceed

15 hours to allow the contractor to prepare the dredge, pipeline, and attendant plant for towing or for lay-up at the site. When the contractor begins preparations to resume operations at the site, or when his dredge and attendant plant are started in tow to the site of the work, as directed by the owner, the 80 per cent provision will apply.

　　C. Non-payment Time. Payment will not be made for lay time on completion of an assignment, or lay time after arrival at location of a new assignment when such time is incurred at the direction of the contractor, or when through negligence of the contractor, the necessary equipment is not available or in operating condition at the new assignment, or for time during suspension of operations as provided for in the contract.

　　Time lost due to shutdowns for the repair or the replacement of worn out or unserviceable equipment, time lost due to pulling a line together when the joints open up, replacing damaged shore pipe or pontoons, and time during which the dredge is engaged in removing misplaced material, will not be paid for.

　　When the dredge is shut down for any reason or purpose that applies to removal of misplaced material, the ensuing time shall remain under that classification until the cause of the shutdown shall have been removed.

173. Mobilization and Demobilization. All costs connected with mobilization and demobilization of all the contractor's plant will be paid for at the contract lump-sum price. Sixty per cent of the lump-sum price will be paid to the contractor upon completion of his mobilization at the worksite. The remaining 40 per cent will be included in the final payment for the work under the contract.

174. Delivery, Prosecution and Termination. The contractor will be required to deliver the dredge and attendant plant ready for operation to

----
(describe fully and exactly the location of the delivery point)

within_____ calendar days after receipt of the notice to proceed. The plant will be finally inspected and the contractor notified of acceptance or rejection of the plant within 24 hours after delivery of the plant to the owner.

175. Technical Provisions. Following are technical provisions which should be used in conjunction with standard specifications in procurement of rental equipment:

　　A. Intent. It is the spirit and intent of these specifications to secure for the owner the lease and operation of a cutterhead, hydraulic, pipeline dredge, complete in all respects, including all attendant plant.

　　B. Size of Plant. The dredge shall be of not less than_____ inch discharge with not less than_____ pump brake horsepower. It shall have a minimum output of_____ cubic yards per 24-hour operating day through a pipeline of_____ feet and a lift of _____ feet. The dredge ladder and spuds shall be of sufficient length and construction that the dredge will dig efficiently in material to a depth of not less than_____ feet below the water surface and in currents up to_____ feet per second. The cutter motor shall be of a type capable of developing at least_____ brake horsepower for a _____ inch dredge and _____ brake horsepower for a_____ inch or larger dredge. The contractor shall have available for use at all times a reasonable variety (at least three) of interchangeable runners to permit the dredge to work under varying conditions of length of line and lift. Discharge lines may be as long as_____ feet, and the lift may be as much as_____ feet.

The contractor shall have available at all times for immediate use one basket-type, smooth blade cutter in addition to that attached to the ladder head. (Adapt this requirement to suit the material to be dredged.)

The following minimum pipeline and fittings will be required:

1. _____ feet of pontoon discharge line with satisfactory pontoons, a sufficient number of which are equipped with hand winches to provide for suitable anchorage for every 400 feet of floating line.

2. _____ pontoon elbows

3. _____ landing pontoons equipped with an A-frame and hand winches

4. A baffle plate for pumping overboard

5. _____ feet of shore pipe equipped with_____ sets of valves, including a wye branch.

The attendant plant shall include the following as minimum requirements: _____ tenders with full crews for 24 hours operation per day, and of such size and design that (it) (they) can serve the dredge, one of which can work efficiently in five feet of water; also one small launch with draft of not to exceed three feet for use in setting buoys, sounding and general inspection.

The dredge will be equipped with recording vacuum and pressure gages to record pipeline pressure and pipe vacuum.

C. Supervision. The entire plant of the contract will be under the control of the owner with regard to hours of work, location of the work, work to be done, type of runner to be used, and other operational factors. A representative of the owner will be present at all times to issue instructions with reference to the work. However, the actual supervision and direction of dredging operations shall be the responsibility of the contractor.

If at any time during the life of the contract the owner shall determine that the plant or any part of it is inadequate for the service required, or it is not being operated at full capacity, or has become unserviceable or incapable of efficient work, or is not being effectively operated because of a reduced or incompetent crew, he will notify the contractor in writing of his decision and direct replacement of unsatisfactory equipment or defects.

D. Duration of Contract. The contract period will be that stated in the contract beginning with the date of acceptance of the plant by the owner, unless it should be necessary to terminate the contract earlier under the provisions provided for in the contract. Unless the contract is terminated under the provisions therein provided, a minimum of _____ calendar days will be guaranteed the contractor. Should this minimum number of days be not obtained under the contract, the owner will pay for the difference on the basis of the average of payments earned during the actual working time. At the option of the owner, the contract with all its terms and provisions may be extended for an additional_____ calendar days, or any fraction thereof.

Table 13. System of Units

| Quantity | ABSOLUTE SYSTEM | | GRAVITATIONAL SYSTEM |
	British (fps)	Metric (cgs)	British (fps)
Fundamental			
Length	feet	centimeters	feet
Mass	pounds	grams	pounds
Time	seconds	seconds	seconds
Derived			
Area	square feet	square centimeters	square feet
Volume	cubic feet	cubic centimeters	cubic feet
Speed	feet per second	centimeters per second	feet per second
Acceleration	feet per second^2	centimeters per second^2	feet per second^2
Force	poundal (lb-ft/sec^2)	dynes (gm-cm/sec^2)	slugs (Mass)
Density	pounds per cubic foot	grams per cubic centimeter	slugs per feet^3
Energy (work)	foot poundal	ergs	foot pounds
Power	foot poundal per second	ergs per second	foot pounds per second

Table 14. Conversion from British to Metric Units

To Convert From	To	Multiply By
inches	mm	25.400
feet	meters	0.305
yards	meters	0.914
sq in	sq mm	645.200
sq ft	sq meters	0.929
cu in	cu mm	16.387
cu in	liters	0.016
cu ft	cu meters	0.028
cu yds	cu meters	0.765
US gal	cu meters	0.004
US gal	liters	3.785
lb/ft	kg/meter	1.488
lb/sq in	kg/sq cm	0.070
lb/cu ft	kg/cu meter	16.018
US gpm	cu meters/hr	0.227

Table 15. Conversion from Metric to British Units

To Convert From	To	Multiply By
mm	inches	0.039
meters	feet	3.281
meters	yards	1.094
sq mm	sq in	0.002
sq meters	sq ft	10.764
cu mm	cu in	0.061
liters	cu in	61.023
cu meters	cu ft	35.314
cu meters	cu yds	1.308
cu meters	US gal	264.200
liters	US gal	0.264
kg/meter	lb/ft	0.672
kg/sq cm	lb/sq in	14.220
kg/cu meter	lb/cu ft	0.063
cu meters/hr	US gpm	4.403

Table 16. Conversion from Inches of Mercury to Feet of Clear Water

Feet = (1.133) (inches of mercury)

Inches Mercury	Feet Water	Inches Mercury	Feet Water	Inches Mercury	Feet Water
1	1.133	11	12.460	21	23.790
2	2.266	12	13.596	22	24.926
3	3.399	13	14.730	23	26.060
4	4.532	14	15.860	24	27.200
5	5.665	15	16.990	25	28.325
6	6.798	16	18.130	26	29.460
7	7.931	17	19.260	27	30.600
8	9.064	18	20.390	28	31.700
9	10.197	19	21.530	29	32.860
10	11.330	20	22.660	30	33.999

Table 17. Conversion from Pounds Per Square Inch to Feet of Clear Water

Feet = (2.31) (PSI)

PSI	Feet Water	PSI	Feet Water	PSI	Feet Water	PSI	Feet Water	PSI	Feet Water
1	2.31	21	48.51	41	94.71	61	140.91	81	187.11
2	4.62	22	50.82	42	97.02	62	143.22	82	189.42
3	6.93	23	53.13	43	99.93	63	145.53	83	191.73
4	9.23	24	55.44	44	101.64	64	147.84	84	194.04
5	11.55	25	57.75	45	103.95	65	150.15	85	196.35
6	13.86	26	60.06	46	106.26	66	152.46	86	198.66
7	16.17	27	62.37	47	108.57	67	154.77	87	200.97
8	18.48	28	64.68	48	110.88	68	157.08	88	203.28
9	20.79	29	66.99	49	113.19	69	159.39	89	205.59
10	23.10	30	69.30	50	115.50	70	161.70	90	207.90
11	25.41	31	71.71	51	117.81	71	164.01	91	210.21
12	27.72	32	73.92	52	120.12	72	166.32	92	212.52
13	30.03	33	76.23	53	122.43	73	168.63	93	214.83
14	32.34	34	78.54	54	124.74	74	170.94	94	217.14
15	34.65	35	80.85	55	127.05	75	173.25	95	219.45
16	36.96	36	83.16	56	129.36	76	175.56	96	221.76
17	39.27	37	85.47	57	131.67	77	177.87	97	224.07
18	41.58	38	87.78	58	133.98	78	180.18	98	226.38
19	43.89	39	90.09	59	136.29	79	182.49	99	228.69
20	46.20	40	92.40	60	138.60	80	184.80	100	231.00

Table 18. Conversion from Feet of Clear Water to Pounds Per Square Inch

PSI = (0.4331) (feet)

Feet	PSI	Feet	PSI	Feet	PSI	Feet	PSI	Feet	PSI	Feet	PSI	Feet	PSI	Feet	PSI
1	0.43	21	9.09	41	17.75	61	26.42	81	35.08	101	43.75	121	52.41	141	61.07
2	0.86	22	9.53	42	18.19	62	26.85	82	35.52	102	44.18	122	52.84	142	61.51
3	1.30	23	9.96	43	18.62	63	27.29	83	35.95	103	44.61	123	53.28	143	61.94
4	1.73	24	10.39	44	19.05	64	27.72	84	36.39	104	45.05	124	53.71	144	62.37
5	2.16	25	10.82	45	19.49	65	28.15	85	36.82	105	45.48	125	54.15	145	62.81
6	2.59	26	11.26	46	19.92	66	28.58	86	37.25	106	45.91	126	54.58	146	63.24
7	3.03	27	11.69	47	20.35	67	29.02	87	37.68	107	46.34	127	55.01	147	63.67
8	3.46	28	12.12	48	20.79	68	29.45	88	38.12	108	46.78	128	55.44	148	64.10
9	3.89	29	12.55	49	21.22	69	29.88	89	38.55	109	47.21	129	55.88	149	64.54
10	4.33	30	12.99	50	21.65	70	30.32	90	38.98	110	47.64	130	56.31	150	64.97
11	4.76	31	13.42	51	22.09	71	30.75	91	39.42	111	48.08	131	56.74	151	65.40
12	5.20	32	13.86	52	22.52	72	31.18	92	39.85	112	48.51	132	57.18	152	65.84
13	5.63	33	14.29	53	22.95	73	31.62	93	40.28	113	48.94	133	57.61	153	66.27
14	6.06	34	14.72	54	23.39	74	32.05	94	40.72	114	49.38	134	58.04	154	66.70
15	6.49	35	15.16	55	23.82	75	32.48	95	41.15	115	49.81	135	58.48	155	67.14
16	6.93	36	15.59	56	24.26	76	32.92	96	41.58	116	50.24	136	58.91	156	67.57
17	7.36	37	16.02	57	24.69	77	33.35	97	42.01	117	50.68	137	59.34	157	68.00
18	7.79	38	16.45	58	25.12	78	33.78	98	42.45	118	51.11	138	59.77	158	68.43
19	8.22	39	16.89	59	25.55	79	34.21	99	42.88	119	51.54	139	60.21	159	68.87
20	8.66	40	17.32	60	25.99	80	34.65	100	43.31	120	51.98	140	60.64	160	69.31

Table 18. (continued)

Feet	PSI	Feet	PSI	Feet	PSI	Feet	PSI
161	69.74	179	77.53	197	85.33	215	93.13
162	70.17	180	77.97	198	85.76	216	93.56
163	70.61	181	78.40	199	86.20	217	93.99
164	71.04	182	78.84	200	86.63	218	94.43
165	71.47	183	79.27	201	87.07	219	94.86
166	71.91	184	79.70	202	87.50	220	95.30
167	72.34	185	80.14	203	87.93	221	95.73
168	72.77	186	80.57	204	88.36	222	96.16
169	73.20	187	81.00	205	88.80	223	96.60
170	73.64	188	81.43	206	89.21	224	97.03
171	74.07	189	81.87	207	89.66	225	97.46
172	74.50	190	82.30	208	90.10	226	97.90
173	74.94	191	82.73	209	90.53	227	98.33
174	75.37	192	83.17	210	90.96	228	98.76
175	75.80	193	83.60	211	91.39	229	99.20
176	76.23	194	84.03	212	91.83	230	99.63
177	76.67	195	84.47	213	92.20	231	100.00
178	77.10	196	84.90	214	92.69		

Table 19. Results of a 16-inch Dredge Test

Item	Run 1	Run 2	Run 3	Run 4
Engine speed, rpm	205	224	258	263
Length of pipeline, feet	1180	1180	1180	1180
Equivalent line, feet	1570	1570	1570	1570
Time for velocity test, seconds	85	78	67	65
Discharge velocity, feet per second	13.9	15.1	17.6	18.2
Suction velocity, feet per second	9.9	10.8	12.5	12.9
Discharge velocity head, feet	3.0	3.5	4.8	5.2
Suction velocity head, feet	1.5	1.8	2.4	2.5
Differential velocity head, feet	1.5	1.7	2.4	2.7
Discharge pressure head, psi	27.8	33.5	44.8	46.5
Discharge pressure head, feet	64.2	77.2	103.3	107.2
Suction head, inches mercury	4.8	5.9	7.1	7.4
Suction head, feet	5.4	6.6	8.0	8.4
Total head, feet (H_t)	71.1	85.5	113.7	118.3
Output, cubic feet per second	19.4	21.2	24.6	25.4
Hydraulic horsepower	161.0	212.0	323.5	350.0
Brake horsepower at 55 per cent eff.	293.0	385.0	588.0	635.0
Runner peripheral velocity, ft/sec	58.2	63.5	73.2	74.8
$H = V^2/2G$, feet (H_r)	53.5	62.5	83.2	87.0
C_p (pump constant) $= H_t/H_r$	1.4	1.4	1.4	1.4
Pressure at stern, psi	27.0	32.0	42.0	44.0
Head at stern, feet	62.3	73.9	97.0	101.6
Net static lift, feet	10.0	10.0	10.0	10.0
Net friction head, feet	52.3	63.9	87.0	91.6
Net friction per 100 feet of line	3.3	4.1	5.5	5.8
Theoretical friction head per 100 feet of line from Table 9, using a SG of 1.03 for salt water	3.5	4.0	5.2	5.5

Bibliography

(1) *Proceedings*, World Dredging Conference, W. V. Crowley, Ed., SYMCON Marine Corp., Long Beach, Cal., Vol. 1, May 1967

(2) Same as reference (1), but 1968

(3) Bird, C. W., *Naval Architecture of Hydraulic Dredges*, paper presented at Dredging Symposium, Tampa, Florida, 1966, Society of Naval Architects and Marine Engineers, New York, N.Y.

(4) Hendry, A. W., *Hydraulic Dredging Operations*, paper presented at Dredging Symposium noted in reference (3)

(5) Woodbury, C. E., *Mechanical Aspects of Hydraulic Cutterhead Dredge Design*, paper presented at Dredging Symposium noted in reference (3)

(6) Blaum/v. Marnitz, *Die Schwimmbagger*, 1st Ed., Springer-Verlag, Berlin, Germany, 1963

(7) Decker, P. M., *Dredging and Dredging Appliances*, 1st Ed., Technical Press, Ltd., London, 1927

(8) Roorda, I. A. and Vertregt, J. J., *Floating Dredges*, The Technical Publishing Co., Haarlem, Netherlands, 1963

(9) Prelini, C., *Dredges and Dredging*, C. Lockwood & Son, London, 1912

(10) Van Veen, Joh., *Dredge Drain and Reclaim*, 3rd Ed., Martinus Nuhoff, The Hague, 1952

(11) Shankland, E. C., *Dredging of Harbours and Rivers*, 1st Ed., Brown, Son & Ferguson, Glasgow, Scotland, 1949

(12) Cooper, H. R., *Practical Dredging*, 1st Ed., Brown, Son & Ferguson, Glasgow, Scotland, 1959

(13) Huston, J. W., *Dredging Fundamentals*, Proceedings, American Society of Civil Engineers, Vol. 93, No. WW3, Paper No. 5390, Aug. 1967

(14) *World Dredging and Marine Construction*, Sam Cummings, Ed., Monthly periodical, SYMCON Marine Corp., Long Beach, Cal.

(15) Scheffauer, F. C., Ed.-in-Chief, *The Hopper Dredge*, Office of the Chief of Engineers, Dept. of the Army, Washington, D.C., 1954

(16) Wilson, N. C., *Pioneering in Hydraulic Dredging*, informal volume, unpublished, author's library, 1950

(17) Terry, L. E., *It's What's Up Front That Counts*, Proceedings, World Dredging Conference, Long Beach, Cal., Vol. 1, May 1967, pp. 91-114 (*see* Ref. 1)

(18) *Standard Handbook for Electrical Engineers*, A. E. Knowlton, Ed.-in-Chief, 7th Ed., McGraw-Hill Book Co., Inc., New York, N.Y., 1941

(19) Heumann, G. W., *Magnetic Control of Industrial Motors*, John Wiley & Sons, Inc., New York, N.Y., 1947

(20) Oberg, Erik and Jones, F. D., *Machinery's Handbook*, 14th Ed., The Industrial Press, New York, N.Y., 1952

(21) *Wire Rope*, Wire Rope Institute, Washington 5, D.C., 1947

(22) *Morse Silent Chain Drives*, Morse Chain Co., Ithaca, N.Y., Bulletin No. 38, 1931

(23) Danforth, R. S. and Ogg, R. D., *Anchors and Anchoring*, Danforth/White, Portland, Maine

(24) Hausmann, E. and Slack, E. P., *Physics*, 3rd Ed., D. Van Nostrand Co., Inc., New York, N.Y., Aug. 1948

(25) *Permits for Work in Navigable Waters*, Corps of Engineers, U.S. Army, Washington, D.C., 1963

(26) *Rules of the Road, International and Inland*, U.S. Coast Guard, U.S. Government Printing Office, Washington, D.C., CG-169, Sept. 1965

(27) Daugherty, R. L., *Hydraulics*, 4th Ed., McGraw-Hill Book Co., Inc., New York, N.Y., 1937

(28) Lunz, B. R., *Oyster Culture with Reference to Dredging Operations*, U.S. Army Corps of Engineers, Charleston, S.C., Jan. 1938, Fla. Board of Conservation, St. Petersburg, Fla.

(29) Ingle, R. M., *Studies of the Effect of Dredging Operations Upon Fish and Shellfish*, Division of Oyster Culture, Board of Conservation, Tallahassee, Fla., 1952, Tech. Series 5

(30) Huston, J. W., *The Oyster and the Dredge*, World Dredging and Marine Construction (*see* Ref. 14), Mar. 1968

(31) Davis, R. E. and Foote, F. S., *Surveying*, 4th Ed., McGraw-Hill Book Co., Inc., New York, N.Y., 1953

(32) *Solar Ephemeris and Surveying Instrument Manual*, Keuffel & Esser Co., Hoboken, New Jersey, Latest Ed.

(33) Cornick, H. F., *Dock and Harbour Engineering*, Vols. 2, 3, 4, Charles Griffin & Co., Ltd., London, England, W.C. 2, 1960

(34) *Nautical Chart Manual*, Coast and Geodetic Survey, 6th Ed., Publication No. 83-1, U.S. Department of Commerce, Washington, D.C., 1963

(35) Abbett, R. W., *Engineering Contracts and Specifications*, 2nd Ed., John Wiley & Sons, New York, N.Y., 1948

(36) Schrampfer, W. H., *Law and Its Application to Business*, Rinehart & Co., Inc., New York, N.Y., 5th Ed., 1947

(37) Cushman, J. F., *Economic Design of Hydraulic Pipe-Line Dredge*, Proceedings, American Society of Civil Engineers, Vol. 56, Nov. 1930

(38) Krynine, D. P. and Judd, W. R., *Principles of Engineering Geology and Geotechnics*, McGraw-Hill Book Co., Inc., New York, N.Y., 1st Ed., 1957.

(39) *Earthmoving and Construction Data*, Allis Chalmers Construction Machinery Division, Milwaukee, Wisc. 53201, 7th Ed., Jan. 1966

(40) *Engineering News-Record*, McGraw-Hill Publ. Co., New York, N.Y., Sept. 1949.

(41) Francis, G. M., *The Small Businessman and His Financial Statements*, Series 70, Small Business Administration, Washington, D.C., 1948

(42) Sanzo, R., *Ratio Analysis for Small Business*, Series 20, Small Business Administration, Washington, D.C., 1957

(43) Cashin, J. A., *Density of Spoil in Suction Dredging*, Dock and Harbour Authority, London, Nov. 1956, pp. 232-235

(44) Denning, R. A., *The Flow of Solids-Water Mixtures in Hydraulic Dredging*, paper presented to American Society of Mechanical Engineers, Applied Mechanics and Fluid Engineering Conference, Washington, D.C., June 1955, published in Symposium on Rheology, A.S.C.E.

(45) Fortino, E. P., *Flow Measurement Techniques for Hydraulic Dredges*, Proceedings, American Society of Civil Engineers, Vol. 92, No. WW1, Paper No. 4683, Feb. 1966

(46) *Engineering Properties and Applications of Ni-Hard*, The International Nickel Co., Inc., 3rd Ed., Revised 1960

(47) Church, A. H., *Centrifugal Pumps and Blowers*, 1st Ed., John Wiley & Sons, New York, N.Y., 1944

(48) Kristal, F. A. and Annett, F. A., *Pumps*, 2nd Ed., McGraw-Hill Book Co., Inc., New York, N.Y., 1953

(49) O'Brien, M. and Fulsom, G. G., *The Transportation of Sand in Pipe Lines*, University of California Publications in Engineering, Vol. 3, No. 7, University of California Press, Nov. 1937, pp. 343-384

(50) Shaw, G. V., and Lomis, A. W., Eds., *Cameron Hydraulic Data*, Compressed Air Magazine, 12th Ed., Phillipsburg, N.J.

(51) Polhemus, J. H. and Du Priest, J. R., *Friction in Dredge Pipes*, Proceedings, American Society of Mechanical Engineers, HYD-50-7, 1928

(52) Paulson, F. O., *Hydraulic Dredge Design*, Proceedings, World Dredging Conference, Long Beach, Cal., Vol. 1, May 1967, pp. 39-51 (*see* Ref. 1)

(53) Erickson, O. P., *Deep Dredging with Suction Pipe Cutter Drive and New Dredge Machinery Developments*, Proceedings, World Dredging Conference, Long Beach, Cal., Vol. 1, May 1967, pp. 561-573 (*see* Ref. 1)

(54) Stepanoff, A. J., *Centrifugal and Axial Flow Pumps*, 1st Ed., John Wiley & Sons, New York, N.Y., 1948

(55) *Power Plant Practice, Steam Engine Principles and Practice*, Croft, T., Ed., 1st Ed., McGraw-Hill Book Co., Inc., New York, N.Y., 1923

(56) Fox, W. J. and McBirnie, S. C., *Marine Steam Engines and Turbines*, 2nd Ed., George Newnes, Ltd., London, 1961

(57) *Weight Handling Equipment*, Design Manual, Technical Publication No. DM-38, Department of the Navy, Bureau of Yards and Docks, Washington, D.C.

(58) Donkin, C. T., *Elementary Practical Hydraulics of Flow in Pipes*, 1st Ed., Oxford University Press, London, 1959

(59) *Marine Crewman's Handbook*, Technical Manual No. 55-501, Department of the Army, Oct. 1967

(60) *Dredging*, Bureau of Yards and Docks, Technical Publication No. NAVDOCKS TP-Pw-19, Department of the Navy, Washington, D.C., July 1953

(61) Feagin, L. B., *Dredging Methods Compared*, Civil Engineering, Nov. 1946, pp. 494-495

(62) Eirich, F. R., Ed., *Rheology of Clay Suspensions*, Vol. 3, Academic Press, New York, N.Y., 1958

(63) *Dredging*, Corps of Engineers Training School, Vicksburg District, Ft. Belvoir, Va., 2nd Ed., Vols. 1, 2, 3, 1948

(64) Erickson, O. P., *Latest Dredging Practice*, Proceedings, American Society of Civil Engineers, Vol. 87, No. WW1, Paper No. 2739, Feb. 1961

(65) Chatley, H., *Dredging Problems in Soil Mechanics*, Dock and Harbour Authority, London, May 1949

(66) *Design Manual*, Bureau of Yards and Docks, Technical Publication No. NAVDOCKS DM-38, Department of the Navy, Washington, D.C.

(67) Cushing, P. J. and Enright, P. M., *Analysis of the Design of a Hydraulc Dredge*, Transactions, Society of Naval Architects and Marine Engineers, New York, N.Y., 1947, pp. 433-446

(68) Dana, R. T., *Handbook of Construction Equipment*, 1st Ed., McGraw-Hill Book Co., Inc., New York, N.Y., 1921

(69) *Handbook of Water Control*, ARMCO Drainage and Metal Products, Inc., 1943

(70) Carter, Karassik and Wright, *Pump Questions and Answers*, 1st Ed., McGraw-Hill Book Co., Inc., New York, N.Y., 1949

(71) Thoenen, J. R., *Sand and Gravel Excavation*, U.S. Bureau of Mines, Washington, D.C., Circular No. 6875, Parts 3 and 5, March 1936

(72) Giroux, C. H., *Modern Hydraulic Dredging*, Civil Engineering, Vol. 740, Sept. 1952, pp. 156-164

(73) Erickson, O. P., *The Hydraulic Dredge*, Dock and Harbour Authority, London, Aug. 1956, pp. 133-135

(74) Erickson, O. P., *Deep Dredging with Suction Pipe Cutter Drive*, World Dredging and Marine Construction (*see* Ref. 14), July-Aug. 1967, pp. 35-38

(75) Mann, M. S., *How to Use System-Head Curves*, Chemical Engineering, Feb. 1953

(76) *Hydraulic Institute Pipe Friction Manual*, Hydraulic Institute, New York, N.Y., 1965, 3rd Ed.

(77) Peurifor, R. L., *Estimating Construction Costs*, McGraw-Hill Book Co., Inc., New York, N.Y. 10036, Dec. 1953

(78) *Marine Catalog*, Marine Engineering/Log, New York, N.Y., 10007, 20th Ed., 1967-68

(79) *Hydrographic Manual*, Coast and Geodetic Survey, Publication No. 20-2, U.S. Department of Commerce, Washington, D.C., 1960

(80) Waldeck, F. F., *The Hofer Automatic Relief Valve for Suction Dredges*, Proceedings, World Dredging Conference, Long Beach, Cal., Vol. 1, May 1967, pp. 197-206 (*see* Ref. 1)

(81) Woodbury, C. E., *Special Mechanical Requirements in Problem Areas of Hydraulic Dredge Design and Operation*, Proceedings, World Dredging Conference, Long Beach, Cal., Vol. 1, May 1967, pp. 207-240 (*see* Ref. 1)

(82) Frazier, D. M., *New Dredging Techniques Using An Annular Jet*, Proceedings, World Dredging Conference, Long Beach, Cal., Vol. 1, May 1967, pp. 115-132 (*see* Ref. 1)

(83) Simon, F. L., *Dredging Engineering*, 1st Ed., McGraw-Hill Book Co., Inc., New York, N.Y., 1920

(84) Irving, R., *Instrumentation in Dredging*, Proceedings, World Dredging Conference, Long Beach, Cal., Vol. 1, May 1967, pp. 397-422 (*see* Ref. 1)

(85) Fraser, W. G., *Development of a Dredge Jet Pump*, Proceedings, World Dredging Conference, Long Beach, Cal., Vol. 1, May 1967, pp. 517-534 (*see* Ref. 1)

(86) Hickerson, T. F., *Route Location and Surveying*, 3rd Ed., McGraw-Hill Book Co., Inc., New York, N.Y. 1953, pp. 45-51

(87) *Low Dams*, National Resources Committee, Superintendent of Documents, Washington, D.C., 1939

(88) *Basic Procedures in Soil Sampling*, Acker Drill Co., Scranton, Pa., 1965

(89) *Principles of Naval Engineering*, U.S. Navy, NAVPERS-10788A, Training Publications Division, Washington, D.C., 1966

(90) Paterson, W. B., *Red Book of Marine Engineering*, 1st Ed., Cornell Maritime Press, Inc., Cambridge, Md., 1962

(91) Seely, F. B., *Resistance of Materials*, 2nd Ed., John Wiley & Sons, New York, N.Y., 1935

(92) *American Civil Engineers' Handbook*, Merriman, M., Ed.-in-Chief, John Wiley & Sons, New York, N.Y., 1920

(93) Hudson, R. G., *The Engineers' Manual*, 2nd Ed., John Wiley & Sons, New York, N.Y., 1939

(94) Aston, J. and Story, E. B., *Wrought Iron*, 4th Ed., A. M. Byers & Co., Pittsburgh, Pa., 1959

(95)   *Major Factors in Cathodic Protection of Steel In Sea Water,*
       U.S. Department of Commerce, NRL Report No. 4596, PB-
       111807, Office of Technical Services, Naval Research Labora-
       tory, Washington, D.C., 1955
(96)   Seely, F. B. and Ensign, N. E., *Analytical Mechanics for Engi-
       neers,* 3rd Ed., John Wiley & Sons, New York, N.Y., 1946
(97)   Puchstein, A. F. and Lloyd, T. C., *Alternating Current
       Machines,* 2nd Ed., John Wiley & Sons, New York, N.Y., 1942
(98)   Quinn, A. DeF., *Design and Construction of Ports and Marine
       Structures,* 1st Ed., McGraw-Hill Book Co., Inc., New York,
       N.Y., 1961
(99)   *Hydraulic Handbook,* Fairbanks Morse Pump Division,
       Kansas City, Kans., 4th Ed., 1965

Index

Hydraulic Dredging

By

JOHN HUSTON, P.E.

Here is the first and only comprehensive book on hydraulic dredging that encompasses the entire field from both the practical and theoretical standpoints.

Dredging is a complicated business and men spend their lives learning almost wholly by experience. Interested principally in the factual aspects of making money, they have put into writing little of what they have done and thusly have created a situation in which there is a dearth of usable, available, organized dredging information. This book, compiled over a considerable number of years, coordinates the story of dredging from its very beginning to the present-day state of the art.

Although written principally for the layman, the student, the beginning dredgeman, the younger engineer, or the engineer or executive in other industries, it will be a valuable asset to anyone interested in this special field.

Where the few other books in the world on dredging merely point out or generally discuss the equipment used in dredging, this book is detailed in the history, layout, operation, control, investigation, bidding, contracts, design, management, cost and troubleshooting of dredging and dredging equipment and projects. It is profusely illustrated, each illustration having a distinct and definite use in the explanation and study of the hydraulic dredge and its operation. The most thorough bibliography on dredging ever compiled is included.

Not only does the book stress the practical information of dredging, but it brings out the theoretical aspects as well. Such subjects as hydraulic principles, mechanics, electrical and civil engineering, pipe friction, and pump hydraulics as applied to dredging, are thoroughly explained in clear and simple language. Numerous tables, graphs, and equations are supplied to provide the reader with the means of making use of all information presented.

Sample problems and situations are given and explained. At every point the author has made this book a usable and practical work. Reference is continually made to the bibliography so that those who are interested can obtain more detailed or additional information on the subject being discussed. A comprehensive and cross-referenced index is supplied.